Table of Contents

D0658496

Scouting the Stamp Frontier

The world comes alive with stamp collecting!

Cherokee Strip Land Run 1893

29 USA

STAMP COLLECTING

can take you back in time to the Old West—and just about anywhere else! Sail with famous explorers, sing with well-known musicians and relive America's adventurous past through U.S. stamps—whether they're classic stamps from decades ago or colorful new releases. Best of all, stamp collecting is more than just fun. It's affordable, too.

You don't need the quickest draw around—take your time building an exciting stamp collection. It's a hobby that's easy to "stick" with, because the enjoyment you get from stamp collecting will last a lifetime.

Read on to see how to start your own stamp collection.

Chief Joseph-National Portrait Gallery
United States Postage 6¢

WHAT IS PHILATELY?

The word philately (fi-lat-el-lee) means the study and collecting of stamps and other postal materials. Stamp collectors are called philatelists.

HOW DO I START COLLECTING STAMPS?

It's easy. You can start by simply saving stamps from letters, packages and postcards. Ask your friends and family to save stamps from their mail. Neighborhood businesses that get a lot of mail—banks, stores, travel agencies—might save their envelopes for you, too.

Or, start your collection by choosing one or two favorite subjects. Then, collect only stamps that fit your theme—art, history, sports, transportation, science—whatever you choose! This is called topical collecting. See the boxes on pages 6 and 13, and the stamps pictured in this article for ideas to get you started on a western theme.

5

Why did people rush to California in 1848?

One word: Gold. In 1848 John Sutter, a pioneer trader, found gold nuggets while building a sawmill on California's American River. News spread quickly, and eager treasure-seekers from all over the world flocked to California in hopes of staking a land claim and striking it rich. In just one year California's population boomed from 15,000 to more than 100,000. The new arrivals were nicknamed "forty-niners" for the year they came. Those who struck gold poured money into cities such as San Francisco and Sacramento. Hard-luck miners who found no gold returned home or started new lives as farmers and ranchers in California's Central Valley.

WILL IT COST ME A LOT TO START A COLLECTION?

No! Start with used stamps and a few inexpensive accessories (such as a small album and a package of hinges), and you can have a great time on a limited budget. Remember to put stamps, albums and hinges on your birthday and holiday wish lists, too!

WHAT KINDS OF STAMPS ARE THERE?

-Definitive
-Commemorative
-Special
-Airmail
-Booklet
-Coil

Definitive stamps are found on most mail. They feature former presidents, statesmen, prominent persons and national shrines. Their denominations range from 1 cent to 14 dollars. Definitives are usually available for several years, since they're printed in large quantities for specific postal rates.

Commemorative stamps are usually larger and more colorful than definitives. They honor important people, events or subjects. Only a limited number of each commemorative is printed, and most post offices only have them for a few months. The U.S. Postal Service's

Definitive

Commemorative

Philatelic Fulfillment Service Center also offers commemorative stamps by mail order for about one year after they are issued.

Special stamps supplement each year's regular stamp issues. They include the Christmas and Love stamps.

Airmail stamps are mainly used for sending mail overseas.

Booklet stamps come in small folders that contain panes of 3 to 20 stamps each. Each booklet stamp has at least one straight edge.

Coil stamps are issued in rolls. Each coil stamp has two straight edges and two edges with either slit-like cuts or little holes, called perforations.

If you wish, you can save whole envelopes with stamps on them and store them anywhere—from shoe boxes to special albums. But if you want to remove stamps from envelopes, it pays to be careful. The best way to remove stamps from envelopes is to soak them. Here's how:

1. Tear or cut off the upper right-hand corner of the envelope.

2. Place it, stamp side down, in a small pan of warm water. After a few minutes, the stamp will sink to the bottom.

3. Wait a few more minutes for any remaining gum to dislodge from the stamp.

Special

Airmail

Booklet

Coil

7

4. Lift the stamp out with tongs (a metal tool, like tweezers) if you have a pair. It's better to handle stamps with tongs because oil from your skin can damage stamps.

5. Place the stamp between two paper towels and put a heavy object, such as a book, on top. This will keep the stamp from curling as it dries. Leave the stamp there overnight.

6. If the stamp is a newer one with "invisible" gum, dry it face down with nothing touching the back, and flatten it later if necessary. Otherwise, it may stick to the paper towel when drying.

HOW SHOULD I ORGANIZE MY STAMPS?

However you want to, of course—it's your collection. But be sure to protect them so they don't get damaged or lost. You can attach your stamps to loose-leaf paper and put them in a three-ring binder. Or, arrange them in a more formal album, which you can buy in stores.

WHAT KINDS OF STAMP ALBUMS CAN I BUY?

Some stamp albums feature specific categories with pictures of the stamps that should appear on each page. You may want to select one with loose-leaf pages so you can add pages as your collection grows. A stock book is an album with plastic or paper pockets on each page. There are no pictures of stamps, so you can organize the album your way.

Edward R. Murrow

HOW DO I PUT A STAMP IN THE ALBUM?

It's best to use a hinge—a small strip of thin plastic with gum on one side. Unlike tape or glue, hinges let you peel the stamp off the page without damaging it. Hinges come either folded or unfolded. Here's how to use a folded hinge:

1. Moisten the short end of the hinge lightly. Press it to the back of the stamp, placing the fold about 1/8 inch from the top of the stamp.

2. Place the stamp in the album and press down to secure it.

3. Using your tongs, gently lift the corners of the stamp to make sure it's not stuck to the page.

Instead of a hinge, you can insert the entire stamp into a mount—a small, clear plastic sleeve. Mounts are more expensive than hinges, but they protect stamps from air, dirt and moisture.

IS THERE ANYTHING ELSE I NEED?

Here's a list of other equipment you may find helpful:

Glassine envelopes are made of a special thin, see-through paper that protects stamps from grease and air. You can use them to keep stamps until you put them in your album.

A **stamp catalog** is a reference book with illustrations to help you identify stamps. It also lists the values of used and unused stamps.

A **magnifying glass** helps you examine stamps by making them appear larger.

A **perforation gauge** measures perforations along the edges of stamps. Sometimes the size and number of perforations (perfs) are needed to identify stamps.

A **watermark tray** and **watermark fluid** help make watermarks on stamps more visible. A watermark is a design or pattern that is pressed into some stamp paper during manufacturing.

Who decides which subjects will become stamps?

The USPS's Citizens' Stamp Advisory Committee meets four times a year to discuss new stamp designs. This committee, established more than 30 years ago, consists of historians, artists, business people, philatelists and others interested in American history and culture.

The committee receives hundreds of suggestions every week. Just a few of these can be recommended because only a limited number of stamps is issued each year. The committee keeps all postal customers in mind as it makes its decisions.

If you think a story should be told on a stamp, submit your idea at least 36 months before the date when it should logically be issued. Send your suggestions and any helpful background information to:

United States Postal Service Citizens' Stamp Advisory Committee
Room 4474-E
475 L'Enfant Plaza West SW
Washington, DC
20260-2437

ow do I collect First Day Covers?

The fastest way to get a First Day Cover is to buy the stamp yourself (it will usually go on sale the day after the first day of issue), attach it to your own envelope (or cover), and send it to the first day post office for cancellation. You can submit up to 50 envelopes, up to 30 days after the stamp's issue date. Here's how:

1. Write your address in the lower right-hand corner of each first day envelope, at least 5/8" from the bottom. Leave plenty of room for the stamp(s) and cancellation. Use a peel-off label if you prefer.

2. Insert a piece of cardboard (about as thick as a postcard) into each envelope. You can tuck the flap in or seal the envelope.

3. Affix your stamp(s) to your first day envelope(s).

4. Put your first day envelope(s) inside another, larger envelope and mail it to "Customer-Affixed Envelopes" in care of the postmaster of the first day city. Your envelopes will be canceled and returned.

Or, you can purchase a plain envelope with the stamp(s) already affixed and canceled. These are now sold directly by mail order through the U.S. Postal Service.

HOW CAN I TELL WHAT A STAMP IS WORTH?

Ask yourself two questions: "How rare is it?" and "What condition is it in?" The price listed in a stamp catalog gives you some idea of how rare it is. However, the stamp may sell at more or less than the catalog price, depending on its condition.

Always try to find stamps in the best possible condition.

HOW SHOULD I JUDGE THE CONDITION OF A STAMP?

Stamp dealers put stamps into categories according to their condition. Look at the pictured examples to see the differences among categories. A stamp in mint

condition is the same as when purchased from the post office. An unused stamp has no cancel but may not have any gum on the back. Mint stamps are usually worth more than unused stamps.

You can begin to judge the condition of a stamp by examining the front of it. Are the colors bright or faded? Is the stamp clean, dirty or stained? Is the stamp torn? Torn stamps are not considered "collectible." Is the stamp design centered on the paper, crooked, or off to one side? Are all the perforations intact? Has the stamp been canceled? A stamp with a light cancellation is in better condition than one with heavy marks across it.

Now look at the back of the stamp. Is there a thin spot in the paper? If so, it may have been caused by careless removal from an envelope or hinge.

The values listed in this book are for used and unused stamps in Fine-Very Fine condition that have been hinged.

Light Cancel–Very Fine

Medium Cancel–Fine

Heavy Cancel

Superb

Very Fine

Fine

Good

11

WHERE ELSE CAN I FIND STAMPS?

Check the classified ads in philatelic newspapers and magazines at your local library. Also, there is a listing of philatelic publishers on page 43 of this book. These publishers will send you one free copy of their publications. Then you can decide if you'd like to subscribe.

WHAT OTHER STAMP MATERIALS CAN I COLLECT?

Postal stationery products are popular among some collectors. These have the stamp designs printed or embossed (printed with a raised design) directly on them.

Stamped Envelopes were first issued in 1853. More than 600 million of them are now printed each year.

Postal Cards were first issued in 1873. The first U.S. multicolored commemorative postal cards came out in 1956. Several different postal cards are issued each year.

Aerogrammes (air letters) are designed to be letters and envelopes all in one. They are specially stamped, marked for folding and already gummed.

Other philatelic collectibles include:

Plate Blocks usually consist of four stamps from the corner of a pane, with the printing plate number in the margin (or selvage) of the pane.

Copyright Blocks feature the copyright symbol © followed by "United States Postal Service" or "USPS" in the margin of the pane. The USPS began copyrighting new stamp designs in 1978.

Booklet Panes are panes of three or more of the same stamp issue. Panes are affixed inside a thin folder to form a booklet. Usually, collectors of booklet panes save the entire pane.

First Day Covers are envelopes bearing new stamps that are postmarked on the first day of sale. For each new postal issue, the USPS selects one location, usually related to the stamp subject, as the place for the first day dedication ceremony and the first day postmark. There is even an annual First Day Cover Collecting Week. See the article on page 10 for information on how to collect these covers.

Souvenir Programs are given to persons who attend first day ceremonies. They contain a list of participants, information on the stamp subject and the actual stamp attached and postmarked.

ARE THERE ANY STAMP GROUPS I CAN JOIN?

Yes! Stamp clubs can be a great source for new stamps and for stamp collecting advice. These clubs often meet at schools, YMCAs and community centers. Write to

**LINN'S CLUB CENTER
P.O. BOX 29
SIDNEY, OH
45365-0029**

for the locations of clubs near you.

Stamping through the West

Over the years, the U.S. Postal Service has honored the people and places that made the American West great. You'll find stamps commemorating them throughout this Guide. Or, start your collection with this list of Western stamps, pardner!

Scott No.	Description	Issue Date
286	Farming in the West	1898
290	Hardships of Emigration	1898
292	Western Cattle in Storm	1898
783	Oregon Territory	1936
954	California Gold	1948
970	Fort Kearny, Neb.	1948
999	Nevada Settlement	1951
1028	Gadsden Purchase	1953
1060	Nebraska Territorial Centennial	1954
1061	Kansas Territorial Centennial	1954
1063	Lewis & Clark Expedition	1954
1120	Overland Mail	1959
1187	Frederic Remington	1961
1198	Homestead Act	1962
1364	Chief Joseph	1968
2178	Buffalo Bill Cody	1986
2512	Grand Canyon	1990
2747	Oregon Trail	1993
2754	Cherokee Strip Land Run	1993
new	Buffalo Soldiers	1994
new	Legends of the West (pane of 20)	1994

Western legends come alive in 1994 stamp release

For the 15 million men and women who moved west in the 1800s, the American frontier represented a dream—the dream of a better life far away from crowded Eastern cities. The West promised fertile ground and wide open spaces for those who were brave enough to make the trek. In 1994, the United States Postal Service honored the West and all those who believed in its promise with a commemorative stamp release—a pane of 20 stamps.

By horse or by wagon, they headed West—wide-eyed explorers, hunters, guides, scouts and, of course, families.

Ever-so-slow wagon trains, hungry hunting parties, watchful army units and hopeful bands of missionaries brought in the 350,000 people who comprised the West's first population boom in the mid-19th century. Eager farmers followed close behind after Congress passed the Homestead Act in 1862. Through the Act, the government offered 165 acres of free land to any person who would live on it and cultivate it for five years.

WHAT WAS WESTERN LIFE LIKE?

Far from easy. Of the 350,000 who rode with the wagon trains, 20,000 died along the way. Members of wagon trains faced mental fatigue and the pressure of trying to cross the continental divide before winter, when snow, wind and freezing temperatures made the Rockies nearly impassable.

Life didn't get much easier for those who finally settled in the West, but those who worked hard were rewarded. Cattle ranching and railroad construction became two of the most crucial new jobs for settlers; expanding rail lines provided access to Eastern cities, and the cattle industry flourished to meet the rising demand for cattle back east. Once-tiny Kansas towns, which sprung up as railroad hubs, quickly grew and attracted testy gunfighters and no-nonsense law officers, many of whom achieved legendary status.

Out of necessity, pioneers learned how to farm or hunt their own food. This became easier in the 1870s with the introduction of barbed wire—a good, cheap substitute for wooden fencing—and improved windmills, which allowed settlers to get their water from far underground. Improved plows and other farm equipment enabled settlers to cultivate huge areas of land by the end of the century.

NO MORE FRONTIERS

In the 20 years preceding 1890, the population west of the Mississippi River had increased from 7 million people to 17 million. By that time the U.S. Bureau of Census declared that no frontiers remained in the U.S., and just about every area once set aside for relocated Native Americans had been opened to white settlement. Westward expansion had come to a close; many forests had been cut down, and much of the frontier's soil now exhausted.

Western movement slowed, but the adventurous spirit of the West remains alive today, in legends that have spawned novels, movies, and songs. With each story and image our knowledge of the West increases, and our culture grows in a richness that is truly American.

WESTERN PROFILES

NINE LEGENDS OF THE WEST

Jim Bridger
1804-1881
Hunter, trapper, fur trader, guide and mountain man. After the Native Americans, he was the first to encounter Utah's Great Salt Lake, as well as the area that became Yellowstone National Park.

Jim Beckwourth
1798-1866
Explorer, fur trader, army guide and mountain man. He discovered Beckwourth Pass, located in the Sierra Nevada Mountains, which opened up a route to California's Sacramento Valley.

Wyatt Earp
1848-1929
Frontiersman and peace officer. Earp honed his shooting skills hunting buffalo for a government surveying party in Kansas, and eventually became a lawman in Tombstone, Ariz., Wichita and Dodge City.

John Frémont
1813-1890
Pioneer and politician. Frémont explored much of the West, including the Oregon Trail, and produced some of the first scientific maps of the American West. In 1856 he ran for president as a Republican and lost to James Buchanan.

"Bat" Masterson
1853-1921
Frontiersman, lawman, gambler and sportswriter. William Barclay Masterson was first known for his sharpshooting, and helped Wyatt Earp enforce the law in Tombstone, Ariz. He went on to run his own gambling hall, and eventually moved to New York, where he covered sports for the New York Morning Telegraph.

USA 29 — JIM BRIDGER

USA 29 — BAT MASTERSON

29 USA

GERONIMO

~~~
**Geronimo**
**1823-1909**
Native American
leader. Geronimo, a
famous resistant
Native American,
escaped from an
Arizona reservation to
battle U.S. soldiers in
Chihuahua and the
Southwest. He joined
and defended
Chiricahua Apaches
in Mexico's Sierra
Madre mountains
until he surrendered
for the last time in
1885.

~~~
Bill Pickett
1870-1932
Cowboy,
showman and
rancher. Of the
many African-
Americans who
helped tame
the Wild West,
Bill Pickett stood
out as one of the
more fearless rodeo
riders. He added his
own style and flair to
bulldogging—a risky
event in which the
rider grabs the bull
by its horns—and
employed Will Rogers
and Tom Mix as
assistants.

~~~
**Chief Joseph**
**1840-1904**
Native American
leader. He led his
tribe in battle against
U.S. troops, which
wanted control of his
Nez Percé homeland
in Oregon. In 1877

he organized a retreat
through Idaho and
Montana, but was
forced to surrender
about 40 miles from
the U.S.-Canadian
border.

**29 USA**

WILD BILL HICKOK

~~~
"Wild Bill" Hickok
1837-1876
Marksman, frontier
scout and peace
officer. James Butler
Hickok, a scout for
the Union Army and
Lieutenant General
George A. Custer,
was marshal of Hays
City, Kansas, before
touring the East with
Buffalo Bill. Hickok
was killed while
playing poker, and his
final cards became
known as the "dead
man's hand:" aces
and eights.

USA 29

CHIEF JOSEPH

omen in the Wild West

Female feats in the new frontier

〰

Have you heard of these women of the West? One was a coal and ore miner, restaurant owner and skilled dogsledder. Another was an explorer and interpreter for the Lewis and Clark Expedition. And another was one of the most accurate gunslingers ever to grace the West. Although nobody ever described them with gutsy nicknames like "No-Nonsense Nellie" or "Quick-Draw," their bold achievements—and those of many other women of the West— are just as notable as those of the men given

nicknames like "Wild Bill," "Buffalo Bill" and "Bat" Masterson.

Here's a look at these women and how they became Legends of the West.

〰

Nellie Cashman
1849-1925

She ran her own restaurant, mined in dozens of coal and ore shafts nationwide and, in her golden years, took up an untraditional hobby: kayaking. The "Angel of Tombstone," Nellie Cashman, was a woman who simply could not sit still.

The Irish-born Cashman, who came to the U.S. after the Civil War, was constantly on the move. In 1880 she became the first female proprietor in Tombstone, Ariz., when she opened her own restaurant. She also ran a boarding

NELLIE CASHMAN

house, raised at least five orphans, and gave money freely to hospitals, missions and injured miners. Even outlaws felt her kindness—Cashman once prepared a gravesite and tombstone for a local prisoner sentenced to die. She kept his hanging from becoming a public spectacle.

Cashman's wit, grace and compassion made her a woman all men sought, but she remained single; adventure was the only thing to which she clung. Later in her life she moved to

Alaska, where she became a skilled kayaker and dogsledder. Cashman spent her last days staked out at a mining claim in Alaska, at the edge of the Arctic Circle.

꘡꘡

Annie Oakley
1860-1926

Annie Oakley had two hobbies: needlepoint and sharpshooting. She was better with a gun than a needle, and became famous for her ability to blast cigars (safely) from her husband's mouth.

Born Phoebe Ann Moses, Oakley proved she had an eagle eye at the age of 15, when she defeated a pro marksman in exhibition shooting. That marksman—Frank Butler—was so impressed that he married Annie one year later, and eventually managed her career. The five-feet-tall Oakley joined Buffalo Bill's Wild West show in 1885, and Sioux Indian chief Sitting Bull dubbed her "Little Sure Shot." Injuries from a train accident forced Annie to leave the show in 1901, but that didn't slow her down. She

enjoyed the spotlight again during World War I, when she starred in the play *The Western Girl*.

Irving Berlin's musical comedy *Annie Get Your Gun* was loosely based on her life.

꘡꘡

Sacagawea
1787-1812

She was born in the Rocky Mountains, captured by enemies at age 11 and later sold to a French-Canadian fur trader. After an unsettled youth, Sacagawea proved to be instrumental in the success of the Lewis and Clark Expedition.

After migrating east, Sacagawea eventually met Lewis and Clark in 1804. She joined their expedition outside Nebraska because they needed a Native American to

translate for them once they neared the Rockies and its inhabitants. After many long months and miles the small group met the same Shoshones that raised Sacagawea. And, much to Sacagawea's surprise, her brother was now the Shoshone chief. Sacagawea persuaded him to provide horses, food and guides for the excursion, which crossed through the Rockies in late fall and eventually made it all the way to the Pacific Ocean.

The Lewis and Clark Expedition was a success, of course. And much of that success is credited to the brave soul they called "Bird Woman:" Sacagawea. In the U.S. today, there are more statues dedicated to her than to any other American woman.

1994 Issues—Commemorative and Special

From the Wild West to the World Cup, the U.S. Postal Service released another colorful collection of stamps in 1994. Ask for them at your local Post Office, or send for the *Stamps etc.* mail-order catalog, Philatelic Fulfillment Service Center, U.S. Postal Service, Box 419424, Kansas City, MO 64179-0997. Most stamps remain on sale at least one year from date of issue, especially by mail order.

Winter Sports
Date of Issue: January 6, 1994
Place of Issue: Salt Lake City, UT

Edward R. Murrow
Date of Issue: January 21, 1994
Place of Issue: Pullman, WA

Dr. Allison Davis
Date of Issue: February 1, 1994
Place of Issue: Williamstown, MA

Happy New Year
Date of Issue: February 5, 1994
Place of Issue: Pomona, CA

Victorian Love Birds
Date of Issue: February 14, 1994
Place of Issue: Niagara Falls, NY
(Note: 29¢ booklet version issued
February 14. The sheet version
followed June 11, also at Niagara
Falls.)

Winter Sports (#2807-11)

Beginning in 1994, the Winter Olympics will alternate at two-year intervals with the Summer Olympics. This five-stamp strip, picturing sports in the Winter Games, captures the action that the world enjoys watching.

Designer: Lon Busch
Printing: Offset

Edward R. Murrow (#2812)

In his deep, resonant voice, Murrow brought events to life for the American public as a radio and TV broadcaster. President Kennedy appointed him director of the U.S. Information Agency. Murrow's portrait adorns this commemorative stamp and reminds us of the high standards he set for broadcast journalism.

Designer: Chris Calle
Printing: Intaglio

Dr. Allison Davis (#2816)

This stamp in the Black Heritage series commemorates Dr. Davis' achievements as a psychologist, educator and author. Dr. Davis taught at the University of Chicago, Columbia University and the University of California at Berkeley, among others.

Designer: Chris Calle
Printing: Intaglio

Happy New Year (#2817)

First there was 1992's popular "Year of the Rooster" stamp. Now comes the colorful follow-up: The "Year of the Dog" stamp featuring a stylized Pekinese.

Designer: Clarence Lee
Printing: Gravure

Victorian Love Bird (#2814: booklet; 2814C: sheet)

This year's Love stamps are sweetly old-fashioned. Victorian in style, featuring doves and roses, they're ideal for mailing Valentine cards.

Designer: Lon Busch
Printing: Gravure (booklet); offset/intaglio (sheet)

Love Birds (#2815)

The coordinated designs for the 1994 Love stamps make them perfect for mailing wedding invitations. The 52¢ stamp pays 2-oz. postage, which is common for many invitations. The 29¢ stamp pays for the R.S.V.P. return.

Designer: Lon Busch
Printing: Offset/intaglio

Buffalo Soldiers (#2818)

Having served with distinction on the Union side in the Civil War, black soldiers were called upon to participate in the Indian conflicts in the West. One fifth of the Cavalry consisted of African-American "Buffalo Soldiers," whose service is honored with this stamp.

Designer: Mort Kuntsler
Printing: Offset/intaglio

Stars of the Silent Screen (#2819-28)

Words can't describe what they brought to the screen in the early days of movies. But this delightful series gives you the idea. Celebrate the comic antics of Charlie Chaplin, Buster Keaton, Harold Lloyd, ZaSu Pitts and the Keystone Cops; the drama of Lon Chaney Sr. (the original "Phantom of the Opera"); and the romance of Rudolph Valentino, Theda Bara, John Gilbert and Clara Bow.

Designer: Al Hirschfeld
Printing: Offset/intaglio

Summer Garden Flowers (#2829-33)

Add a bright, summery touch to your mail. Like 1993's Garden Flowers booklet, this new series is blooming with color.

Designer: Ned Seidler
Printing: Offset/intaglio

1994 Issues—Postal Stationery

Lincoln Home (19¢) (#UX174)	February 12, 1994	Postal Card
Meyrs Hall (19¢) (#UX175)	March 11, 1994	Postal Card
Canyon de Chelly (19¢)	August 11, 1994	Postal Card
St. Louis Union Station (19¢)	September 3, 1994	Postal Card
Football (29¢)	September 17, 1994	Envelope

1994 Issues—New Printings

Tractor Trailer (10¢ coil)
New printing, released May 25, 1994, at Secaucus, NJ, is printed by gravure rather than intaglio. Printed lines are not as "raised" above the surface as the intaglio version, colors are a bit lighter, and plate numbers include two digits instead of one. Originally issued in 1991 (see #2457).

Fishing Boat (19¢ coil) (#2529c)
New printing, released June 25, 1994, at Arlington, VA, is distinguished by a single loop of rope fastening the boat to the mooring, rather than a double loop. Originally issued in 1991 (see #2529) and reprinted in 1993 (see #2529a).

Buffalo Soldiers
Date of Issue: April 22, 1994
Place of Issue: Dallas, TX

Stars of the Silent Screen
Date of Issue: April 27, 1994
Place of Issue: San Francisco, CA

Summer Garden Flowers
Date of Issue: April 28, 1994
Place of Issue: Cincinnati, OH

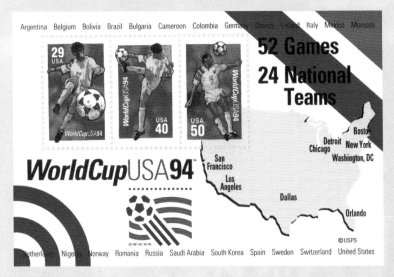

World Cup Soccer
Date of Issue: May 26, 1994
Place of Issue: East Rutherford, NJ

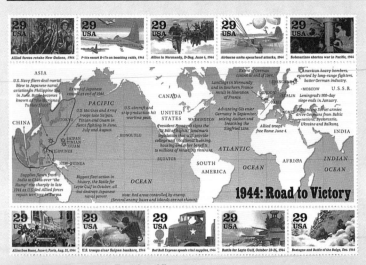

World War II - 1944: Road to Victory
Date of Issue: June 6, 1994
Place of Issue: USS Normandy

World Cup Soccer (#2834-36: single; 2837: souvenir sheet)

The world's most widely followed single-sport event comes to the United States in 1994. Played in nine U.S. cities, the World Cup tournament will determine which of the 24 national soccer teams will take the top prize. The stamp designs, in 29-, 40-, and 50- cent denominations, capture peak moments of play.

Designer: Michael Dudash
Printing: Gravure

World War II - 1994: Road to Victory (#2838)

This 10-stamp sheet, including a world map, portrays notable events of the next-to-last year of World War II. The single most dramatic event of the year was the Normandy invasion on June 6, but Allied forces were advancing on many fronts. Fourth in a series of miniature sheets commemorating the 50th anniversary of American participation in the war.

Designer: Bill Bond
Printing: Offset/intaglio

Migratory Bird Hunting and Conservation Stamps ("Duck Stamps") are sold as bird hunting permits and are not usable for postage.

Red-breasted Merganser ($15)
Date of Issue: June 30, 1994
Place of Issue: Washington, DC
(Issued by the U.S. Department of the Interior)

Some details, including catalog numbers, were not available at press time.

Four Freedoms (#2840)

This four-stamp souvenir sheet reproduces Norman Rockwell's paintings of the Four Freedoms proclaimed by President Roosevelt during World War II.

Designer: Richard Sheaff
Illustrator: Norman Rockwell
Printing: Offset

Norman Rockwell (#2839)

The artist Norman Rockwell captured the ideal of traditional small-town American life. His paintings, many of them magazine cover illustrations, also found humor in the incidents of daily life. Rockwell's birth centennial is celebrated with his popular "triple self-portrait."

Designer: Richard Sheaff
Illustrator: Norman Rockwell
Printing: Offset/intaglio

Moon Landing (#2841: sheet; 2841a: 29¢; 2842: $9.95)

Shortly after the first moon landing, noted artist Paul Calle designed a 10¢ airmail stamp, in celebration of the event. Twenty years later, his son Chris designed a $2.40 stamp in honor of the anniversary. Now, to celebrate the 25th anniversary, Paul and Chris Calle have teamed up to design a 29¢ commemorative stamp and a $9.95 stamp for Express Mail, providing a tribute to this landmark of human endeavor and U.S. space achievement.

Designer:
Chris Calle and
Paul Calle
Printing:
Offset/intaglio
($9.95);
gravure (29¢)

Four Freedoms
Date of Issue: July 1, 1994
Place of Issue: Stockbridge, MA

Norman Rockwell
Date of Issue: July 1, 1994
Place of Issue: Stockbridge, MA

29¢ Moon Landing
Date of Issue: July 20, 1994
Place of Issue: Washington, DC

$9.95 Moon Landing
Date of Issue: July 20, 1994
Place of Issue: Washington, DC

George Meany
Date of Issue: August 16, 1994
Place of Issue: Washington, DC

Locomotives
Date of Issue: July 28, 1994
Place of Issue: Chama, NM

James Thurber
Date of Issue: September 10, 1994
Place of Issue: Columbus, OH

Jazz and Blues Singers
Date of Issue: September 17, 1994
Place of Issue: Greenville, MS

Popular Singers
Date of Issue: September 1, 1994
Place of Issue: New York, NY

Locomotives (#2847a: booklet)

Across mountains and prairies, they towed passengers and freight from sea to shining sea. Steam engines, like those shown in the series, once knit the country together with treads of steel. The romance of the railroads is captured in this tribute to the "Iron Horse."

Designer: Richard Leech
Printing: Gravure

George Meany

Meany's portrait dominates the stamp that pays tribute to him as one of the United States's foremost labor leaders. For many years the head of the American Federation of Labor (AFL), Meany presided over the AFL's merger with the Congress of Industrial Organizations (CIO), which united divergent elements in the labor movement.

Designer: Chris Calle
Printing: Intaglio

James Thurber

One of America's great humorists, Thurber overcame a loss of eyesight to become a longtime New Yorker contributor. He was equally fluent as a short story writer, essayist, and cartoonist. A self-portrait sketch of Thurber, and New Yorker-style typography, give this stamp its character.

Designer: Richard Sheaff
Illustrator: James Thurber
Printing: Offset/intaglio

Popular Singers

Through movies, the Broadway stage, radio, and TV, these vocalists put wings on melodies and sent them to every corner of America. This series showcases five great talents who set the life of a nation to music—Al Jolson, Bing Crosby, Ethel Waters, Nat "King" Cole and Ethel Merman.

Designer: Chris Payne
Printing: Gravure

Jazz and Blues Singers

Here's another installment in the Legends of American Music series. These performers sang about heartbreak and trouble, and in so doing brought a new, authentic, soulful music to America. On back porches in the Mississippi Delta, in Chicago speakeasies, in New York nightclubs, they forged two of our country's original art forms—jazz and blues. This "portrait gallery" of stamps recognizes artists who added to the vitality of our popular culture, namely Bessie Smith, Muddy Waters, Billie Holiday, Robert Johnson, Jimmy Rushing, "Ma" Rainey, Mildred Bailey and Howlin' Wolf.

Designers: Howard Koslow/Julian Allen
Printing: Offset

Wonders of the Seas

If you could bring together amazing sights from oceans all over the world, what would the scene look like? This block of four gives you an imaginative picture.

Designer: Charles Lynn Bragg
Printing: Offset

Cranes

World Post Day, October 9, will mark the joint issuance by the People's Republic of China and the U.S. of two stamps featuring endangered species: the Black Necked Crane and the Whooping Crane. The birds are the symbols of peace and friendship.

Designer: Clarence Lee (U.S.)
Illustrator: Zhan Gengxi (People's Republic of China)
Printing: Offset/intaglio

Legends of the West

This 20-stamp sheetlet blazes new trails in the stamp world. It's the first in the Classic Collection series. Features include a banner of title and artwork above the actual stamps, a theme uniting all 20 stamps, and descriptive text on the gummed side.

Designer: Mark Hess
Printing: Gravure

To receive your own souvenir edition, hardcover *Legends of the West* tabletop book featuring exciting stories, colorful illustrations and more of these great stamps, please send $24.95 plus 50 cents for postage and handling to:

Legends of the West Book Offer
U.S. Postal Service
Post Office Box 449997
Kansas City, MO 64144-9997

Please allow four to six weeks for delivery. Offer expires October 1, 1995, while supplies last.

Native American Culture	Annie Oakley	Jim Bridger	Buffalo Bill	Home on the Range
Early travelers to the West encouraged rich and complex societies living close to the land in harmony with nature. Tribal lore and extensive archaeological ruins attested to centuries of habitation.	Phoebe Anne Oakley Mozee 1860-1926 "Little Sure Shot," she was a major star of Buffalo Bill Cody's Wild West Show for 17 years. Sharpshooter and entertainer. Source for *Annie Get Your Gun*.	James Bridger 1804-1981 Hunter, trapper, scout, fur trader, mountain man, teller of tall tales. Earliest visitor to the Great Salt Lake. Built Fort Bridger on the Oregon Trail.	William Frederick Cody 1846-1917 Frontier scout, pony express rider, buffalo hunter, army guide. Indian fighter, flamboyant Wild West showman, and hero of Ned Buntline dime novels.	The cowboy is an enduring figure in American folk history. The tall tales of self-reliant trailhands told 'round the chuck wagon and campfire breathed life into the popular legend of the rugged individual.
Wyatt Earp	John Frémont	Bat Masterson	Bill Pickett	Chief Joseph
Wyatt Berry Stapp Earp 1848-1929 Lawman in Wichita, Dodge City & Tombstone. Gunfight at the O.K. Corral. Rode stagecoach shotgun for Wells, Fargo; owned interests in saloons and gambling halls.	John Charles Frémont 1813-1890 Explorer (known as 'The Pathfinder') general, governor, senator, and anti-slavery presidential candidate. Explored and mapped the Oregon Trail.	William Barclay Masterson 1853-1921 Lawman, buffalo hunter, scout, gambler, editor. Died at his typewriter, a New York sportswriter. "Sky Masterson" in *Guys & Dolls* is based on his character.	Willie M. Pickett 1870-1932 Fearless black cowboy, rodeo showman and rancher, said to have invented bulldogging. Both Will Rogers and Tom Mix served as his assistants.	Hin-mah-too-yah-lat-kekht 'Thunder-traveling-to-loftier-heights' c.1840-1904 Eloquent, noble Nez Percé chief whose brilliant tactics allowed his people to fight off the U.S. army across several states.
Wild Bill Hickok	Kit Carson	Geronimo	Charles Goodnight	Nellie Cashman
James Butler Hickok 1837-1876 Scout for Custer, stage driver, trick rider, gunslinger, lawman. Killed while playing poker, holding aces and eights, now known as the "dead man's hand."	Christopher Carson 1809-1868 Frontiersman, trapper, hunter, soldier, guide to Frémont, Indian agent, brevetted brigadier-general. He had close contact with Native Americans in many states and territories.	Goyahkla 'One-who-yawns' c.1829-1909 Chiricahua Apache war leader. A fine horseman, guerilla leader and tactician who led war parties for 30 years. Widely believed to have spiritual powers.	Charles Goodnight 1836-1929 Texas Ranger, Indian fighter and pioneer cattle rancher. Both the Goodnight Trail and the Goodnight-Loving Trail are named for him. First bred the 'cattalo.'	Nellie Cashman c.1849-1925 'The Angel of Tombstone,' anti-violence peacemaker who ran a boarding house, raised orphans, campaigned against public hangings, and once saved a man from an angry mob.
Overland Mail	Sacagawea	Bill Tilghman	Jim Beckwourth	Western Wildlife
Many adventurous tales of the Old West sprang from the delivery of mail by stagecoach and Pony Express, which advertised for young orphans willing to brave the untamed countryside.	'Bird-woman' c.1787-1812 Born Shoshone, she was captured by rival Native Americans and later sold to a French trapper. Both joined the Lewis & Clark Expedition, which she served as guide.	William Matthew Tilghman 1854-1924 Frontiersman, scout, buffalo hunter and one of the best old-time Western lawmen. Brought many an outlaw to justice. Became an Oklahoma state senator.	James Pierson Beckwourth c.1798-1866 Black pioneer mountain man, fur trader and scout. Lived as a war leader with the Crow. Early explorer of Beckwourth Pass in the Sierra Nevada mountains.	As Easterners moved West, pioneers found animals as exotic as the landscape . . . buffalo, prairie dogs, bears, beavers, bighorn sheep, cougars, wolves and rattlesnakes. The eagle became a national symbol.

Cranes
Date of Issue: October 9, 1994
Place of Issue: Washington, DC

Wonders of the Seas
Date of Issue: October 3, 1994
Place of Issue: Honolulu, HI

Legends of the West
Date of Issue: October 18, 1994
Place of Issue: Tucson, AZ and Laramie, WY

Greetings

Contemporary Holiday
Date of Issue: October 20, 1994
Place of Issue: Harmony, MN

CHRISTMAS

Elisabetta Sirani, 1663
National Museum of Women in the Arts

Traditional Holiday
Date of Issue: October 20, 1994
Place of Issue: Washington, DC

Bureau of Engraving and Printing
Date of Issue: November 3, 1994
Place of Issue: New York, NY

Definitive Stamps

Victory at Saratoga
Date of Issue: May 5, 1994
Place of Issue: New York, NY

Washington & Jackson
Date of Issue: August 19, 1994
Place of Issue: Pittsburgh, PA

Virginia Apgar
Date of Issue: October 24, 1994
Place of Issue: Dallas, TX

Contemporary Holiday

This year's Contemporary Holiday issue will delight children and conjure up happy memories for grown-ups. The Holiday stocking— dangling from the "e" in the word "Greetings"—is packed with presents, including a teddy bear and candy cane.

Designer: Lou Nolan
Printing: Offset

Traditional Holiday

This year's Traditional Holiday edition derived its image from a Madonna and Child painted by the Italian Baroque artist Elisabetta Sirani. The picture, in The National Museum of Women in the Arts, continues a European tradition of painting this subject that goes back to the Middle Ages.

Designer: Bradbury Thompson
Printing: Offset/intaglio

Bureau of Engraving and Printing

This issue celebrates the centennial of U.S. postage stamp production by the Bureau of Engraving and Printing. It reproduces the $2 James Madison stamp of 1894, one of the first stamps produced entirely by the Bureau of Engraving and Printing.

Printing: Offset/intaglio

Definitive Stamps

Victory at Saratoga (#2590)

Based on a design originally proposed for a stamp in 1869 (but not used), this issue features an engraving of the John Trumbull painting, "The Surrender of General Burgoyne at Saratoga."

Designer: Joe Brockert/Richard Sheaff/Czeslaw Slania
Printing: Intaglio

Washington & Jackson

Based on a design originally proposed for a stamp in 1869 (but not used), this issue features portraits of Presidents George Washington and Andrew Jackson.

Designer: Yves Baril/Joe Brockert/Richard Sheaff
Printing: Intaglio

Virginia Apgar

This new stamp in the Great Americans series depicts Dr. Virginia Apgar, physician, anesthesiologist and pioneer in research of the prevention and treatment of birth defects. She developed the widely used Apgar Score for evaluating the health of newborns.

Printing: Intaglio

1994 Issues—Self-adhesive

Love Sunrise (#2813)

Issued in sheets of 18 and coil rolls of 5,004.

Designer: Peter Good
Printing: Offset/intaglio

Eagle (#2598)

Issued in sheets of 18 and coil rolls of 5,004.

Designer: Richard Sheaff
Printing: Gravure

Statue of Liberty (#2599)

Issued in sheets of 18 and coil rolls of 5,004.

Designer: Tom Engeman
Printing: Gravure

Santa

A cheerful Santa Claus bearing gifts is featured on the self-adhesive Holiday stamp.

Designer: Harry Zelenko
Printing: Gravure

Cardinal ATM

A cardinal in the snow graces this year's self-adhesive designed specifically for use in Automated Teller Machines (ATMs). Issued in sheets of 18.

Designer: Peter Good
Printing: Gravure

Automated Vending

Postage & Mailing Center (PMC-Unisys version)

Coil stamp on which denomination is imprinted by dispensing equipment. Denomination can be set between 19¢ and $99.99 by customer.

Designer: Richard Sheaff
Printing: Gravure

In 1992, this earlier version of the PMC stamp was released. It was printed by intaglio.

1994 Issues—Self-adhesive

Love Sunrise
Date of Issue: January 27, 1994
Place of Issue: Loveland, OH

Eagle
Date of Issue: February 4, 1994
Place of Issue: Sarasota, FL

Statue of Liberty
Date of Issue: June 24, 1994
Place of Issue: Haines City, FL

Santa
Date of Issue: October 20, 1994
Place of Issue: Harmony, MN

Cardinal ATM
Date of Issue: October 20, 1994
Place of Issue: Harmony, MN

Automated Vending

**Postage & Mailing Center
(PMC-Unisys version)**
Date of Issue: February 19, 1994
Place of Issue: Merrifield, VA

Share the Excitement of New Stamp Issues

- Provides a great way to collect new U.S. postal issues
- Includes postmark with date and place of official issuance for a complete historical record

First day covers are a great way to enjoy the best elements of stamp collecting, and the U.S. Postal Service now offers first day covers for all new issues.

First Day Benefits

In addition to providing the new stamps, each envelope includes blank covers (no cachets) with stamps affixed. Stamps are postmarked with the official United States Postal Service "first day of issue" cancellation, to complete the historical record of the stamps' date and place of issuance.

Different Sizes

Depending on the size or number of stamps in a particular issue, covers come in one of three sizes: *Personal* (#6³/₄) for single stamps and many blocks, *Monarch* (@ 7¹/₂" x 4") for larger blocks and booklet panes, or *Legal* (#10) for larger items and panes. Customers may have self-addressed envelopes canceled through the office of the Postmaster of any official First Day city.

For More Information

Send the postage-paid request card in this book or write to:

U.S. POSTAL SERVICE GUIDE
FIRST DAY COVERS
PHILATELIC FULFILLMENT SERVICE CENTER
PROMOTIONS
PO BOX 419219
KANSAS CITY MO 64179-0998

Stamp Collecting Words and Phrases

Accessories
The tools used by stamp collectors, such as tongs, hinges, etc.

Adhesive
A gummed stamp made to be attached to mail.

Aerophilately
Stamp collecting that focuses on stamps or postage relating to air mail.

Album
A book designed to hold stamps and covers.

Approvals
Stamps sent by a dealer to a collector for examination. Approvals must either be bought or returned to the dealer within a specified time.

Auction
A sale at which philatelic material is sold to the highest bidder.

Block
An unseparated group of stamps, at least two stamps high and two stamps wide.

Black Jack
The nickname for the very popular U.S. two-cent black Andrew Jackson stamp, which was issued in various forms between 1863 and 1875.

Bogus
A completely fictitious, worthless "stamp," created only for sale to collectors. Bogus stamps include labels for nonexistent values added to regularly issued sets, issues for nations without postal systems, etc.

Booklet Pane
A small sheet of stamps specially cut to be sold in booklets.

Bourse
A marketplace, such as stamp exhibition, where stamps are bought, sold or exchanged.

Bluish Paper
Used to print portions of several issues in 1909; the paper was made with 35 percent rag stock instead of all wood pulp. The color goes through the paper, showing clearly on back and face.

Cachet (ka-shay')
A design on an envelope describing an event. Cachets appear on first day of issue, first flight and stamp exhibition covers, etc.

Cancellation
A mark placed on a stamp by a postal authority to show that it has been used.

Centering
The position of the design on a postage stamp. On perfectly centered stamps the design is exactly in the middle.

Classic
An early stamp issue. Most people consider these to be rare stamps, but classic stamps aren't necessarily rare.

Coils
Stamps issued in rolls (one stamp wide)

for use in dispensers or vending machines.

Commemoratives
Stamps that honor anniversaries, important people or special events.

Compound Perforations
Different gauge perforations on different (normally adjacent) sides of a single stamp.

Condition

Condition is the most important characteristic in determining a stamp's value. It refers to the state of a stamp regarding such details as centering, color and gum.

Cover

An envelope that has been sent through the mail.

Cracked Plate

A term used to describe stamps which show evidence that the plate from which they were printed was cracked.

Definitives

Regular issues of postage stamps, usually sold over long periods of time.

Denomination

The postage value appearing on a stamp, such as 5 cents.

Directory Markings

Postal markings that indicate a failed delivery attempt, stating reasons such as "No Such Number" or "Address Unknown."

Double Transfer

The condition on a printing plate that shows evidence of a duplication of all or part of the design.

Dry Printing

Begun as an experiment in 1953, this type of printing results in a whiter paper, a higher sheen on the surface, a thicker and stiffer feel and designs that stand out more clearly than on more standard "wet" printings.

Duplicates

Extra copies of stamps that can be sold or traded. Duplicates should be examined carefully for color and perforation variations.

Entire

An intact piece of postal stationery, in contrast to a cut-out of the printed design.

Error

A stamp with something incorrect in its design or manufacture.

Exploded

A stamp booklet is said to be "exploded" when it has been separated into its various components for show.

Face Value

The monetary value or denomination of a stamp.

Fake

A genuine stamp that has been altered in some way to make it more attractive to collectors. It may be repaired, reperfed or regummed to resemble a more valuable variety.

First Day Cover (FDC)

An envelope with a new stamp and cancellation showing the date the stamp was issued.

Franks

Marking on the face of a cover, indicating it is to be carried free of postage. Franks may be written, handstamped, imprinted or represented by special adhesives. Such free franking is usually limited to official correspondence, such as soldier's mail.

Freak

An abnormal variety of stamps occurring because of paper fold, over-inking, perforation shift, etc., as opposed to a continually appearing variety or a major error.

Grill

A pattern of small, square pyramids in parallel rows impressed or embossed on the stamp to break paper fibers, allowing cancellation ink to soak in and preventing washing and reuse.

Gum

The coating of glue on the back of an unused stamp.

Hinges

Small strips of gummed material used by collectors to affix stamps to album pages.

Imperforate

Indicates stamps without perforations or separating holes. They usually are separated by scissors and collected in pairs.

Label
Any stamp-like adhesive that is not a postage stamp.

Laid Paper
When held to the light, the paper shows alternate light and dark crossed lines.

Line Pairs (LP)
Most coil stamp rolls prior to #1891 feature a line of ink printed between two stamps at varying intervals.

Miniature Sheet
A single stamp or block of stamps with a margin on all sides bearing some special wording or design.

Overprint
Additional printing on a stamp that was not part of the original design.

On Paper
Stamps "on paper" are those that still have portions of the original envelope or wrapper stuck to them.

Packet
A presorted unit of all different stamps. One of the most common and economical ways to begin a collection.

Pane
A full "sheet" of stamps as sold by a Post Office. Four panes typically make up the original sheet of stamps as printed.

Par Avion
French for mail transported "by air."

Perforations
Lines of small holes or cuts between rows of stamps that make them easy to separate.

Philately
The collection and study of postage stamps and other postal materials.

Pictorials
Stamps with a picture of some sort, other than portraits or static designs such as coats of arms.

Plate Block (PB) (or Plate Number Block)
A block of stamps with the margin attached that bears the plate number used in printing that sheet.

Plate Number Coils (PNC)
For most coil stamps rolls beginning with #1891, a small plate number appears at varying intervals in the roll in the design of the stamp.

Postage Due
A stamp issued to collect unpaid postage.

Postal Stationery
Envelopes, postal cards and aerogrammes with stamp designs printed or embossed on them.

Postmark
A mark put on envelopes or other mailing pieces showing the date and location of the post office where it was mailed.

Precancels
Cancellations applied to stamps before the stamps were affixed to mail.

Registered Mail
First class mail with a numbered receipt, including a valuation of the registered item. This guarantees customers will get their money back if an item is lost in the mail.

Reissue
An official reprinting of a stamp that was no longer being printed.

Replicas
Reproductions of stamps sold during the early days of collecting. Usually printed in one color in a sheet containing a number of different designs. Replicas were never intended to deceive either the post office or the collector.

Reprint
A stamp printed from the original plate after the issue is no longer valid for postage. Official reprints are sometimes made for presentation purposes, official collections, etc., and are often distinguished in some way from the "real" ones.

Revenue Stamps
Stamps not valid for postal use but issued for collecting taxes.

Ribbed Paper
Paper which shows fine parallel ridges on one or both sides of a stamp.

Se-tenant
An attached pair, strip or block of stamps that differ in design, value or surcharge.

Secret Marks
Many stamps have included tiny reference points in their designs to foil attempts at counterfeiting and to differentiate issues.

Selvage
The unprinted paper around panes of stamps, sometimes called the margin.

Series
All the variations of design and value of a particular issue.

Set
A unit of stamps with a common design or theme issued at one time for a common purpose or over an extended period.

Souvenir Sheet
A small sheet of stamps with a commemorative inscription of some sort.

Speculative
A stamp or issue released primarily for sale to collectors, rather than to meet any legitimate postal need.

Strip
Three or more unseparated stamps in a row.

Surcharge
An overprint that changes the denomination of a stamp from its original face value.

Sweatbox
A closed box with a grill over which stuck-together unused stamps are placed. A wet, sponge-like material under the grill creates humidity so the stamps can be separated without removing the gum.

Thematic
A stamp collection that relates to a specific theme and is arranged to present a logical story and progression.

Tied On
Indicates a stamp whose postmark touches the envelope.

Tongs
A tool, used to handle stamps, that resembles a tweezers with rounded or flattened tips.

Topicals
Indicates a group of stamps with the same theme—space travel, for example.

Unhinged
A stamp without hinge marks, but not necessarily with original gum.

Unused
The condition of a stamp that has no cancellation or other sign of use.

Used
The condition of a stamp that has been canceled.

Want List
A list of philatelic material needed by a collector.

Watermark
A design pressed into stamp paper during its manufacture.

Wet Printing
Has a moisture content of 15-35 percent, compared to 5-10 percent for "dry" printings; also, has a duller look than "dry" printings.

Wove Paper
A uniform paper which, when held to the light, shows no light or dark figures.

Organizations, Publications and Resources

For Your Information ...

Here's a list of philatelic resources that can increase your knowledge of stamps as well as your collecting enjoyment.

Organizations

Please enclose a stamped, self-addressed envelope when writing to these organizations.

American Air Mail Society
Stephen Reinhard
PO Box 110
Mineola, NY 11501-0110

Specializes in all phases of aerophilately. Membership services include Advance Bulletin Service, Auction Service, free want ads, Sales Department, monthly journal, discounts on Society publications, translation service.

American First Day Cover Society
Founder-Member
2 Vreeland Road
Florham Park, NJ 07932

A full-service, not-for-profit, noncommercial society devoted exclusively to First Day Covers and First Day Cover collecting. Offers information on 300 current cachet producers, expertizing, foreign covers, translation service, color slide programs and archives covering First Day Covers.

American Philatelic Society
Robert E. Lamb
Executive Director
PO Box 8000
Dept. PG
State College, PA
        16803-8000

A full complement of services and resources for stamp collectors. Annual membership offers: library services, educational seminars and correspondence courses, expertizing service, estate advisory service, translation service, a stamp theft committee that functions as a clearinghouse for philatelic crime information, intramember sales service and a monthly journal, The American Philatelist, *sent to all members. Membership 57,000 worldwide.*

American Society for Philatelic Pages and Panels
Gerald Blankenship
PO Box 475
Crosby, TX 77532-0475

American Stamp Dealers' Association
Joseph B. Savarese
3 School St.
Glen Cove, NY 11542-2517

Association of dealers engaged in every facet of philately, with 11 regional chapters nationwide. Sponsors national and local shows. Will send you a complete listing of dealers in your area or collecting specialty. A #10 SASE must accompany your request.

American Topical Association
Donald W. Smith
PO Box 630
Johnstown, PA 15907-0630

A service organization concentrating on the specialty of topical stamp collecting. Offers handbooks and checklists on specific topics; exhibition awards; Topical Time, *a bimonthly publication dealing with topical interest areas; a slide loan service, and information, translation and sales services.*

Booklet Collectors Club
Jim Natele
PO Box 2461-U
Cinnaminson, NJ
        08077-2461

Devoted to the study of worldwide booklets and booklet collecting, with special emphasis on U.S. booklets. Publishes The Interleaf, *a quarterly journal.*

Bureau Issues Association
PO Box 23707
Belleville, IL 62223-0707

Devoted to the study of all U.S. stamps, principally those produced by the Bureau of Engraving and Printing.

**Junior Philatelists
of America**
Central Office
PO Box 850
Boalsburg, PA 16827-0850

*Publishes a bimonthly
newsletter,* The Philatelic
Observer, *and offers auction,
exchange, pen pal and other
services to young stamp
collectors. Adult supporting
membership and gift
memberships are available.
The Society also publishes
various brochures on stamp
collecting.*

Linn's Stamp Club Center
PO Box 29
Sidney, OH 45365-0029

*Write for the address of a
stamp club near your ZIP
Code. Will also provide
information on specialized
national societies.*

**Mailer's Postmark
Permit Club**
Florence M. Sugarberg
PO Box 5793
Akron, OH 44372-5793

*Publishes bimonthly
newsletter,* Permit Patter,
*which covers all aspects
of mailer's precancel
postmarks, as well as a
catalog and two checklists.*

**Modern Postal
History Society**
Bill DiPaolo
404 Dorado Ct.
High Point, NC 27265-9650

*Emphasizes the collection
and study of postal history,
procedures and rates
beginning with the early
20th century and including
rates as shown by use of
definitive stamps on
commercial covers, modern
markings such as bar codes
and ink-jet postmarks, and
auxiliary markings such as
"Return to Sender," etc.
Publishes the quarterly*
Modern Postal History
Journal.

Philatelic Foundation
501 Fifth Ave. Rm. 1901
New York, NY 10017-6103

*A nonprofit organization
known for its excellent
expertization service.
The Foundation's broad
resources, including
extensive reference
collections, 5,000-volume
library and Expert
Committee, provide collectors
with comprehensive
consumer protection. Slide
and cassette programs are
available on such subjects as
the Pony Express, classic
U.S. stamps, Confederate
Postal History and collecting
basics for beginners. Book
series include expertizing
case histories in* Opinions,
*Foundation seminar
subjects in "textbooks" and
specialized U.S. subjects in
monographs.*

Postal History Society
Kalman V. Illyefalvi
8207 Daren Ct.
Pikesville, MD 21208-2211

*Devoted to the study of
various aspects of the
development of the mails
and local, national and
international postal systems;
UPU treaties; and means of
transporting mail.*

**Souvenir Card
Collectors Society**
Dana M. Marr
PO Box 4155
Tulsa, OK 74159-4155

*Provides member auctions,
a quarterly journal and
access to limited-edition
souvenir cards.*

**United Postal
Stationery Society**
Mrs. Joann Thomas
PO Box 48
Redlands, CA 92373-0601

**Universal Ship
Cancellation Society**
David Kent
PO Box 127
New Britain, CT
06050-0127

*Specializes in naval ship
postmarks.*

Free Periodicals

*The following publications
will send you a free copy of
their magazine or newspaper
upon request:*

Linn's Stamp News
PO Box 29
Sidney, OH 45365-0029

*The largest weekly stamp
newspaper.*

**Mekeel's Weekly
Stamp News**
PO Box 5050-ff
White Plains, NY 10602

*World's oldest stamp
weekly, for intermediate and
advanced collectors.*

Stamps etc.
Philatelic Fulfillment
Service Center
United States Postal Service
Kansas City, MO
64144-9997

*Published quarterly; includes
every philatelic item offered
by the USPS.*

Stamp Collector
PO Box 10
Albany, OR 97321-0006

*For beginning and advanced
collectors of
all ages.*

Stamps Auction News
85 Canisteo St.
Hornell, NY 14843-1544

*The monthly financial
journal of the stamp market.*

Stamps Magazine
85 Canisteo St.
Hornell, NY 14843-1544

*The weekly magazine of
philately.*

Museums, Libraries and Displays

There is no charge to visit any of the following institutions. Please contact them before visiting because their hours may vary.

American Philatelic Research Library
PO Box 8338
State College, PA
　　16803-8338

Founded in 1968; now the largest philatelic library in the U.S. Currently receives more than 400 worldwide periodical titles and houses extensive collections of bound journals, books, auction catalogs and dealer pricelists. Directly serves members of the APS and APRL (library members also receive the quarterly Philatelic Literature Review*). The public may purchase photocopies directly or borrow materials through the national interlibrary loan system.*

Cardinal Spellman Philatelic Museum
235 Wellesley St.
Weston, MA 02193-1538

America's only fully accredited museum devoted to the display, collection and preservation of stamps and postal history. It has three galleries of rare stamps, a philatelic library and a post office/philatelic counter. Telephone: (617) 894-6735.

The Collectors Club
22 E. 35th St.
New York, NY 10016-3806

Bimonthly journal, publication of various reference works, one of the most extensive reference libraries in the world, reading and study rooms. Regular meetings on the first and third Wednesdays of each month at 6:30 p.m., except July, August. Telephone: (212) 683-0559.

Friends of the Western Philatelic Library
P.O. Box 2219
Sunnyvale, CA 94087-2219

Hall of Stamps
United States Postal Service
475 L'Enfant Plaza
Washington, DC
　　20260-0001

Located at USPS headquarters, this exhibit features more than $500,000 worth of rare U.S. stamps, a moon rock and letter canceled on the moon, original stamp design art, etc.

National Postal Museum
Smithsonian Institution
2 Massachusetts Ave. NE
Washington, DC
　　20560-0001

Houses more than 16 million items for exhibition and study purposes. Research may be conducted by appointment only on materials in the collection and library. This new museum, which is housed in the old Washington, D.C. Post Office next to Union Station, opened to the public in mid-1993. Telephone: (202) 633-9360.

The Postal History Foundation
PO Box 40725
Tucson, AZ 85717-0725

Regular services include a library, USPS contract post office, philatelic sales, archives, artifacts and collections and a Youth Department. Membership includes subscription to a quarterly journal, The Heliograph. *Telephone: (602) 623-6652.*

San Diego County Philatelic Library
4133 Poplar St.
San Diego, CA 92105-4541

Western Philatelic Library
Sunnyvale Public Library
665 W. Olive Ave.
Sunnyvale, CA 94086-7622

Wineburgh Philatelic Research Library
University of Texas at Dallas
PO Box 830643
Richardson, TX 75083-0643

Open Monday - Thursday, 9 a.m. – 6 p.m.; Friday, 9 a.m. – 5 p.m.; first Saturday each month (except May and June), 1 p.m. – 5 p.m.

Exchange Service

Stamp Master
PO Box 17
Putnam Hall, FL 32685

An "electronic connection" for philatelists via modem and computer to display/review members' stamp inventories for trading purposes, etc.

Literature

Basic Philately
Stamp Collector
PO Box 10
Albany, OR 97321-0006

Brookman Disney, Baseball & Entertainment Topical Price Guide
Arlene Dunn
Brookman Stamp Company
10 Chestnut Dr.
Bedford, NH 03110-5566

Illustrated, 128-page, perfect-bound book.

1995 Brookman Price Guide of U.S., U.N. and Canada Stamps and Postal Collectibles
Arlene Dunn
Brookman Stamp Company
10 Chestnut Dr.
Bedford, NH 03110-5566

Illustrated, 304-page, perfect-bound catalog.

Catalogue of U.S. Souvenir Cards
Washington Press
2 Vreeland Rd.
Florham Park, NJ
07932-1587

Commemorative Cancellation Catalog
General Image, Inc.
PO Box 335
Maplewood, NJ 07040-0335

Catalog covering all pictorial cancellations used in the U.S. during 1988 to 1990 is available. Please send self-addressed, stamped envelope for prices and description.

Compilation of U.S. Souvenir Cards
PO Box 4155
Tulsa, OK 74159-4155

Durland Plate Number Catalog
c/o: Bureau Issues Association
P.O. Box 23707
Belleville, Il 62223-0707

First Day Cover Catalogue (U.S.-U.N.)
Washington Press
2 Vreeland Rd.
Florham Park, NJ
07932-1587

Includes Presidential Inaugural covers.

Fleetwood's Standard First Day Cover Catalog
Fleetwood
Cheyenne, WY 82008-0001

The Fun of Stamp Collecting
Arlene Dunn
Brookman Stamp Company
10 Chestnut Dr.
Bedford, NH 03110-5566

Illustrated, 96-page, perfect-bound book.

The Hammarskjold Invert
Washington Press
2 Vreeland Rd.
Florham Park, NJ
07932-1587

Tells the story of the Dag Hammarskjold error/invert. FREE for #10 SASE.

Linn's U.S. Stamp Yearbook
PO Box 29
Sidney, OH 45365-0029

A series of books providing facts and figures on every collectible variety of U.S. stamps, postal stationery and souvenir cards issued since 1983.

Linn's World Stamp Almanac
P.O. Box 29
Sidney, OH 45365-0029

The most useful single reference source for stamp collectors. Contains detailed information on U.S. stamps.

19th Century Envelopes Catalog
PO Box 48
Redlands, CA 92373-0601

Postage Stamp Identifier and Dictionary of Philatelic Terms
Washington Press
2 Vreeland Rd.
Florham Park, NJ
07932-1587

1992 edition, with new country listings.

Precancel Stamp Society Catalog of U.S. Bureau Precancels
108 Ashwamp Rd.
Scarborough, ME 04074

Precancel Stamp Society Catalog of U.S. Local Precancels
108 Ashwamp Rd.
Scarborough, ME 04074

Scott Specialized Catalogue of U.S. Stamps
PO Box 828
Sidney, OH 45365-8959

Scott Stamp Monthly
PO Box 828
Sidney, OH 45365-8959

Scott Standard Postage Stamp Catalogue
PO Box 828
Sidney, OH 45365-8959

Stamp Collecting Made Easy
PO Box 29
Sidney, OH 45365-0029

An illustrated, easy-to-read, 96-page booklet for beginning collectors.

The 24c 1918 Air Mail Invert
Washington Press
2 Vreeland Rd.
Florham Park, NJ
07932-1587

Tells all there is to know about this famous stamp. FREE for #10 SASE.

20th Century Envelopes Catalog
PO Box 48
Redlands, CA 92373-0601

U.S. Postal Card Catalog
PO Box 48
Redlands, CA 92373-0601

The U.S. Transportation Coils
Washington Press
2 Vreeland Rd.
Florham Park, NJ
07932-1587

FREE for #10 SASE.

Philatelic Centers

In addition to the more than 20,000 postal facilities authorized to sell philatelic products, the U.S. Postal Service also maintains more than 450 Philatelic Centers located in major population centers.

These Philatelic Centers have been established to serve stamp collectors and make it convenient for them to acquire an extensive range of current postage stamps, postal stationery and philatelic products issued by the Postal Service.

Centers are located at Main Post Offices unless otherwise indicated.

Note: ZIP + 4 is 9998 unless otherwise indicated.

Alabama
351 N. 24th
St.Birmingham, AL
35203-

2000 Riverchase
Galleria, Space 102
Birmingham, AL
35244-

307 N. Oates St.
Dothan, AL 36302-

615 Clinton Street
Huntsville, AL 35801-

250 St. Joseph
Mobile, AL 36601-

Downtown Station
135 Catoma St.
Montgomery, AL
36104-

Alaska
Downtown Station
3rd & C Streets
Anchorage, AK 99510-

Arizona
2400 N. Postal Blvd.
Flagstaff, AZ 86004-

Osborn Station
3905 N. 7th Ave.
Phoenix, AZ 85013-

General Mail Facility
4949 E. Van Buren
Phoenix, AZ 85026-

1501 S. Cherrybell
Tucson, AZ 85726-

Arkansas
30 S. 6th St.
Fort Smith, AR 72901-

600 W. Capitol
Little Rock, AR 72201-

California
Holiday Station
1180 W. Ball Road
Anaheim, CA 92802-

2730 W. Tregallas Road
Antioch, CA 94509-

Cerritos Branch
18122 Carmencita
Artesia, CA 90701-

General Mail Facility
3400 Pegasus Drive
Bakersfield, CA 93380-

2000 Allston Way
Berkeley, CA 94704-

135 East Olive St.
Burbank, CA
91502-1820

6330 Fountains
Square Dr.
Citrus Heights, CA
95621-

2121 Meridian Park
Blvd.
Concord, CA 94520-

2020 Fifth Street
Davis, CA 95616-

8111 East Firestone
Downey, CA 90241-

401 W. Lexington Ave.
El Cajon, CA 92020-

Cotten Station
3901 Walnut Dr.
Eureka, CA 95501-

600 Kentucky St.
Fairfield, CA 94533-

1900 E St.
Fresno, CA 93706-

313 E. Broadway
Glendale, CA 91209-

Hillcrest Station
303 E. Hillcrest
Inglewood, CA 90311-

5200 Clark Ave.
Lakewood, CA 90712-

300 Long Beach Blvd.
Long Beach, CA
90801-

Terminal Annex
900 N. Alameda
Los Angeles, CA
90052-

407 C St.
Marysville, CA 95901-

2334 M St.
Merced, CA 95340-

715 Kearney Ave
Modesto, CA 99350-

Civic Center Annex
201 13th St.
Oakland, CA 94612-

211 Brooks
Oceanside, CA 92054-

281 E. Colorado Blvd.
Pasadena, CA 91109-

4300 Black Ave.
Pleasanton, CA 94566-

1647 Yuba St.
Redding, CA 96001-

1201 N. Catalina
Redondo Beach, CA
90277-

Downtown Station
3890 Orange St.
Riverside, CA 92501-

330 Vernon St.
Roseville, CA 95678-

2000 Royal Oaks Dr.
Sacramento, CA 95813-

2535 Midway Dr.
San Diego, CA 92199-

180 Stewart St.
San Francisco, CA
94119-3737

1750 Meridian Dr.
San Jose, CA 95125-

St. Matthews Station
210 S. Ellsworth
San Mateo, CA
94401-9991

Simms Station
41 Simms Street
San Rafael, CA 94901-

Spurgeon Station
615 North Bush
Santa Ana, CA 92701-

836 Anacapa St.
Santa Barbara, CA
93102-

201 E. Battles Rd.
Santa Maria, CA 93454-

730 Second St.
Santa Rosa, CA 95404-

Hammer Ranch Station
7554 Pacific Ave.
Stockton, CA 95213-

4245 W. Lane
Stockton, CA 95208

200 Prairie Ct.
Vacaville, CA 95687-

15701 Sherman Way
Van Nuys, CA 91408-

Channel Islands Station
675 E. Santa Clara St.
Ventura, CA 93001-

396 S. California St.
West Covina, CA
91790-

Area Mail Processing
Center
3775 Industrial Blvd.
West Sacramento, CA
95647-

Colorado
16890 E. Alameda
Pkwy.
Aurora, CO 80017-

1905 15th St.
Boulder, CO 80302-

201 E. Pikes Peak
Colorado Springs, CO
80901-

Downtown Station
951 20th St.
Denver, CO 80202-

222 W. Eighth St.
Durango, CO 81301-

241 N. 4th St.
Grand Junction, CO
81501-

5733 S. Prince St.
Littleton, CO 80120-

421 N. Main St.
Pueblo, CO 81003-

Connecticut
141 Weston St.
Hartford, CT 06101-

11 Silver St.
Middletown, CT 06457-

50 Brewery St.
New Haven, CT 06510-

27 Masonic St.
New London, CT
06320-

469 Main St.
Ridgefield, CT 06877-

421 Atlantic St.
Stamford, CT 06904-

Stratford Branch
3100 Main St.
Stratford, CT 06497-

135 Grand St.
Waterbury, CT 06701-

Delaware
55 The Plaza
Dover, DE 19801-

Federal Station
110 E. Main St.
Newark, DE 19711-

Airport Industrial Park
General Mail Facility
147 Quigley Blvd.
New Castle, DE 19720-

Rodney Square Station
1101 N. King St.
Wilmington, DE 19850-

District of
Columbia
Headquarters Center
475 L'Enfant Plaza SW.
Washington, DC 20260-

National Postal Museum
2 Massachusetts Ave.
NE.
Washington, DC 20560-

Old Post Office Bldg.
1100 Pennsylvania NW.
Washington, DC 20004-

Florida
824 Manatee Ave. West
Bradenton, FL 33506-

100 South Belcher Road
Clearwater, FL 33515-

Downtown Station
220 N. Beach St.
Daytona Beach, FL
32115-

1900 W. Oakland Pk.
Fort Lauderdale, FL
33310-

2655 N. Airport Rd.
Fort Myers, FL 33906-

1717 Orange Ave.
Fort Pierce, FL 34950-

4600 SW. 34th St.
Gainesville, FL 32608-

1801 Polk St.
Hollywood, FL 33022-

Southpoint Station
4150 Belfort Rd.
Jacksonville, FL 32255

1100 Kings Rd.
Jacksonville, FL 32203

210 N. Missouri Ave.
Lakeland, FL 33802-

50 8th Ave. SW.
Largo, FL 34640-

Suntree Branch
6105 N. Wickham Rd.
Melbourne, FL 32940-

2200 NW. 72nd Ave.
Miami, FL 33101-

1200 Goodlette
Naples, FL 33940-

1111 E. Nebraska Ave.
New Port Richey, FL
34653-

400 SW. 1st Ave.
Ocala, FL 34478-

1335 Kingsley Ave.
Orange Park, FL 32073-

46 E. Robinson St.
Orlando, FL 32801-

421 Jenks Ave.
Panama City, FL 32401-

1400 West Jordan St.
Pensacola, FL 32501-

99 King St.
St. Augustine, FL 32084

3135 First Avenue N.
St. Petersburg, FL
33730-

Open Air Postique
76 Fourth St. N.
St. Petersburg, FL
33701-

1661 Ringland Blvd.
Sarasota, FL 34230-

2800 S. Adams St.
Tallahassee, FL 32301-

5201 W. Spruce St.
Tampa, FL 33630-

850 E. Lime St.
Tarpon Springs, FL
34689-

3200 Summit Blvd.
West Palm Beach, FL
33401-

Georgia
575 Olympic Dr.
P.O. Box 80308
Athens, GA 30608-

Downtown Station
101 Marietta St. NW.
Atlanta, GA 30301-

Perimeter Branch
Perimeter Mall Shopping
Center
I-285 & Ashford
Dunwoody Rd.
Atlanta, GA 30346-

Downtown Station
120 12th St.
Columbus, GA 31908-

3470 McClure
Bridge Rd.
Duluth, GA 30136-

364 Green St.
Gainesville, GA 30501-

451 College St.
Macon, GA 31201-

257 Lawrence St.
Marietta, GA 30060-

5600 Spaulding Dr.
Norcross, GA 30092-

2 N. Fahm St.
Savannah, GA 31401-

904 Russell Pky.
Warner Robins, GA
31088-

Hawaii
3600 Aolele St.
Honolulu, HI 96819-

Idaho
770 S. 13th St.
Boise, ID 83708-

220 E. 5th St.
Moscow, ID 83843-

730 E. Clark St.
Pocatello, ID 83201-

Illinois
909 W. Euclid Ave.
Arlington Heights, IL
60004-

525 N. Broadway
Aurora, IL 60507-

Moraine Valley Station
7401 100th Place
Bridgeview, IL
60455-2405

1301 E. Main St.
Carbondale, IL 62901-

Loop Station
211 S. Clark St.
Chicago, IL 60604-

433 W. Van Buren St.
Chicago, IL 60607-

1000 E. Oakton
Des Plaines, IL 60018-

1101 Davis St.
Evanston, IL 60204-

2359 Madison Ave.
Granite City, IL 62040-

2000 McDonough St.
Joliet, IL 60436-

1750 W. Ogden Ave.
Naperville, IL 60566-

901 Lake St.
Oak Park, IL
60301-1203

123 Indianwood
Park Forest, IL 60466-

N. University Station
6310 N. University
Peoria, IL 61614-3454

5225 Harrison Ave.
Rockford, IL 61125-

211 19th St.
Rock Island, IL 61201-

Schaumburg Station
450 W. Schaumburg
Roselle, IL 60194-

*In addition to these Philatelic Centers, some larger Post Offices have
dedicated "Philatelic" Windows with many current stamps and products.*

47

2105 E. Cook St.
Springfield, IL 62703-

Edison Square Station
1520 Washington
Waukegan, IL
          60085-5347

1241 Central Ave.
Wilmette, IL 60099-

Indiana
North Park Branch
44928 1st Ave.
Evansville, IN 47710-

Fort Wayne Postal
Facility
1501 S. Clinton St.
Fort Wayne, IN
          46802-3509

5530 Sohl St.
Hammond, IN 46320-

125 W. South Street
Indianapolis, IN 46206-

2719 S. Webster
Kokomo, IN 46902-

3450 State Rd. 26 East
Lafayette, IN 47901-

424 S. Michigan
South Bend, IN 46624-

Cross Roads Station
70 Rose Ave.
Terre Haute, IN 47803-

Iowa
615 6th Ave. SE.
Cedar Rapids, IA
          52401-1923

1165 Second Ave.
Des Moines, IA 50318-

214 Jackson St.
Sioux City, IA
          51101-9706

Kansas
Indian Springs Station
4953 State Ave.
Kansas City, KS 66102-

6029 Broadmoor
Shawnee Mission, KS
          66202-

Santa Fe Room
424 S. Kansas Ave.
Topeka, KS 66603-

Downtown Station
330 W. 2nd Street
Wichita, KS 67202-

Kentucky
1088 Nadino Rd.
Lexington, KY
          40511-1207

Okolona Branch
7400 Jefferson Blvd.
Louisville, KY 40219-

St. Mathews Station
4600 Shelbyville Rd.
Louisville, KY 40207-

Louisiana
1715 Odom St.
Alexandria, LA 71301-

750 Florida St.
Baton Rouge, LA
          70821-

General Mail Facility
1105 Moss St.
Lafayette, LA 70501-

3301 7th St.
Metairie, LA 70004-

501 Sterlington Rd.
Monroe, LA 71201-

701 Loyola Ave.
New Orleans, LA
          70113-

Vieux Carre Station
1022 Iberville St.
New Orleans, LA
          70112-

2400 Texas Ave.
Shreveport, LA 71102-

Maine
40 Western Ave.
Augusta, ME 04330-

202 Harlow St.
Bangor, ME 04401-

125 Forest Ave.
Portland, ME 04101-

Maryland
1 Church Cir.
Annapolis, MD 21401-

900 E. Fayette St.
Baltimore, MD 21233-

Chevy Chase
Finance Unit
5910 Connecticut Ave.
Bethesda, MD 20815-

215 Park St.
Cumberland, MD
          21502-

201 E. Patrick St.
Frederick, MD 21701-

6411 Baltimore Ave.
Riverdale, MD 20840-

500 N. Washington St.
Rockville, MD 20850-

U.S. Rte. 50 &
Naylor Rd.
Salisbury, MD 21801-

Silver Spring Centre
Finance Station
8455 Colesville Rd.
Silver Spring, MD
          20911-

Massachusetts
120 Commercial St.
Brockton, MA 02401-

2 Government Center
Fall River, MA 02722-

881 Main St.
Fitchburg, MA 01420-

330 Cocituate Rd.
Framingham, MA
          01701-

431 Common St.
Lawrence, MA 01842-

Main Post Office
Post Office Square
Lowell, MA 01853-

695 Pleasant St.
New Bedford, MA
          02741-

212 Fenn St.
Pittsfield, MA 01201-

2 Margin St.
Salem, MA 01970-

Main St. Station
1883 Main St.
Springfield, MA 01101-

Turner Falls Post Office
178 Ave. A
Turner Falls, MA
          01376-

462 Washington St.
Woburn, MA 01888-

4 E. Central St.
Worcester, MA 01603-

Michigan
2075 W. Stadium Blvd.
Ann Arbor, MI 48106-

90 S. McCamly
Battle Creek, MI
          49016-

26200 Ford Rd.
Dearborn Hgts., MI
          48127-

1401 W. Fort St.
Detroit, MI 48233-

250 E. Boulevard Dr.
Flint, MI 48502-

225 Michigan Ave.
Grand Rapids, MI
          49501-

200 S. Otsego
Jackson, MI 49201-

1121 Miller Rd.
Kalamazoo, MI 49001-

General Mail Facility
4800 Collins Rd.
Lansing, MI 48924-

735 W. Huron St.
Pontiac, MI 48056-

1300 Military St.
Port Huron, MI 48060-

30550 Gratiot St.
Roseville, MI 48066-

200 W. 2nd St.
Royal Oak, MI 48068-

500 S. Washington
Saginaw, MI 48605-

6300 N. Wayne Rd.
Westland, MI 48185-

Minnesota
2800 W. Michigan
Duluth, MN 55806-

100 S. First St.
Minneapolis, MN
          55401-

Downtown Station
102 S. Broadway
Rochester, MN 55904-

Burnsville Branch
12212 12th Avenue S.
Savage, MN 55378-

Mississippi
2421 13th St.
Gulfport, MS 39501-

La Fleur Station
1501 Jacksonian Plaza
Jackson, MS 39211-

P.O. Box 332
Jackson, MS
          39205-9714

500 W. Miln St.
Tupelo, MS 38801-

Missouri
920 Washington
Chillicothe, MO 64601-

Columbia Mall Station
Columbia, MO 65203-

315 Pershing Rd.
Kansas City, MO 64108-

Northwest Plaza Station
500 Northwest Plaza
St. Ann, MO 63074-

Pony Express Station
8th & Edmond
St. Joseph, MO 64503-

Clayton Branch
7750 Maryland
St. Louis, MO 63105-

Trading Post
1720 Market St.
St. Louis, MO 63155-

500 W. Chestnut Expwy.
Springfield, MO 65801-

48

Please detach at perforation.

UNITED STATES
POSTAL SERVICE™

Philatelic Fulfillment Service Center
Kansas City MO 64179–0997

Official Business

BUSINESS REPLY MAIL
FIRST-CLASS MAIL   PERMIT NO. 73026   WASHINGTON DC

POSTAGE WILL BE PAID BY THE ADDRESSEE

United States Postal Service
Philatelic Fulfillment Service Center
Customer Service
Box 419424
Kansas City MO 64179–1009

Additional information on stamp collecting products

You can expand your stamp collection and keep it updated with philatelic products from the USPS. Check the box next to the products you'd like to learn more about.

❑ *American Commemorative Panels*
❑ *Commemorative Stamp Collections*
❑ *Commemorative Stamp Club*
❑ *Souvenir Pages Program*
❑ *Standing Order Service*
❑ *Topical Stamp Collections*
❑ *StampFolios*

...And a free offer!

Let us know if you're interested in receiving:
❑ *A copy of **Stamps, etc.,** our catalog which contains details and mail-order information on all stamps and stamp products currently available from the Postal Service.*

Neatly print your name and address below, and drop this card in the mail—no postage necessary. (Information that you provide is protected and only disclosed in accordance with the Privacy Act of 1974.)

Mr./Mrs./Ms.

Street Address
(Include P.O. Box, Apt. no., R.D. Route, etc. where appropriate)

City   State   ZIP Code

Please detach at perforation.

Montana
841 S. 26th
Billings, MT 59101-

215 First Ave. N.
Great Falls, MT 59401-

1100 W. Kent
Missoula, MT 59801-

Nebraska
204 W. South Front St.
Grand Island, NE
68801-

700 R St.
Lincoln, NE 68501-

300 E. Third St.
North Platte, NE
69101-

1124 Pacific
Omaha, NE 68108-

Nevada
1001 Sunset Rd.
Las Vegas, NV 89199-

200 Vassar St.
Reno, NV 89510-

New Hampshire
55 Pleasant St.
Concord, NH 03301-

50 S. Main St.
Hanover, NH 03755-

955 Goffs Falls Rd.
Manchester, NH 03103-

80 Daniel St.
Portsmouth, NH 03801-

New Jersey
1701 Pacific Ave.
Atlantic City, NJ 08401-

Veterans Plaza
Bergenfield, NJ 07621-

3 Miln St.
Cranford, NJ 07016-

229 Main St.
Fort Lee, NJ 07024-

Haag Ave. & Benigno
Gloucester, NJ 08099-

Bellmawr Branch
Route 35 & Hazlet Ave.
Hazlet, NJ 07730-

Borough Complex
East End & Van Sant
Ave.
Island Heights, NJ
08732-

69 Montgomery St.
Jersey City, NJ 07305-

160 Maplewood Ave.
Maplewood, NJ 07040-

150 Ridgedale
Morristown, NJ 07960-

Federal Square
Newark, NJ 07102-

86 Bayard St.
New Brunswick, NJ
08906-

Nutley Branch
372 Franklin Ave.
Nutley, NJ 07110-

194 Ward St.
Paterson, NJ 07510-

171 Broad St.
Red Bank, NJ 07701-

680 Highway 130
Trenton, NJ 08650-

Sheffield Station
150 Pompton Plains
Crossing
Wayne, NJ 07470-9994

155 Clinton Rd.
West Caldwell, NJ
07006-

41 Greenwood Ave.
Wyckoff, NJ 07481-

New Mexico
1135 Broadway NE.
Albuquerque, NM
87101-

200 E. Las Cruces Ave.
Las Cruces, NM 88001-

415 N. Pennsylvania
Ave.
Roswell, NM 88201-

New York
Superintendent USPS
Albany, NY 12220-

General Mail Facility
30 Old Karner Rd.
Albany, NY 12288-

115 Henry St.
Binghamton, NY 13902-

Bronx General P.O.
149th St. & Grand
Concourse
Bronx, NY 10451-

Parkchester Station
1449 West Ave.
Bronx, NY 10462-

Riverdale Station
5951 Riverdale Ave.
Bronx, NY 10471-

Throggs Neck Station
3630 East Tremont Ave.
Bronx, NY 10465-

Wakefield Station
4165 White Plains Rd.
Bronx, NY 10466-

Bayridge Station
5501 7th Ave.
Brooklyn, NY 11220-

Brooklyn General P.O.
271 Cadman Plaza E.
Brooklyn, NY 11201-

Greenpoint Station
66 Meserole Ave.
Brooklyn, NY 11222

Homecrest Station
2002 Ave. U
Brooklyn, NY 11229-

1200 William St.
Buffalo, NY 14240-

1764 Rte. 9
Clifton Park, NY 12065-

Baron DeHirsch Rd.
Crempond, NY 10517-

Downtown Station
255 Clemens Center
Pkwy.
Elmira, NY 14901-

4165 Main St.
Flushing, NY 11351-

Broadway & Maple St.
Glenham, NY 12527-

16 Hudson Ave.
Glens Falls, NY 12801-

185 W. John St.
Hicksville, NY 11802-

8840 164th St.
Jamaica, NY 11431-

300 E. 3rd St.
Jamestown, NY
14701-998

324 Broadway
Monticello, NY 12701-

Ansonia Station
1980 Broadway
New York, NY 10023-

Bowling Green Station
25 Broadway
New York, NY 10036-

Church St. Station
90 Church St.
New York, NY 10007-

Empire State Station
350 Fifth Ave.
New York, NY 10001-

F.D.R. Station
909 Third Ave.
New York, NY 10022-

Grand Central Station
45th St. & Lexington
Ave.
New York, NY 10017-

Madison Square Station
149 E. 23rd St.
New York, NY 10010-

New York General P.O.
33rd St. and 8th Ave.
New York, NY 10001-

Rockefeller Center
610 Fifth Ave.
New York, NY
10020-9991

Times Square Station
340 West 42nd St.
New York, NY 10036-

Main St. & Hunt St.
Oneonta, NY 13820-

Franklin St. &
S. Main St.
Pearl River, NY 10965-

10 Miller St.
Plattsburgh, NY 12901-

Branch Office
407 East Main St.
Port Jefferson, NY
11777-

55 Mansion St.
Poughkeepsie, NY
12601-

1335 Jefferson Rd.
Rochester, NY 14692-

250 Merrick Rd.
Rockville Ctr., NY
11570-

29 Jay St.
Schenectady, NY 12305-

25 Route 11
Smithtown, NY 11787-

New Springville Station
2843 Richmond Ave.
Staten Island, NY
10314-

10 Broad St.
Utica, NY 13503-

108 Main St.
Warwick, NY 10990-

100 Fisher Ave.
White Plains, NY
10602-

7881 Main St.
Yonkers, NY 10701-

North Carolina
West Asheville Station
1300 Patton Ave.
Asheville, NC
28806-2604

Eastway Station
3065 Eastway Dr.
Charlotte, NC 28210-

301 Green St.
Fayetteville, NC 28302-

Four Seasons Station
Four Seasons Town Ctr.
Ste. 303
Greensboro, NC 27427-

310 New Bern Ave.
Raleigh, NC 27611-

North Dakota
220 East Rosser Ave.
Bismarck, ND 58501-

675 2nd Ave. N.
Fargo, ND 58102-

Ohio
675 Wolf Ledges Pky.
Akron, OH 44309-

2650 Cleveland St.
Canton, OH 44702-

Fountain Square Station
5th & Walnut St.
Cincinnati, OH 45202-

2400 Orange Ave.
Cleveland, OH 44101-

850 Twin Rivers Dr.
Columbus, OH 43216-

1111 E. 5th St.
Dayton, OH 45401-

345 E. Bridge St.
Elyria, OH 44035-

105 Court St.
Hamilton, OH 45011-

200 N. Diamond St.
Mansfield, OH 44901-

200 N. 4th St.
Steubenville, OH
        43952-2104

435 S. St. Clair St.
Toledo, OH 43601-

99 S. Walnut St.
Youngstown, OH
        44503-

Oklahoma
208 First Street SW.
Ardmore, OK 73401-

101 E. First
Edmond, OK 73034-

115 W. Broadway
Enid, OK 73701-

102 S. 5th
Lawton, OK 73501-

525 W. Okmulgee
Muskogee, OK 74401-

129 W. Gray
Norman, OK 73069-

320 SW. 5th St.
Oklahoma City, OK
        73125-

116 E. 9th St.
Shawnee, OK 74801-

333 W. 4th
Tulsa, OK 74101-

12 S. 5th
Yukon, OK 73099-

Oregon
311 SW 2nd St.
Corvallis, OR 97333-

520 Willamette St.
Eugene, OR 97401-2627

751 NW. Hoyt
Portland, OR 97208-

1050 25th St. SW.
Salem, OR 97301-

Pennsylvania
442-456 Hamilton St.
Allentown, PA 18101-

535 Wood St.
Bethlehem, PA 18016-

115 Boylston St.
Bradford, PA 16701-

229 Beaver Dr.
Du Bois, PA 15801-

Griswold Plaza
Erie, PA 16501-

115 Buford Ave.
Gettysburg, PA
        17325-9990

238 S. Pennsylvania
Greensburg, PA
        15601-3007

10th and Market St.
Harrisburg, PA 17105-

Johnstown Main Post
Office
111 Franklin St.
Johnstown, PA 15901-

Downtown Station
48-50 W. Chestnut St.
Lancaster, PA 17603-

980 Wheeler Way
Langhorne, PA 19047-

Lehigh Valley Branch
Airport Rd. & Rte. 22
Lehigh Valley, PA
        18001-

Monroeville Mall
Branch
348 Mall Circle Dr.
Monroeville, PA 15146-

435 S. Cascade St.
New Castle, PA 16101-

501 11th St.
New Kensington, PA
        15068-

28 East Airy St.
Norristown, PA 19401-

B. Free Franklin Station
316 Market St.
Philadelphia, PA 19106-

30th St. & Market St.
Philadelphia, PA 19104-

William Penn Annex
Station
9th & Chestnut St.
Philadelphia, PA 19107-

General Mail Facility
1001 California Ave.
Pittsburgh, PA 15290-

Main Post Office
Pittsburgh, PA 15219

59 N. 5th St.
Reading, PA 19603-

North Washington Ave.
& Linden St.
Scranton, PA 18503-

237 S. Frazer St.
State College, PA
        16801-

7th & Ann St.
Stroudsburg, PA 18360-

300 S. Main St.
Wilkes Barre, PA
        18701-

Center City Finance
Station
240 West Third St.
Williamsport, PA
        17703-

200 S. George St.
York, PA 17405-

Puerto Rico
General Post Office
Roosevelt Ave.
San Juan, PR 00936-

Plaza Las Americas
Station
San Juan, PR 00938-

Rhode Island
320 Thames St.
Newport, RI 02840-

40 Montgomery St.
Pawtauket, RI 02860-

24 Corliss St.
Providence, RI 02904-

South Carolina
4290 Daley Ave.
Charleston, SC 29402-

1601 Assembly St.
Columbia, SC 29201-

600 W. Washington
Greenville, SC 29602-

South Dakota
500 E. Boulevard
Rapid City, SD 57701-

320 S. 2nd Ave.
Sioux Falls, SD 57101-

Tennessee
5424 Bell Forge Lane E.
Antioch, TN 37013-

111 Sixth St.
Bristol, TN 37620

General Mail Facility
6050 Shallowford Rd.
Chattanooga, TN 37401-

200 Martin Luther King
Jr. Blvd.
Jackson, TN 38301-

530 E. Main St.
Johnson City, TN 37601-

General Mail Facility
1237 E. Weisgarber Rd.
Knoxville, TN
        37950-9608

Colonial Finance Unit
4695 Southern Ave.
Memphis, TN 38124-

Crosstown Finance Unit
1520 Union Ave.
Memphis, TN
        38174-3725

901 Broadway
Nashville, TN 37202-

Texas
341 Pine St.
Abilene, TX 79604-

2300 S. Ross
Amarillo, TX 79105-

300 E. South St.
Arlington, TX 76010-

Downtown Station
300 East 9th
Austin, TX 78767-

General Mail Facility
8225 Cross Park Dr.
Austin, TX 78710-

300 Willow
Beaumont, TX 77704-

1535 Los Ebanos
Brownsville, TX 78520-

2121 E. Wm. J. Bryan
Pky.
Bryan, TX 77801-

2201 Hilltop Dr.
College Station, TX
        77840-

809 Nueces Bay
Corpus Christi, TX
        78408-

Byran St. and Ervay St.
Dallas, TX 75221-

Olla Podrida
Finance Station
12215 Coit Rd.
Dallas, TX 75251-

5300 E. Paisano Dr.
El Paso, TX 79910-

251 W. Lancaster
Fort Worth, TX 76101-

401 Franklin Ave.
Houston, TX 77201-

Central Station
2300 W. Story Rd.
Irving, TX 75038-

300 N. 10th
Killeen, TX 76541-

411 Ave. L
Lubbock, TX 79408-

601 E. Pecan
McAllen, TX 78501-

100 E. Wall
Midland, TX 79702-

433 Belle Grove
Richardson, TX 75080-

1 N. Bryant
San Angelo, TX 76902-

Downtown Station
615 E. Houston
San Antonio, TX 78205-

10410 Perrin Beitel Rd.
San Antonio, TX 78284-

1411 Wunsche Loop
Spring, TX 77373-

2211 N. Robinson
Texarkana, TX 75501-

221 W. Ferguson
Tyler, TX 75702-

800 Franklin
Waco, TX 76701-

1000 Lamar St.
Wichita Falls, TX
76307-

Utah
3680 Pacific Ave.
Ogden, UT 84401-

95 W. 100 S.
Provo, UT 84601-

1760 W. 2100 S.
Salt Lake City, UT
84119-

Vermont
204 Main St.
Brattleboro, VT 05301-

1 Elmwood Ave.
Burlington, VT 05401-

151 West St.
Rutland, VT
05701-2859

White River Junction,
VT 05001-

Virginia
111 Sixth St.
Bristol, VA 24201-

1155 Seminole Trail
Charlottesville, VA
22906-

1425 Battlefield Blvd. N.
Chesapeake, VA 23320-

700 Main St.
Danville, VA 24541-

Merrifield Branch
8409 Lee Hwy.
Fairfax, VA 22116-

809 Aberdeen Rd.
Hampton, VA 23670-

300 Odd Fellows Rd.
Lynchburg, VA 24506-

Denbigh Station
14104 Warwick Blvd.
Newport News, VA
23602-

600 Church St.
Norfolk, VA 23501-

Thomas Corner Station
6274 E. Virginia
Beach Blvd.
Norfolk, VA 23502-

1801 Brook Rd.
Richmond, VA 23232-

419 Rutherford Ave. NE.
Roanoke, VA 24022-

1430 N. Augusta
Staunton, VA 24401-

501 Viking Dr.
Virginia Beach, VA
23454-

Washington
11 3rd St. NW.
Auburn, WA 98001-

Crossroads Station
15800 NE. 8th
Bellevue, WA
98008-3906

315 Prospect St.
Bellingham, WA 98225-

3102 Hoyt
Everett, WA 98201

3500 W. Court
Pasco, WA 99301-4532

424 E. 1st St.
Port Angeles, WA
98362-

301 Union St.
Seattle, WA 98101-

W. 904 Riverside
Spokane, WA 99210-

1102 A St.
Tacoma, WA 98402-

205 W. Washington
Yakima, WA 98903-

West Virginia
301 North St.
Bluefield, WV
24701-4307

Lee & Dickinson St.
Charleston, WV 25301-

500 W. Pike St.
Clarksburg, WV
26301-2664

1000 Virginia Ave.
W. Huntington, WV
25704-1726

217 King St.
Martinsburg, WV
25401-

Wisconsin
126 N. Barstow St.
Eau Claire, WI 54703-

325 E. Walnut
Green Bay, WI 54301-

425 State St.
La Crosse, WI 54601-

3902 Milwaukee St.
Madison, WI 53707-

345 W. St. Paul Ave.
Milwaukee, WI 53203-

1025 W. 20th Ave.
Oshkosh, WI 54901

235 Forrest St.
Wausau, WI 54401

Wyoming
150 E. B Street
Casper, WY 82601-

2120 Capitol Ave.
Cheyenne, WY 82001-

FOREIGN CENTERS
U.S. Postal Service stamps and products are available at face value from agencies in foreign countries, as follows:

Australia
Max Stern & Co.
Port Phillip Arcade
234 Flinders St.
Melbourne 3000

Denmark
Nordfrim
DK 5450 Otterup

France
Theodore Champion
8 Rue des Messageries
75010 Paris

Germany
Hermann W. Sieger
Venusbert 3234
73545 Lorch/
Wurttemberg

Great Britain
Harry Allen
P.O. Box 5
Watford, Herts
WD2 5SW

Japan
Japan Philatelic Agency
P. O. Box 350
Shinjuku
Tokyo 163-91

Netherlands
J.A. Visser
P. O. Box 184
3300 Ad Dordrecht

Switzerland
De Rosa International S.A.
Av Du Tribunal
Federal 34
Ch-1005 Lausanne

Significant Stamp Details

1¢ Franklin Types I-V of 1851-57

5

Bust of **5**

Detail of **5, 18, 40** Type I
Has curved, unbroken lines outside labels. Scrollwork is substantially complete at top, forms little balls at bottom.

Detail of **5A** Type Ib
Lower scrollwork is incomplete, the little balls are not so clear.

Bust of **5**

Detail of **6, 19** Type Ia
Same as Type I at bottom but top ornaments and outer line partly cut away. Lower scrollwork is complete.

Bust of **5**

Detail of **7, 20** Type II
Lower scrollwork incomplete (lacks little balls and lower plume ornaments). Side ornaments are complete.

Bust of **5**

Detail of **8, 21** Type III
Outer lines broken in the middle. Side ornaments are substantially complete.

Detail of **8A, 22** Type IIIa
Outer lines broken top or bottom but not both.

Bust of **5**

Detail of **9, 23** Type IV
Similar to Type II, but outer lines recut top, bottom or both.

What does the color of the stamp signify?

In the 1940s, the United States Postal Service sought to create some uniformity among stamps. This was achieved through the printing process and ink selection. Different, distinctly colored inks were used to indicate different stamp prices. For example, stamps printed in green were worth 1 cent, red stamps were worth 2 cents, purple stamps were worth 3 cents, blue stamps were worth 5 cents and dark brown stamps were worth 10 cents (**#859-93**). There were some exceptions, however, and this stamp uniformity only lasted a few years.

Bust of 5

Detail of 24 Type V
Similar to Type III of 1851-57 but with side ornaments partly cut away.

3¢ Washington Types I-IIa of 1851-57

10

Bust of 10

Detail of 10, 11, 25, 41 Type I
There is an outer frame line at top and bottom.

Bust of 10

Detail of 26 Type II
The outer frame line has been removed at top and bottom. The side frame lines were recut so as to be continuous from the top to the bottom of the plate.

Bust of 10

Detail of 26a Type IIa
The side frame lines extend only to the bottom of the stamp design.

5¢ Jefferson Types I-II of 1851-57

12

Bust of 12

Detail of 12, 27-29 Type I
There are projections on all four sides.

Bust of 12

Detail of 30-30A Type II
The projections at top and bottom are partly cut away.

10¢ Washington Types I-V of 1851-57

15

Bust of 15

Detail of 13, 31, 43 Type I
The "shells" at the lower corners are practically complete. The outer line below the label is very nearly complete. The outer lines are broken above the middle of the top label and the "X" in each upper corner.

Bust of 15

Detail of 14, 32 Type II
The design is complete at the top. The outer line at the bottom is broken in the middle. The shells are partly cut away.

Bust of 15

Detail of 15, 33 Type III
The outer lines are broken above the top label and the "X" numerals. The Outer line at the bottom and the shells are partly cut away, as in Type II.

Bust of 15

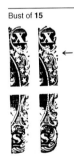

Detail of 16, 34 Type IV
The outer lines have been recut at top or bottom or both. Types I, II, III and IV have complete ornaments at the sides of the stamps and three pearls at each outer edge of the bottom panel.

Bust of 15

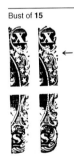

Detail of 35 Type V
(Two typical examples). Side ornaments slightly cut away. Outer lines complete at top except over right "X". Outer lines complete at bottom and shells nearly so.

53

1¢ Franklin of 1861-75

55

3¢ Washington of 1861-75

56

5¢ Jefferson of 1861-75

57

Detail of **55**

Detail of **56**

Detail of **57**

Detail of **63, 86, 92**
In 63, 86 and 92, a dash has been added under the tip of the ornament at right of the numeral in upper left corner.

Detail of **64-66, 74, 79, 82-83, 85, 85C, 88, 94**
In 64-66, 74, 79, 82-83, 85, 85C, 88 and 94, ornaments at corners have been enlarged and end in a small ball.

Detail of **67, 75, 80, 95**
In 67, 75, 80 and 95, a leaf has been added to the foliated ornaments at each corner.

How can a stamp get printed upside down?

When stamps were first issued in the mid-1800s, printing stamps in two colors required running the paper through the printing press twice. Because this process was done by hand, in a few rare instances, the paper would get turned around and the second color would print upside down or on the opposite side of the paper. One of the most valuable errors is the center-inverted 24-cent Curtiss Jenny **(#C3a)**. Today, most multiple-colored stamps are printed in a single process.

10¢ Washington of 1861-75

58

Detail of **58, 62B**

Detail of **68, 85D, 89, 96**
In 68, 85D, 89 and 96, a heavy, curved line has been cut below the stars and an outer line added to the ornaments above them.

12¢ Washington of 1861-75

59

Detail of **59**

Detail of **69, 85E, 90, 97**
In 69, 85E, 90 and 97, ovals and scrolls have been added at the corners.

90¢ Washington of 1861-75

62

Detail of **62**

Detail of **72, 101**
In 72 and 101, parallel lines form an angle above the ribbon containing "U.S. Postage"; between these lines a row of dashes has been added, along with a point of color to the apex of the lower line.

15¢ Columbus Landing Types I-III of 1869-75

118

Vignette of **118**

Detail of **118** Type I
Picture unframed.

Vignette of **118**

Detail of **119** Type II
Picture framed.

Vignette of **118**

129 Type III
Same as Type I but without fringe of brown shading lines around central vignette.

#55-62 are now considered essays.

55

134   135   136   137   138

Comparison of Issue of 1870-71: Printed by National Bank Note Company. Issued without secret marks (134-41, 145-52, 187) and **Issues of 1873-80: Printed by Continental and American Bank Note Companies.** Issued with secret marks (156-63, 167-74, 178, 180, 182-84, 186, 188-90, 192-99).

Detail of **134, 145**

Detail of **156, 167, 182, 192**
1¢. In the pearl at the left of the numeral "1" there is a small crescent.

Detail of **136, 147**

Detail of **158, 169, 184, 194**
3¢. The under part of the upper tail of the left ribbon is heavily shaded.

Detail of **138, 149**

Detail of **160, 171, 196**
7¢. Two small semicircles are drawn around the ends of the lines that outline the ball in the lower righthand corner.

Detail of **135, 146**

Detail of **157, 168, 178, 180, 183, 193**
2¢. Under the scroll at the left of "U.S." there is small diagonal line. This mark seldom shows clearly.

Detail of **137, 148**

Detail of **159, 170, 186, 195**
6¢. The first four vertical lines of the shading in the lower part of the left ribbon have been strengthened.

What are secret marks?

When stamps were first issued, printing companies would print stamps for certain periods, as specified by their contracts with the United States Postal Service. After their contracts expired, however, they had to relinquish the printing plates to new printers. When the new printing company received the plates, it would purposely insert secret marks to distinguish its stamps from the previous printer **(#134-138)**. Additionally, as time went on, pieces of the printing plate would wear down, crack or break after years of use. Stamps that exhibit "cracked plate" markings are more valuable than stamps without these markings.

139   140   141   143   206   207

Detail of **139, 150, 187**

Detail of **206**
1¢. Upper vertical lines have been deepened, creating a solid effect in parts of background. Upper arabesques shaded.

Detail of **140, 151**

Detail of **161, 172, 188, 197**
10¢. There is a small semi-circle in the scroll at the right end of the upper label.

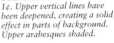

Detail of **207**
3¢. Shading at sides of central oval is half its previous width. A short horizontal dash has been cut below the "TS" of "CENTS."

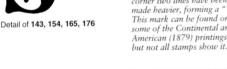

Detail of **141, 152**

Detail of **162, 173, 198**
12¢. The balls of the figure "2" are crescent-shaped.

S

Detail of **143, 154, 165, 176**

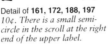

Detail of **163, 174, 189, 199**
In the lower part of the triangle in the upper left corner two lines have been made heavier, forming a "V". This mark can be found on some of the Continental and American (1879) printings, but not all stamps show it.

208   209

S

Detail of **190**
30¢. In the "S" of "CENTS," the vertical spike across the middle section of the letter has been broadened.

Detail of **208**
6¢. Has three vertical lines instead of four between the edge of the panel and the outside of the stamp.

Detail of **209**
10¢. Has four vertical lines instead of five between left side of oval and edge of the shield. Horizontal lines in lower part of background strengthened.

57

2¢ Washington Types of I-III of 1894-98

248

10¢ Webster Types I-II of 1898

282C

3¢ Washington Types I-IV of 1908-19

333

Triangle of **248-50, 265** Type I
Horizontal lines of uniform thickness run across the triangle.

Detail of **282C** Type I
The tips of the foliate ornaments do not impinge on the white curved line below "TEN CENTS."

Detail of **333, 345, 359, 376, 389, 394, 426, 445, 456, 464, 483, 493, 501-01b** Type I
Top line of toga rope is weak and rope shading lines are thin. Fifth line from left is missing. Line between lips is thin.

Triangle of **251, 266** Type II
Horizontal lines cross the triangle, but are thinner within than without.

Detail of **283** Type II
The lips of the ornaments break the curved line below the "E" of "TEN" and the "T" of "CENTS."

2¢ Washington of 1903

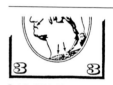

Detail of **484, 494, 502, 541** Type II
Top line of toga rope is strong and rope shading lines are heavy and complete. Line between lips is heavy.

Triangle of **252, 267, 279B-279Be** Type III
The horizontal lines do not cross the double frame lines of the triangle.

$1 Perry Types I-II of 1894

319

Detail of **259** Type III
Top row of toga rope is strong but fifth shading line is missing as in Type I. Toga button center shading line consists of two dashes, central dot. "P," "O" of "POSTAGE" are separated by line of color.

261

Detail of **319a, 319b, 319g** Die I

Detail of **261, 276** Type I
The circles enclosing $1 are broken.

Detail of **319c, 319f, 319h, 319i** Die II

Detail of **261A, 276A** Type II
The circles enclosing $1 are complete.

58

Detail of **530, 535** Type IV
*Toga rope shading lines are
complete. Second, fourth toga
button shading lines are
broken in middle; third line is
continuous with dot in center.
"P," "O" of "POSTAGE"
are joined.*

**2¢ Washington Types I-VII
of 1912-21**

406

Detail of **406-06a, 411, 413, 425-
25e, 442, 444, 449, 453, 461,
463-63a, 482, 499-99f**
Type I
*One shading line in first curve
of ribbon above left "2" and
one in second curve of ribbon
above right "2". Toga button
has only a faint outline. Top
line of toga rope, from button
to front of the throat, is very
faint. Shading lines of face end
in the front of the ear, with
little or no joining, to form
lock of hair.*

Detail of **482a, 500** Type Ia
*Similar to Type I but all lines
are stronger.*

Detail of **454, 487, 491, 539**
Type II
*Shading lines in ribbons as in
Type I. Toga button, rope and
rope shading lines are heavy.
Shading lines of face at lock of
hair end in strong vertical
curved line.*

Detail of **450, 455, 488, 492,
540, 546** Type III
*Two lines of shading in curves
of ribbons.*

Detail of **526, 532** Type IV
*Top line of toga rope is
broken. Toga button shading
lines form "DID". Line of
color in left "2" is very thin
and usually broken.*

Detail of **527, 533** Type V
*Top line of toga is complete.
Toga button has five vertical
shading lines. Line of color in
left "2" is very thin and
usually broken. Nose shading
dots are as shown.*

Detail of **528, 534** Type Va
*Same as Type V except third
row from bottom of nose
shading dots has four dots
instead of six. Overall height
of design is 1/3mm shorter
than Type V.*

Detail of **528A, 534A** Type VI
*Generally same as Type V
except line of color in left "2"
is very heavy.*

Detail of **528B, 534B** Type VII
*Line of color in left "2" is
continuous, clearly defined and
heavier than in Type V or Va
but not as heavy as Type VI.
An additional vertical row of
dots has been added to upper
lip. Numerous additional dots
appear in hair at top of head.*

**2¢ Washington Types I-II
of 1923-29**

599

Detail of **599, 634** Type I
*No heavy hair lines at top
center of head.*

Detail of **599A, 634A** Type II
*Three heavy hair lines at top
center of head.*

59

Explanation of Catalog Prices

The United States Postal Service sells only the commemoratives released during the past few years, current regular and special stamps, and current postal stationery.

Prices in this book are called "catalog prices" by stamp collectors. Collectors use catalog prices as guidelines when buying or trading stamps. It is important to remember the prices are simply guidelines to the stamp values. Stamp condition (see pp 10-11) is very important in determining the actual value of a stamp.

Condition Affects Value

The catalog prices are given for unused (mint) stamps and used (canceled) stamps, which have been hinged and are in Fine condition. Stamps in Superb condition that have never been hinged may cost more than the listed price. Stamps in less than Fine condition may cost less.

The prices for used stamps are based on a light cancellation; a heavy cancellation lessens a stamp's value. Canceled stamps may be worth more than uncanceled stamps. This happens if the cancellation is of a special type or for a significant date. Therefore, it is important to study an envelope before removing a stamp and discarding its "cover."

Prices are Estimated

Listed prices are estimates of how much you can expect to pay for a stamp from a dealer. A 15-cent minimum valuation has been established which represents a fair-market price to have a dealer locate and provide a single stamp to a customer. Dealers may charge less per stamp to provide a group of such stamps, and may charge less for such a single stamp. Similarly, a $1.00 minimum has been established for First Day Covers (FDCs). If you sell a stamp to a dealer, he or she may offer you much less than the catalog price. Dealers pay based on their interest in owning a particular stamp. If they already have a full supply, they may only buy additional stamps at a low price.

Sample Listing

			Un	U	PB/LP/PNC	#	FDC		Q
2636	29¢	Kentucky Statehood, June 1	.00	.00	0.00	( )	0.00		000,000,000

Scott Catalog Number (bold type indicates stamp is pictured)

Denomination

Description

First Day of Issue

Unused Catalog Price

Used Catalog Price

Plate Block Price, Line Pair Price or Plate Number Coil Price

# of stamps in Plate Block, Line Pair or Plate Number Coil

First Day Cover Price

Quantity Issued (where known)

2636

Understanding the Listings

- Prices in regular type for single unused and used stamps are taken from the *Scott 1995 Standard Postage Stamp Catalogue, Volume 1* ©1994, whose editors have based these prices on **actual retail values** as they found them in the marketplace. The Scott numbering system for stamps is used in this book. Prices quoted for unused and used stamps are for "Fine" condition, except where Fine is not available.

- Stamp values in *italic* generally refer to items difficult to value accurately.

- A dash (—) in a value column means the item is known to exist but information is insufficient for establishing a value.

- The stamp listings contain a number of additions designated "a," "b," "c," etc. These represent recognized variations of stamps as well as errors. These listings are as complete as space permits.

- Occasionally, a new stamp or major variation may be inserted by the catalog editors into a series or sequence where it was not originally anticipated. These additions are identified by capital letters "A," "B" and so forth. For example, a new stamp which logically belonged between 1044 and 1045 is designated 1044A, even though it is entirely different from 1044. The insertion was preferable to a complete renumbering of the series.

- Prices for Plate Blocks, First Day Covers, American Commemorative Panels and Souvenir Pages are taken from *Scott's Specialized Catalogue of U.S. Stamps*, 1994 Edition, ©1993.

Sample Variation Listing

			Un	U	PB/LP/PNC	#	FDC	Q
2281	25¢	Honeybee, Sept. 2	.45	.15	3.75	(3)	1.00	000,000,000
a		Imperf. pair	45.00					
b		Black omitted	100.00					
d		Pair, imperf. between	—					

Scott Catalog Number (bold type indicates stamp is pictured)

Description Denomination

First Day of Issue

Unused Catalog Price

Used Catalog Price

Plate Block Price, Line Pair Price or Plate Number Coil Price

# of stamps in Plate Block, Line Pair or Plate Number Coil

First Day Cover Price

Quantity Issued (where known)

2281

61

Commemorative and Definitive Stamps

1847-1861

1

2

3

4

5

11

12

14

17

Issues of 1847, Thin, Bluish Wove Paper, July 1, Imperf., Unwmkd.

		Un	U
1	5¢ Benjamin Franklin	4,500.00	425.00
b	5¢ orange brown	5,000.00	525.00
c	5¢ red orange	10,000.00	4,000.00
	Pen cancel	—	225.00
	Double transfer of top, or top and bottom, or bottom and lower left frame lines		525.00
	Double transfer of top, bottom and left frame lines and numerals		900.00
2	10¢ George Washington	20,000.00	900.00
	Pen cancel	—	425.00
	Vertical line through second "F" of "OFFICE," or with "stick pin" in tie, or with "harelip," or double transfer in lower right "X," or in "POST OFFICE," or of left and bottom frame lines	—	1,150.00

Issues of 1875, Reproductions of 1 and 2, Bluish Paper, Without Gum

		Un	U
3	5¢ Franklin	700.00	—
4	10¢ Washington	900.00	—

5¢. On the original, the left side of the white shirt frill touches the oval on a level with the top of the "F" of "Five." On the reproduction, it touches the oval about on a level with the top of the figure "5."

10¢. On the reproduction, line of coat at left points to right of "X" and line of coat at right points to center of "S" of CENTS. On the original, line of coat points to "T" of TEN and between "T" and "S" of CENTS.

On the reproduction, the eyes have a sleepy look, the line of the mouth is straighter and in the curl of hair near the left cheek is a strong black dot, while the original has only a faint one.

Issues of 1851-57, Imperf.

		Un	U
5	1¢ Franklin, type I	200,000.00	17,500.00
5A	1¢ blue, type Ib	8,500.00	3,500.00
	#6-9: Franklin (5), 1851		
6	1¢ dark blue, type Ia	22,500.00	6,000.00
7	1¢ blue, type II	575.00	110.00
	Cracked plate	750.00	275.00
8	1¢ blue, type III	6,500.00	1,500.00
8A	1¢ pale blue, type IIIa	2,500.00	600.00
9	1¢ blue, type IV	425.00	90.00
	Triple transfer, one inverted	550.00	125.00

#10-11, 25-26a all had plates on which at least four outer frame lines (and usually much more) were recut, adding to their value.

Issues of 1851-57 (continued), Imperf.

		Un	U
10	3¢ orange brown Washington, type I (11)	1,600.00	40.00
	3¢ copper brown	1,500.00	75.00
	On part-India paper		250.00
11	3¢ Washington, type I	130.00	7.00
	3¢ deep claret	185.00	13.50
	Double transfer, "GENTS" for "CENTS"	200.00	25.00
12	5¢ Jefferson, type I	11,000.00	875.00
13	10¢ green Washington, type I (14)	9,000.00	575.00
14	10¢ green, type II	2,100.00	190.00
15	10¢ Washington, type III	2,100.00	190.00
16	10¢ green, type IV (14)	12,500.00	1,100.00
17	12¢ Washington	2,600.00	225.00

Issues of 1857-61, Perf. 15½ (Issued in 1857 except #18, 27, 28A, 29, 30, 30A, 35, 36b, 37, 38, 39)

		Un	U
	#18-24: Franklin (5)		
18	1¢ blue, type I	800.00	325.00
19	1¢ blue, type Ia	11,500.00	3,250.00
20	1¢ blue, type II	450.00	150.00
21	1¢ blue, type III	5,000.00	1,250.00
22	1¢ blue, type IIIa	800.00	275.00
23	1¢ blue, type IV	2,750.00	325.00
24	1¢ blue, type V	120.00	25.00
	"Curl" on shoulder	150.00	37.50
	"Earring" below ear	200.00	52.50
	Long double "curl" in hair	185.00	42.50
b	Laid paper		—
	#25-26a: Washington (11)		
25	3¢ rose, type I	1,000.00	30.00
	Cracked plate	1,200.00	175.00
26	3¢ dull red, type II	40.00	3.00
	3¢ brownish carmine	75.00	10.00
	3¢ claret	90.00	12.50
	Left or right frame line double	60.00	8.75
	Cracked plate	475.00	150.00
26a	3¢ dull red, type IIa	110.00	20.00
	Double transfer	175.00	45.00
	Left frame line double	—	65.00

Issues of 1857-61 (continued), Perf. 15½		Un	U
	#27-29: Jefferson (12)		
27	5¢ brick red, type I	9,000.00	600.00
28	5¢ red brown, type I	1,350.00	250.00
b	5¢ brt. red brn., type I	1,850.00	400.00
28A	5¢ Indian red, type I	12,000.00	1,750.00
29	5¢ brown, type I	950.00	200.00
	Defective transfer	—	—
30	5¢ orange brown, type II	800.00	1,000.00
30A	5¢ brown, type II (30)	525.00	185.00
b	Printed on both sides	3,750.00	4,500.00
	#31-35: Washington (15)		
31	10¢ green, type I	8,000.00	500.00
32	10¢ green, type II	2,800.00	165.00
33	10¢ green, type III	2,800.00	165.00
	"Curl" on forehead or in left "X"	—	225.00
34	10¢ green, type IV	17,500.00	1,400.00
35	10¢ green, type V	200.00	50.00
	Small "curl" on forehead	235.00	60.00
	"Curl" in "e" or "t" of "Cents"	250.00	70.00
	Plate I—Outer frame lines complete.		
36	12¢ blk. Washington (17), plate I	400.00	95.00
	Triple transfer	525.00	—
36b	12¢ black, plate III	350.00	100.00
	Vertical line through rosette	450.00	145.00
37	24¢ gray lilac	675.00	200.00
a	24¢ gray	675.00	200.00
b	24¢ red lilac	1,000.00	
38	30¢ orange Franklin	850.00	300.00
	Recut at bottom	900.00	400.00

Issues of 1857-61 (continued), Perf. 15½		Un	U
39	90¢ blue Washington	1,150.00	5,000.00
	Double transfer at top or bottom	1,250.00	—
	90¢ Same, with pen cancel		900.00

Note: Beware of forged cancellations of #39. Genuine cancellations are rare.

Issues of 1875, Government Reprints, White Paper, Without Gum, Perf. 12

		Un	U
40	1¢ bright blue Franklin (5)	425.00	
41	3¢ scarlet Wash. (11)	2,000.00	
42	5¢ orange brown Jefferson (30)	900.00	
43	10¢ blue green Washington (14)	1,750.00	
44	12¢ greenish black Washington (17)	2,000.00	
45	24¢ blackish violet Washington (37)	2,000.00	
46	30¢ yellow orange Franklin (38)	2,000.00	
47	90¢ deep blue Washington (39)	3,250.00	
48-54	Not assigned		

Issue of 1861, Thin, Semi-Transparent Paper

		Un	U
	#55-62 are considered essays.		
55	1¢ Franklin		
56	3¢ Washington		
58	10¢ Washington		
59	12¢ Washington		
60	24¢ Washington		
61	30¢ Franklin		
62	90¢ Washington		
62B	10¢ dark green Washington (58)	5,000.00	450.00
	Double transfer	5,500.00	525.00

Who wrote under the name "Mrs. Silence Dogood"?

Benjamin Franklin never excelled in writing at school. After his father could no longer afford to educate him, he began studying printing methods under his brother, James. At the same time, he was teaching himself to write with a style all his own, and submitted news articles to his brother's print shop under the name of "Mrs. Silence Dogood." James appreciated many of the articles, printing them until he found they were actually his brother's. Ben left home for Philadelphia at 17, and was running his own print shop by the age of 22. (**#40**)

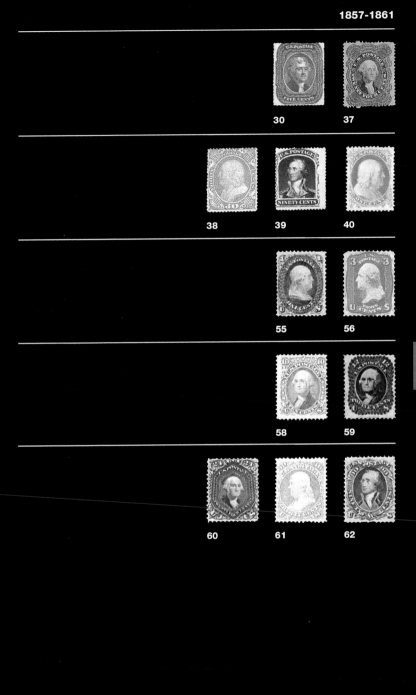

30   37

38   39   40

55   56

58   59

60   61   62

Have you noticed? We expanded the stamp listings. They are now grouped according to historical eras.

67   **73**   **77**

*Now there are more stamps than ever
before and dozens of new illustrations
of your favorite stamps!*

Issues of 1861-62, Perf. 12	Un	U
63 1¢ blue Franklin (55)	140.00	15.00
a 1¢ ultramarine	350.00	100.00
b 1¢ dark blue	350.00	25.00
c Laid paper	—	—
d Vert. pair, imperf. horiz.		—
e Printed on both sides	—	2,500.00
Double transfer	—	22.50
Dot in "U"	150.00	17.50
64 3¢ pink Washington (56)	4,500.00	450.00
a 3¢ pigeon blood pink	10,000.00	2,500.00
b 3¢ rose pink	300.00	90.00
65 3¢ rose Washington (56)	90.00	1.00
b Laid paper	—	—
d Vertical pair, imperf. horizontally	3,500.00	750.00
e Printed on both sides	1,650.00	1,000.00
f Double impression		6,000.00
Cracked plate	—	—
Double transfer	85.00	2.50
66 3¢ lake Washington (56)	1,650.00	
Double transfer	2,000.00	
67 5¢ buff Jefferson	6,000.00	425.00
68 10¢ yellow green Washington (58)	275.00	30.00
10¢ deep yellow green on thin paper	350.00	40.00
a 10¢ dark green	290.00	31.00
b Vert. pair, imperf. horiz.		3,500.00
Double transfer	325.00	40.00
69 12¢ blk. Washington (59)	550.00	55.00
12¢ intense black	575.00	60.00
Double transfer of top or bottom frame line	575.00	65.00
Double transfer of top and bottom frame lines	600.00	70.00
70 24¢ red lilac Washington (60)	800.00	80.00
a 24¢ brown lilac	600.00	67.50
b 24¢ steel blue	5,000.00	300.00
c 24¢ violet	6,500.00	550.00
d 24¢ grayish lilac	1,400.00	350.00
Scratch under "A" of "POSTAGE"		—
71 30¢ orange Franklin (61)	625.00	70.00
a Printed on both sides		—
72 90¢ bl. Washington (62)	1,450.00	250.00
b 90¢ dark blue	1,600.00	275.00
73 2¢ blk. Andrew Jackson	175.00	22.50
Double transfer	200.00	25.00
Major double transfer of top left corner and "POSTAGE"		6,000.00
Cracked plate	—	—

Issues of 1861-66, Perf. 12	Un	U
#74 was not regularly issued.		
74 3¢ scarlet Washington (56)	6,500.00	
75 5¢ red brown Jefferson (57)	2,000.00	250.00
76 5¢ brown Jefferson (57)	500.00	70.00
a 5¢ dark brown	550.00	80.00
Double transfer of top or bottom frame line	425.00	80.00
77 15¢ blk. Abraham Lincoln	650.00	70.00
Double transfer	600.00	75.00
78 24¢ lilac Washington (60)	400.00	50.00
c 24¢ black violet	17,500.00	1,100.00
Scratch under "A" of "POSTAGE"	—	—

Grills on U.S. Stamps

Between 1867 and 1870, postage stamps were embossed with pyramid-shaped grills that absorbed cancellation ink to prevent reuse of canceled stamps.

Issues of 1867, With Grills

Grills A, B, C: Points Up

A. Grill Covers Entire Stamp

	Un	U
79 3¢ rose Washington (56)	2,000.00	550.00
b Printed on both sides		—
80 5¢ brown Jefferson (57)	—	—
a 5¢ dark brown		—
81 30¢ orange Franklin (61)		—

B. Grill about 18 x 15mm

	Un	U
82 3¢ rose Washington (56)		100,000.00

C. Grill about 13 x 16mm

	Un	U
83 3¢ rose Washington (56)	3,000.00	475.00
Double grill	4,000.00	1,500.00

Grills, D, Z, E, F: Points Down

D. Grill about 12 x 14mm

	Un	U
84 2¢ black Jackson (73)	9,000.00	1,450.00
85 3¢ rose Washington (56)	3,000.00	450.00
Split grill		500.00

Z. Grill about 11 x 14mm

	Un	U
85A 1¢ blue Franklin (55)		—
85B 2¢ black Jackson (73)	3,000.00	400.00
Double transfer	2,000.00	425.00
85C 3¢ rose Washington (56)	5,000.00	1,100.00
Double grill	6,000.00	
85D 10¢ grn. Washington (58)		45,000.00
85E 12¢ blk. Washington (59)	2,500.00	575.00
Double transfer of top frame line		625.00
85F 15¢ black Lincoln (77)		100,000.00

E. Grill about 11 x 13mm

	Un	U
86 1¢ blue Franklin (55)	1,000.00	275.00
Double grill	—	375.00
Split grill	1,050.00	275.00

Issues of 1867 (continued), With Grills, Perf. 12	Un	U
87	2¢ black Jackson (73)	450.00	70.00
	2¢ intense black	475.00	75.00
	Double grill	—	—
	Double transfer	475.00	75.00
88	3¢ rose Washington (56)	350.00	10.00
a	3¢ lake red	400.00	12.50
	Double grill	—	—
	Very thin paper	375.00	11.00
89	10¢ grn. Washington (58)	2,000.00	175.00
	Double grill	2,500.00	300.00
90	12¢ blk. Washington (59)	2,250.00	200.00
	Double transfer of top or bottom frame line	2,100.00	220.00
91	15¢ black Lincoln (77)	5,000.00	450.00
	Double grill	—	700.00

F. Grill about 9 x 13mm

		Un	U
92	1¢ blue Franklin (55)	450.00	100.00
	Double transfer	475.00	120.00
	Double grill	—	200.00
93	2¢ black Jackson (73)	175.00	25.00
	Double grill	—	100.00
	Very thin paper	190.00	30.00
94	3¢ red Washington (56)	125.00	2.50
c	Vertical pair, imperf. horizontally	1,000.00	
d	Printed on both sides	1,100.00	
	Double grill	—	—
	End roller grill		200.00
	Quadruple split grill	275.00	75.00
95	5¢ brown Jefferson (57)	1,500.00	275.00
a	5¢ dark brown	1,600.00	275.00
	Double transfer of top frame line	—	—
	Double grill	—	—
96	10¢ yellow green Washington (58)	1,200.00	110.00
	Double transfer	—	—
	Quadruple split grill		350.00
97	12¢ blk. Washington (59)	1,500.00	125.00
	Double transfer of top or bottom frame line	950.00	135.00
	Triple grill	—	
98	15¢ black Lincoln (77)	1,500.00	175.00
	Double transfer of upper right corner	—	—
	Double grill	—	250.00
	Quadruple split grill	1,750.00	350.00
99	24¢ gray lilac Washington (60)	2,000.00	425.00
100	30¢ orange Franklin (61)	2,750.00	400.00
	Double grill	3,000.00	700.00
101	90¢ bl. Washington (62)	5,000.00	800.00
	Double grill	7,000.00	

Issues of 1875, Reissue of 1861-66 Issue, Without Grill, Perf. 12	Un	U
102	1¢ blue Franklin (55)	500.00	800.00
103	2¢ black Jackson (73)	2,250.00	4,000.00
104	3¢ brown red Washington (56)	2,500.00	4,250.00
105	5¢ brown Jefferson (57)	1,850.00	2,250.00
106	10¢ grn. Washington (58)	2,000.00	3,750.00
107	12¢ blk. Washington (59)	2,750.00	4,500.00
108	15¢ black Lincoln (77)	2,750.00	4,750.00
109	24¢ deep violet Washington (60)	3,750.00	6,000.00
110	30¢ brownish orange Franklin (61)	4,250.00	6,000.00
111	90¢ bl. Washington (62)	5,250.00	20,000.00

Issues of 1869, With Grill

G. Grill about 9¹/₂ x 9mm

		Un	U
112	1¢ Franklin, Mar. 27	275.00	65.00
b	Without grill	750.00	
	Double grill	450.00	150.00
113	2¢ br. Post Rider, Mar. 27	200.00	25.00
	Split grill	225.00	35.00
	Double transfer		30.00
114	3¢ Locomotive, Mar. 27	175.00	7.00
a	Without grill	600.00	
d	Double impression		3,500.00
	Triple grill	—	—
	Sextuple grill	2,000.00	
	Gray paper	—	—
115	6¢ Washington	900.00	95.00
	Quadruple split grill	—	400.00
116	10¢ Shield and Eagle	1,000.00	85.00
	End roller grill	—	—
117	12¢ S.S. Adriatic, Apr. 5	950.00	95.00
	Split grill	850.00	105.00
118	15¢ Columbus Landing, type I, Apr. 2	2,400.00	325.00
119	15¢ type II (118)	1,000.00	150.00
b	Center inverted	220,000.00	14,000.00
c	Center double, one inverted	—	—
120	24¢ Declaration of Independence, Apr. 7	4,000.00	500.00
b	Center inverted	220,000.00	15,000.00
121	30¢ Shield, Eagle and Flags, May 15	2,400.00	250.00
b	Flags inverted	165,000.00	55,000.00
	Double grill	—	500.00
122	90¢ Lincoln	5,000.00	1,150.00
	Split grill	—	—

Issues of 1875, Reissue of 1869 Issue, Without Grill, Hard, White Paper

		Un	U
123	1¢ buff (112)	325.00	225.00
124	2¢ brown (113)	375.00	325.00
125	3¢ blue (114)	3,000.00	10,000.00
126	6¢ blue (115)	850.00	550.00

112   113   114

115   116   117

118   120

121   122

Make your stamp search quick and easy! Use the improved index, now featuring larger type.

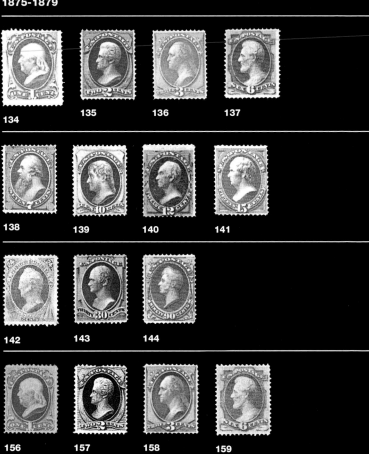

134   135   136   137

138   139   140   141

142   143   144

156   157   158   159

160   161   162   163

179

Issues of 1875 (continued), Perf. 12		Un	U
127	10¢ yellow (116)	1,400.00	1,200.00
128	12¢ green (117)	1,500.00	1,200.00
129	15¢ brown and blue, type III (118)	1,300.00	750.00
a	Imperf. horizontally	1,600.00	—
130	24¢ grn. & violet (120)	1,250.00	850.00
131	30¢ bl. & carmine (121)	1,750.00	1,500.00
132	90¢ car. & black (122)	4,000.00	4,250.00
Issue of 1880, Reissue of 1869 Issue, Soft, Porous Paper			
133	1¢ buff (112)	200.00	175.00
a	1¢ brown orange, issued without gum	175.00	150.00
Issues of 1870-71, With Grill, White Wove Paper, No Secret Marks			
H. Grill about 10 x 12mm			
134	1¢ Franklin, April 1870	900.00	60.00
	End roller grill		300.00
135	2¢ Jackson, April 1870	525.00	37.50
136	3¢ Washington	400.00	10.00
	Cracked plate	—	50.00
137	6¢ Lincoln, April 1870	2,100.00	300.00
	Double grill	—	500.00
138	7¢ Edwin M. Stanton	1,500.00	275.00
139	10¢ Jefferson	1,800.00	450.00
140	12¢ Henry Clay	13,000.00	2,000.00
141	15¢ Daniel Webster	2,750.00	750.00
142	24¢ Gen. Winfield Scott	—	11,500.00
143	30¢ Alexander Hamilton	5,750.00	950.00
144	90¢ Commodore Perry	7,500.00	850.00
	Split grill		825.00
Without Grill, White Wove Paper, No Secret Marks			
145	1¢ ultra. Franklin (134)	225.00	7.50
146	2¢ red brn. Jackson (135)	140.00	5.00
147	3¢ grn. Washington (136)	170.00	.50
148	6¢ carmine Lincoln (137)	325.00	12.00
	6¢ violet carmine	350.00	15.00
149	7¢ verm. Stanton (138)	425.00	55.00
150	10¢ brown Jefferson (139)	325.00	12.00
151	12¢ dull violet Clay (140)	750.00	80.00
152	15¢ brt. or. Webster (141)	725.00	85.00
153	24¢ purple Scott (142)	775.00	85.00
154	30¢ black Hamilton (143)	1,500.00	100.00
155	90¢ carmine Perry (144)	1,700.00	185.00
Issues of 1873, Without Grill, White Wove Paper, Thin to Thick, Secret Marks			
156	1¢ ultra. Franklin	120.00	1.75
	Paper with silk fibers	—	15.00
f	Imperf. pair	—	500.00
157	2¢ br. Jackson	250.00	10.00
	Double paper	325.00	20.00
c	With grill	1,100.00	600.00

Issues of 1873 (continued), Perf. 12		Un	U
158	3¢ gr. Washington	75.00	.15
	3¢ olive green	90.00	2.50
	Cracked plate	—	27.50
159	6¢ dull pk. Lincoln	275.00	10.00
b	With grill	1,000.00	
160	7¢ or. verm. Stanton	600.00	57.50
	Ribbed paper	—	70.00
161	10¢ br. Jefferson	335.00	11.50
162	12¢ bl. vio. Clay	900.00	67.50
163	15¢ yel. or. Webster	800.00	62.50
a	With grill	3,000.00	
164	24¢ pur. Scott		
165	30¢ gray blk. Hamilton	925.00	65.00
166	90¢ rose carm. Perry	1,800.00	185.00
Issues of 1875, Special Printing, Hard, White Wove Paper, Without Gum, Secret Marks			
Although perforated, these stamps were usually cut apart with scissors. As a result, the perforations are often much mutilated and the design is frequently damaged.			
167	1¢ ultra. Franklin (156)	7,500.00	
168	2¢ dk. br. Jackson (157)	3,500.00	
169	3¢ blue green Washington (158)	9,500.00	—
170	6¢ dull rose Lincoln (159)	8,500.00	
171	7¢ reddish vermilion Stanton (160)	2,250.00	
172	10¢ pale brown Jefferson (161)	8,250.00	
173	12¢ dark vio. Clay (162)	3,000.00	
174	15¢ bright orange Webster (163)	8,250.00	
175	24¢ dull pur. Scott (142)	1,850.00	—
176	30¢ greenish black Hamilton (143)	6,000.00	
177	90¢ vio. car. Perry (144)	7,500.00	
Yellowish Wove Paper			
178	2¢ verm. Jackson (157)	210.00	5.00
c	With grill	300.00	
179	5¢ Zachary Taylor, June	260.00	9.00
	Cracked plate	—	100.00
	Double paper	325.00	
c	With grill	600.00	
	Paper with silk fibers	—	15.00
Special Printing, Hard, White Wove Paper, Without Gum			
180	2¢ carmine vermilion Jackson (157)	17,500.00	
181	5¢ br. bl. Taylor (179)	27,500.00	
Issues of 1879, Soft, Porous Paper, Thin to Thick			
182	1¢ dark ultramarine Franklin (156)	175.00	1.25
183	2¢ verm. Jackson (157)	80.00	1.25
a	Double impression	—	500.00

Issues of 1879 (continued), Perf. 12	Un	U
184	3¢ grn. Washington (158)	60.00	.15
	Double transfer	—	4.00
	Short transfer	—	5.00
185	5¢ blue Taylor (179)	325.00	8.00
186	6¢ pink Lincoln (159)	600.00	13.00
187	10¢ brown Jefferson (139) (no secret mark)	975.00	15.00
188	10¢ brown Jefferson (161) (with secret mark)	700.00	16.00
	10¢ black brown	750.00	25.00
	Double transfer		30.00
189	15¢ red or. Webster (163)	225.00	15.00
190	30¢ full blk. Hamilton (143)	625.00	35.00
191	90¢ carmine Perry (144)	1,300.00	155.00

Issues of 1880, Special Printing, Soft, Porous Paper, Without Gum

		Un	U
192	1¢ dark ultramarine Franklin (156)	10,000.00	
193	2¢ blk. br. Jackson (157)	6,000.00	
194	3¢ blue green Washington (158)	15,000.00	
195	6¢ dull rose Lincoln (159)	11,000.00	
196	7¢ scarlet vermilion Stanton (160)	2,250.00	
197	10¢ deep brown Jefferson (161)	10,000.00	
198	12¢ blk. pur. Clay (162)	3,500.00	
199	15¢ or. Webster (163)	11,000.00	
200	24¢ dk. vio. Scott (142)	3,500.00	
201	30¢ greenish black Hamilton (143)	8,500.00	
202	90¢ dull carmine Perry (144)	9,000.00	
203	2¢ scarlet vermilion Jackson (157)	18,000.00	
204	5¢ dp. bl. Taylor (179)	30,000.00	

Issues of 1882

205	5¢ Garfield, Apr. 10	135.00	4.50

Special Printing, Soft, Porous Paper, Without Gum

205C	5¢ gray brown Garfield (205)	20,000.00	

Issues of 1881-82, Designs of 1873 Re-engraved

206	1¢ Franklin, Aug. 1881	40.00	.40
	Double transfer	52.50	4.00
207	3¢ Washington, July 16, 1881	45.00	.15
	Double transfer	—	7.50
	Cracked plate	—	
208	6¢ Lincoln, June 1882	250.00	45.00
a	6¢ brown red	225.00	55.00
209	10¢ Jefferson, Apr. 1882	90.00	2.50
	10¢ pur. or olive brown	90.00	2.50
b	10¢ black brown	140.00	10.00

Issues of 1883, Perf. 12	Un	U
210	2¢ Washington, Oct. 1	37.50	.15
	Double transfer	40.00	1.25
211	4¢ Jackson, Oct. 1	160.00	8.00
	Cracked plate	—	

Special Printing, Soft, Porous Paper

211B	2¢ pale red brown Washington (210)	600.00	—
c	Horizontal pair, imperf. between	2,000.00	
211D	4¢ deep blue green Jackson (211) no gum	15,000.00	

Issues of 1887

212	1¢ Franklin, June	65.00	.65
	Double transfer	—	
213	2¢ green Washington (210), Sept. 10	25.00	.15
b	Printed on both sides	—	
	Double transfer	—	3.00
214	3¢ vermilion Washington (207), Oct. 3	50.00	37.50

Issues of 1888

215	4¢ carmine Jackson (211), Nov.	160.00	11.00
216	5¢ indigo Garfield (205), Feb.	160.00	6.50
217	30¢ orange brown Hamilton (165), Jan.	360.00	75.00
218	90¢ pur. Perry (166), Feb.	850.00	150.00

Issues of 1890-93

219	1¢ Franklin, Feb. 22, 1890	18.50	.15
	Double transfer	—	—
219D	2¢ lake Washington (220), Feb. 22, 1890	150.00	.45
	Double transfer	—	—
220	2¢ Washington, 1890	15.00	.15
a	Cap on left "2"	35.00	1.00
c	Cap on both "2s"	125.00	8.00
	Double transfer	—	3.00
221	3¢ Jackson, Feb. 22, 1890	50.00	4.50
222	4¢ Lincoln, June 2, 1890	50.00	1.50
	Double transfer	65.00	—
223	5¢ Grant, June 2, 1890	50.00	1.50
	Double transfer	65.00	1.75
224	6¢ Garfield, Feb. 22, 1890	55.00	15.00
225	8¢ Sherman, Mar. 21, 1893	40.00	8.50
226	10¢ Webster, Feb. 22, 1890	95.00	1.75
	Double transfer	—	—
227	15¢ Clay, Feb. 22, 1890	150.00	15.00
	Double transfer	—	—
	Triple transfer	—	
228	30¢ Jefferson, Feb. 22, 1890	225.00	20.00
	Double transfer	—	—
229	90¢ Perry, Feb. 22, 1890	350.00	95.00
	Short transfer at bottom	—	—

205   206   207   208

209   210   211   212

319   220   221   222

223   224   225   226

227   228   229

230

231

232

233

234

235

236

237

238

239

240

241

242

243

244

245

	Issues of 1893, Perf. 12	Un	U	PB	#	FDC	Q
	Columbian Exposition Issue, Printed by The American Bank Note Co., Jan. 2 (8¢ March)						
230	1¢ Columbus in Sight of Land	21.00	.25	300.00	(6)	*3,500.00*	449,195,550
	Double transfer	25.00	.50				
	Cracked plate	80.00					
231	2¢ Landing of Columbus	19.00	.15	250.00	(6)	*2,600.00*	1,464,588,750
	Double transfer	22.50	.25				
	Triple transfer	57.50	—				
	Quadruple transfer	85.00					
	Broken hat on third figure left of Columbus	50.00	.20				
	Broken frame line	20.00	.15				
	Recut frame lines	20.00	—				
	Cracked plate	80.00	—				
232	3¢ *Santa Maria,* Flagship of Columbus	50.00	12.50	650.00	(6)	*6,000.00*	11,501,250
	Double transfer	67.50	—				
233	4¢ ultramarine Fleet of Columbus	70.00	5.50	1,000.00	(6)	*6,000.00*	19,181,550
a	4¢ blue (error)	*10,000.00*	*4,000.00*	*45,000.00*	(4)		
	Double transfer	100.00	—				
234	5¢ Columbus Soliciting Aid from Isabella	75.00	6.50	1,250.00	(6)	*6,250.00*	35,248,250
	Double transfer	120.00	—				
235	6¢ Columbus Welcomed at Barcelona	70.00	18.00			*6,750.00*	4,707,550
a	6¢ red violet	70.00	18.00	1,100.00	(6)		
	Double transfer	90.00	25.00				
236	8¢ Columbus Restored to Favor	60.00	8.00	725.00	(6)		10,656,550
	Double transfer	70.00	—				
237	10¢ Columbus Presenting Natives	115.00	5.50	2,750.00	(6)	*7,500.00*	16,516,950
	Double transfer	150.00	10.00				
	Triple transfer	—					
238	15¢ Columbus Announcing His Discovery	190.00	50.00	*3,500.00*	(6)		1,576,950
	Double transfer	—	—				
239	30¢ Columbus at La Rábida	260.00	70.00	*7,000.00*	(6)		617,250
240	50¢ Recall of Columbus	450.00	120.00	*10,500.00*	(6)		243,750
	Double transfer	—	—				
	Triple transfer	—	—				
241	$1 Isabella Pledging Her Jewels	1,350.00	525.00	*35,000.00*	(6)		55,050
	Double transfer	—	—				
242	$2 Columbus in Chains	1,400.00	450.00	*40,000.00*	(6)	*18,000.00*	45,550
243	$3 Columbus Describing His Third Voyage	2,000.00	800.00				27,650
a	$3 olive green	2,000.00	800.00	*60,000.00*	(6)		
244	$4 Isabella and Columbus	2,600.00	1,000.00				26,350
a	$4 rose carmine	2,600.00	1,000.00	*165,000.00*	(6)		
245	$5 Portrait of Columbus	3,000.00	1,200.00	*150,000.00*	(6)		27,350

	Issues of 1894, Unwmkd., Perf. 12	Un	U	PB	#

Bureau Issues Starting in 1894 and continuing until 1979, the Bureau of Engraving and Printing in Washington produced all U.S. postage stamps except #909-21, 1335, 1355, 1410-18 and 1789. Beginning in 1979, security printers in addition to the Bureau of Engraving and Printing started producing postage stamps under contract with the U.S. Postal Service.

#	Description	Un	U	PB	#
246	1¢ Franklin, Oct.	16.00	2.00	200.00	(6)
	Double transfer	21.00	3.00		
247	1¢ blue Franklin (246)	40.00	.85	400.00	(6)
	Double transfer	—	2.50		
248	2¢ pink Washington, type I, Oct.	12.50	1.50	145.00	(6)
	Double transfer	—	—		
249	2¢ carmine lake, type I (248)	77.50	1.00	850.00	(6)
	Double transfer	—	1.50		
250	2¢ carmine, type I (248)	15.00	.25	200.00	(6)
a	Vertical pair, imperf. horizontally	1,500.00			
b	Horizontal pair, imperf. between	1,500.00			
	Double transfer	—	1.10		
251	2¢ carmine, type II (248)	125.00	1.50	1,450.00	(6)
252	2¢ carmine, type III (248)	70.00	2.00	950.00	(6)
b	Horizontal pair, imperf. between	1,500.00			
253	3¢ Jackson, Sept.	52.50	4.25	700.00	(6)
254	4¢ Lincoln, Sept.	60.00	2.00	850.00	(6)
255	5¢ Grant, Sept.	50.00	2.50	575.00	(6)
c	Vertical pair, imperf. horiz.	1,350.00			
	Worn plate, diagonal lines missing in oval background	60.00	3.00		
	Double transfer	67.50	3.00		
256	6¢ Garfield, July	90.00	12.00	1,500.00	(6)
a	Vertical pair, imperf. horizontally	850.00			
257	8¢ Sherman, Mar.	80.00	8.00	800.00	(6)
258	10¢ Webster, Sept.	115.00	5.00	1,600.00	(6)
	Double transfer	150.00	6.00		
259	15¢ Clay, Oct.	185.00	30.00	2,750.00	(6)

246 248 253

254 255 256

257 258 259

260

261

262

263

Watermark 191

277

		Un	U	PB	#
	Issues of 1894 (continued), Unwmkd., Perf. 12				
260	50¢ Jefferson, Nov.	250.00	60.00	4,250.00	(6)
261	$1 Perry, type I, Nov.	650.00	160.00	11,000.00	(6)
261A	$1 black Perry, type II (261), Nov.	1,650.00	350.00	18,500.00	(6)
262	$2 James Madison, Dec.	2,250.00	400.00	26,000.00	(6)
263	$5 John Marshall, Dec.	3,500.00	750.00	10,000.00	(4)
	Issues of 1895, Wmkd. (191)				
264	1¢ blue Franklin (246), Apr.	3.50	.15	130.00	(6)
265	2¢ carmine Washington, type I (248), May	18.00	.40	225.00	(6)
	Double transfer	27.50	3.00		
266	2¢ carmine, type II (248)	15.00	1.75	200.00	(6)
267	2¢ carmine, type III (248)	3.00	.15	90.00	(6)
	Triple transfer	—			
	Triangle at right without shading	17.50	5.00		
268	3¢ purple Jackson (253), Oct.	22.50	.65	375.00	(6)
	Double transfer	32.50	2.25		
269	4¢ dark brown Lincoln (254), June	24.00	.75	400.00	(6)
	Double transfer	25.00	2.25		
270	5¢ chocolate Grant (255), June 11	22.50	1.20	400.00	(6)
	Double transfer	32.50	2.50		
	Worn plate, diagonal lines missing in oval background	25.00	1.60		
271	6¢ dull brown Garfield (256), Aug.	42.50	2.50	1,100.00	(6)
	Very thin paper	47.50	2.50		
a	Wmkd. USIR	2,250.00	350.00		
272	8¢ violet brown Sherman (257), July	35.00	.65	475.00	(6)
a	Wmkd. USIR	1,750.00	110.00	5,500.00	(3)
	Double transfer	50.00	2.00		
273	10¢ dark green Webster (258), June	45.00	.80	800.00	(6)
	Double transfer	65.00	2.75		
274	15¢ dark blue Clay (259), Sept.	125.00	5.50	2,100.00	(6)
275	50¢ orange Jefferson (260), Nov.	175.00	14.00	4,000.00	(6)
a	50¢ red orange	195.00	16.00		
276	$1 black Perry, type I (261), Aug.	500.00	45.00	7,500.00	(6)
276A	$1 black Perry, type II (261)	1,000.00	95.00	15,000.00	(6)
277	$2 bright blue Madison (262), Aug.	850.00	225.00	14,000.00	(6)
a	$2 dark blue	825.00	235.00		
278	$5 dark green Marshall (263), Aug.	1,750.00	300.00	50,000.00	(6)

Who forced James and Dolley Madison from their home?

The War of 1812 took its toll on the Madisons when the British captured Washington, D.C., and burned the White House and the Capitol, among other buildings. Damage forced the President and First Lady into the Octagon House — just west of the White House — and later into a house at the corner of Pennsylvania Avenue and 19th Street in Washington. The White House wasn't restored until nine months after Madison left office in 1817. **(#277)**

American Legends One and All

- U.S. commemorative stamps issued during the year
- Large-format, informative book for displaying stamps
- Clear acetate mounts to protect stamps

A Tribute to America's Best

Whether it's people, places, ideals or events, you'll meet America's winners through U.S. commemorative stamps.

Fun, Informative and Valuable

Commemorative Stamp Collections gather the year's honorees in one convenient, collectible and colorful package. The upcoming Collection will contain 1994 commemoratives, including the following: Legends of the West; Moon Landing; Wonders of the Sea; Locomotives; Summer Garden Flowers; the fourth World War II miniature sheet of 10; Popular Singers; Jazz & Blues Singers; Norman Rockwell; Endangered Birds; World Cup Soccer; Legends of the Silent Screen; Buffalo Soldiers; Winter Olympics and more.

The 1994 Commemorative Stamp Collection is available (approximately November 1994) for $29.95.

1993 Collection Includes:

Circus; Sports Horses; National Postal Museum; Youth Classics; the third World War II miniature sheet of 10; Space Fantasy; Garden Flowers; Broadway Musicals; Country Music; Rock & Roll/Rhythm & Blues; Elvis; Grace Kelly; Joe Lewis; Hank Williams; etc. ($24.95)

To Obtain a Commemorative Stamp Collection

The 1994 Collection and one or two earlier sets may be obtained at your local post office or Philatelic Center. You may also fill out the postage-paid request card in this book or write directly to:

U.S. POSTAL SERVICE GUIDE
COMMEMORATIVE STAMP COLLECTIONS
PHILATELIC FULFILLMENT SERVICE CENTER
PROMOTIONS
PO BOX 419219
KANSAS CITY MO 64179-0998

	Issues of 1898-1900, Wmkd. (191), Perf. 12 (279Be issued in 1900, rest in 1898)	Un	U	PB	#	FDC	Q
279	1¢ dp. grn. Franklin (246), Jan.	6.00	.15	110.00	(6)		
	Double transfer	9.00	.75				
279B	2¢ red Washington, type III (248)	5.50	.15	120.00	(6)		
c	2¢ rose carmine, type III	185.00	25.00	1,750.00	(6)		
d	2¢ orange red, type III	6.50	.15	120.00	(6)		
e	Booklet pane of 6, Apr. 16, 1900	300.00					
f	2¢ deep red, type III	12.50	.75				
280	4¢ rose brn. Lincoln (254), Oct.	20.00	.45				
a	4¢ lilac brown	20.00	.45				
b	4¢ orange brown	20.00	.45	400.00	(6)		
	Extra frame line at top	32.50	3.50				
281	5¢ dark blue Grant (255), Mar.	22.50	.40	425.00	(6)		
	Double transfer	32.50	1.75				
	Worn plate, diagonal lines missing in oval background	26.00	.55				
282	6¢ lake Garfield (256), Dec.	32.50	1.40	650.00	(6)		
a	6¢ purple lake	35.00	1.65	750.00	(6)		
	Double transfer	42.50	2.50				
282C	10¢ brown Webster (258), type I, Nov.	125.00	1.20	1,600.00	(6)		
	Double transfer	150.00	3.00				
283	10¢ orange brown Webster (258), type II	75.00	1.00	950.00	(6)		
284	15¢ olive grn. Clay (259), Nov.	100.00	4.50	1,600.00	(6)		
	Issues of 1898, Trans-Mississippi Exposition Issue, June 17						
285	1¢ Marquette on the Mississippi	21.00	4.00	250.00	(6)	5,500.00	70,993,400
	Double transfer	30.00	5.25				
286	2¢ Farming in the West	19.00	1.00	210.00	(6)	5,000.00	159,720,800
	Double transfer	27.50	1.75				
	Worn plate	21.00	1.25				
287	4¢ Indian Hunting Buffalo	110.00	16.00	1,150.00	(6)		4,924,500
288	5¢ Fremont on the Rocky Mountains	95.00	14.00	1,000.00	(6)	6,250.00	7,694,180
289	8¢ Troops Guarding Train	140.00	30.00	2,250.00	(6)	9,250.00	2,927,200
a	Vertical pair, imperf. horizontally	13,500.00		55,000.00	(4)		
290	10¢ Hardships of Emigration	135.00	18.00	2,500.00	(6)		4,629,760
291	50¢ Western Mining Prospector	400.00	150.00	13,000.00	(6)	11,000.00	530,400
292	$1 Western Cattle in Storm	1,050.00	400.00	37,500.00	(6)	15,000.00	56,900
293	$2 Mississippi River Bridge	1,700.00	700.00	90,000.00	(6)		56,200
	Issues of 1901, Pan-American Exposition Issue, May 1						
294	1¢ Great Lakes Steamer	16.00	2.50	210.00	(6)	3,750.00	91,401,500
a	Center inverted	10,000.00	5,500.00	40,000.00	(3)		
295	2¢ An Early Locomotive	15.00	.75	210.00	(6)	3,250.00	209,759,700
a	Center inverted	30,000.00	13,500.00	210,000.00	(4)		
296	4¢ Automobile	75.00	12.50	2,250.00	(6)	4,250.00	5,737,100
a	Center inverted	12,500.00		55,000.00	(4)		
297	5¢ Bridge at Niagara Falls	90.00	11.00	2,600.00	(6)	4,500.00	7,201,300
298	8¢ Canal Locks at Sault Ste. Marie	100.00	45.00	4,250.00	(6)		4,921,700
299	10¢ American Line Steamship	160.00	20.00	6,500.00	(6)		5,043,700

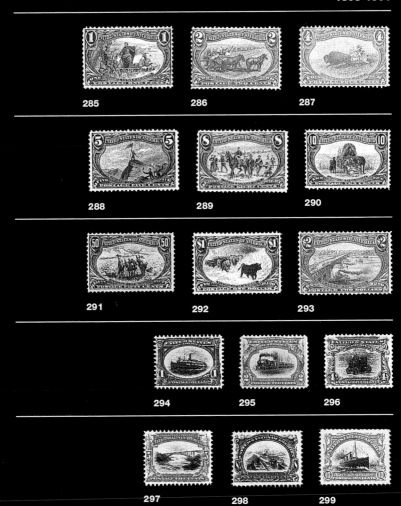

300   301   302

303   304   305

306   307   308

309   310   311

312   313   319

Issues of 1902-03, Wmkd. (191), Perf. 12 (All issued in 1903 except #300b, 306, 308)		Un	U	PB/LP	#	FDC
300	1¢ Franklin, Feb.	6.00	.15	130.00	(6)	
b	Booklet pane of 6, Mar. 6, 1907	400.00	—			
	Double transfer	10.00	1.00			
	Worn plate	7.50	.25			
	Cracked plate	—	—			
301	2¢ Washington, Jan. 17	8.00	.15	130.00	(6)	2,750.00
c	Booklet pane of 6, Jan. 24	375.00	—			
	Double transfer	14.00	.90			
	Cracked plate	—				
302	3¢ Jackson, Feb.	30.00	2.00	535.00	(6)	
	Double transfer	52.50	3.00			
	Cracked plate	—				
303	4¢ Grant, Feb.	30.00	.90	535.00	(6)	
	Double transfer	47.50	2.50			
304	5¢ Lincoln, Jan.	35.00	1.10	600.00	(6)	
305	6¢ Garfield, Feb.	40.00	2.00	625.00	(6)	
	6¢ brownish lake	47.50	2.00			
	Double transfer	60.00	2.50			
306	8¢ M. Washington, Dec. 1902	27.50	1.50	450.00	(6)	
	8¢ lavender	35.00	1.75			
307	10¢ Webster, Feb.	30.00	.70	700.00	(6)	
308	13¢ B. Harrison, Nov. 18, 1902	27.50	5.00	425.00	(6)	
309	15¢ Clay, May 27	90.00	3.75	2,000.00	(6)	
	Double transfer	135.00	7.50			
310	50¢ Jefferson, Mar. 23	285.00	17.50	4,750.00	(6)	
311	$1 David G. Farragut, June 5	550.00	45.00	10,000.00	(6)	
312	$2 Madison, June 5	800.00	140.00	17,500.00	(6)	
313	$5 Marshall, June 5	2,250.00	550.00	45,000.00	(6)	
	For listings of #312 and 313 with perf. 10, see #479 and 480.					
	Issues of 1906-08, Imperf. (All issued in 1908 except #314)					
314	1¢ bl. grn. Franklin (300), Oct. 2, 1906	20.00	15.00	150.00	(6)	
314A	4¢ brown Grant (303), Apr.	22,500.00	15,000.00			
	#314A was issued imperforate, but all copies were privately perforated at the sides.					
315	5¢ blue Lincoln (304), May 12	300.00	350.00	2,900.00	(6)	
	Coil Stamps, Perf. 12 Horizontally					
316	1¢ bl. grn. pair Franklin (300), Feb. 18	75,000.00	—	100,000.00	(2)	
317	5¢ blue pair Lincoln (304), Feb. 24	6,000.00	—	9,000.00	(2)	
	Coil Stamp, Perf. 12 Vertically					
318	1¢ bl. grn. pair Franklin (300), July 31	5,500.00	—	7,500.00	(2)	
	Issue of 1903, Perf. 12					
319	2¢ Washington, Nov. 12	4.00	.15	67.50	(6)	
a	2¢ lake, type I	—	—			
b	2¢ carmine rose, type I	6.00	.20	125.00	(6)	
c	2¢ scarlet, type I	4.00	.15	60.00	(6)	
d	Vertical pair, imperf. horizontally	2,000.00				
f	2¢ lake, type II	5.00	.20			
g	Booklet pane of 6, carm., type I, Dec. 3	75.00	125.00			
h	Booklet pane of 6, carm., type II	125.00				
i	2¢ carmine, type II	17.50	—			
q	Booklet pane of 6, lake, type II	165.00				

	Issues of 1906, Washington (319), Imperf.	Un	U	PB/LP	#	FDC	Q
320	2¢ carmine, Oct. 2	17.50	11.00	200.00	(6)		
a	2¢ lake, die II	50.00	40.00	625.00	(6)		
b	2¢ scarlet	16.00	12.00	175.00	(6)		
	Double transfer	24.00	15.00				
	Issues of 1908, Coil Stamp (319), Perf. 12 Horizontally						
321	2¢ carmine pair, Feb. 18	95,000.00	—				
	Coil Stamp, Perf. 12 Vertically						
322	2¢ carmine pair, July 31	6,500.00	5,000.00	8,000.00	(2)		
	Issues of 1904, Louisiana Purchase Exposition Issue, Apr. 30, Perf. 12						
323	1¢ Robert R. Livingston	19.50	3.00	200.00	(6)	3,000.00	79,779,200
	Diagonal line through left "1"	35.00	10.00				
324	2¢ Thomas Jefferson	17.00	1.00	200.00	(6)	3,250.00	192,732,400
325	3¢ James Monroe	65.00	24.00	750.00	(6)	3,750.00	4,542,600
326	5¢ William McKinley	67.50	15.00	800.00	(6)	5,500.00	6,926,700
327	10¢ Map of Louisiana Purchase	130.00	21.00	1,600.00	(6)	8,000.00	4,011,200
	Issues of 1907, Jamestown Exposition Issue, Apr. 26, Wmkd. (191), Perf. 12						
328	1¢ Captain John Smith	13.00	2.00	175.00	(6)	3,750.00	77,728,794
	Double transfer	16.00	3.00				
329	2¢ Founding of Jamestown, 1607	17.00	1.75	250.00	(6)	5,500.00	149,497,994
330	5¢ Pocahontas	72.50	16.00	1,600.00	(6)		7,980,594

How much land was bought in the Louisiana Purchase?

Part or all of 15 states were bought in an 1803 U.S. treaty with France. The territory covered 827,987 square miles, and doubled the area of the United States. The U.S. acquired the area after Napoleon feared a battle over the territory from the U.S. and the British. Total price paid for the land: 60 million francs, or about $15 million in U.S. currency. **(#327)**

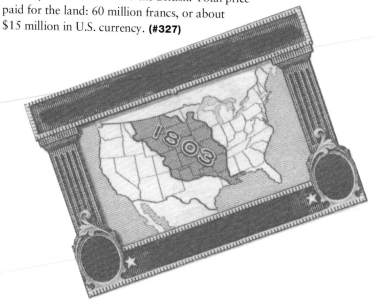

323

324

325

326

327

328

329

330

Have you noticed? We expanded the stamp listings. They are now grouped according to historical eras.

331

332

333

334

335

336

334

335

336

337

338

339

340

341

342

	Issues of 1908-09, Wmkd. (191) Perf. 126 (All issued in 1908 except #336, 338-42, 345-47)	Un	U	PB/LP	#	
331	1¢ Franklin, Dec.	4.75	.15	45.00	(6)	
a	Booklet pane of 6, Dec. 2	130.00	*90.00*			
	Double transfer	6.75	.60			
332	2¢ Washington, Nov.	4.50	.15	42.50	(6)	
a	Booklet pane of 6, Nov. 16	125.00	*90.00*			
	Double transfer	9.00	—			
	Cracked plate	—	—			
333	3¢ Washington, type I, Dec.	21.00	1.75	200.00	(6)	
334	4¢ Washington, Dec.	25.00	.55	250.00	(6)	
	Double transfer	40.00	—			
335	5¢ Washington, Dec.	32.50	1.50	345.00	(6)	
336	6¢ Washington, Jan. 1909	40.00	3.50	550.00	(6)	
337	8¢ Washington, Dec.	30.00	1.75	300.00	(6)	
	Double transfer	40.00	—			
338	10¢ Washington, Jan. 1909	47.50	1.00	650.00	(6)	
a	"China Clay" paper	*1,250.00*				
	Very thin paper	—				
339	13¢ Washington, Jan. 1909	27.50	14.00	300.00	(6)	
	Line through "TAG" of "POSTAGE"	47.50	—			
340	15¢ Washington, Jan. 1909	42.50	3.75	400.00	(6)	
a	"China Clay" paper	*1,500.00*				
341	50¢ Washington, Jan. 13, 1909	190.00	10.00	*4,500.00*	(6)	
342	$1 Washington, Jan. 29, 1909	350.00	50.00	*10,000.00*	(6)	
	Imperf.					
343	1¢ green Franklin (331), Dec.	5.50	4.00	47.50	(6)	
	Double transfer	11.50	5.50			
344	2¢ carmine Washington (332), Dec. 10	7.50	2.50	90.00	(6)	
	Double transfer	12.50	3.50			
	Double transfer, design of 1¢	*1,250.00*	*1,000.00*			
	#345-47: Washington (333-35)					
345	3¢ deep violet, type I, Mar. 3, 1909	14.00	17.50	180.00	(6)	
	Double transfer	22.50	—			
346	4¢ orange brown, Feb. 25, 1909	24.00	17.50	210.00	(6)	
	Double transfer	42.50	—			
347	5¢ blue, Feb. 25, 1909	42.50	30.00	350.00	(6)	
	Cracked plate	—				
	Issues of 1908-10, Coil Stamps, Perf. 12 Horizontally					
	#350-51, 354-56: Washington (Designs of 334-35, 338)					
348	1¢ green Franklin (331), Dec. 29, 1908	21.00	10.00	150.00	(2)	
349	2¢ carmine Washington (332), Jan. 1909	37.50	6.00	265.00	(2)	
	Double transfer, design of 1¢	—	*1,750.00*			
350	4¢ orange brown, Aug. 15, 1910	80.00	60.00	575.00	(2)	
351	5¢ blue, Jan. 1909	90.00	90.00	575.00	(2)	
	Issues of 1909, Coil Stamps, Perf. 12 Vertically					
352	1¢ green Franklin (331), Jan.	40.00	25.00	275.00	(2)	
	Double transfer	—	—			

	Issues of 1909 (continued), Coil Stamps, Perf. 12 Vertically						
		Un	**U**	**PB/LP**	**#**		**Q**
353	2¢ carmine Washington (332), Jan. 12	40.00	6.00	275.00	(2)		
354	4¢ orange brown, Feb. 23	100.00	45.00	700.00	(2)		
355	5¢ blue, Feb. 23	110.00	65.00	725.00	(2)		
356	10¢ yellow, Jan. 7	1,750.00	750.00	7,000.00	(2)		
	Issues of 1909, Bluish Paper, Perf. 12, #359-66: Washington (Designs of 333-40)						
357	1¢ green Franklin (331), Feb. 16	80.00	65.00	875.00	(6)		
358	2¢ carmine Washington (332), Feb. 16	75.00	55.00	850.00	(6)		
	Double transfer	—					
359	3¢ deep violet, type I	1,500.00	*1,300.00*	15,000.00	(6)		
360	4¢ orange brown	*13,500.00*		75,000.00	(3)		
361	5¢ blue	3,250.00	*3,500.00*	30,000.00	(6)		
362	6¢ red orange	1,150.00	850.00	13,000.00	(6)		
363	8¢ olive green	*13,500.00*		75,000.00	(3)		
364	10¢ yellow	1,350.00	1,000.00	13,500.00	(6)		
365	13¢ blue green	2,250.00	*1,250.00*	18,500.00	(6)		
366	15¢ pale ultramarine	1,150.00	800.00	*10,000.00*	(6)		
	Lincoln Memorial Issue, Feb. 12, Wmkd. (191)						
367	2¢ Bust of Abraham Lincoln	4.25	1.40	100.00	(6)	*350.00*	148,387,191
	Double transfer	6.75	2.50				
	Imperf.						
368	2¢ carmine (367)	20.00	16.00	175.00	(6)	*7,000.00*	1,273,900
	Double transfer	40.00	24.00				
	Bluish Paper						
369	2¢ carmine (367)	170.00	175.00	*2,400.00*	(6)		637,000
	Alaska-Yukon Pacific Exposition Issue, June 1						
370	2¢ Willam H. Seward	7.50	1.25	175.00	(6)	*1,800.00*	152,887,311
	Double transfer	10.00	4.00				
	Imperf.						
371	2¢ carmine (370)	27.50	20.00	200.00	(6)		525,400
	Double transfer	40.00	25.00				
	Hudson-Fulton Celebration Issue, Sept. 25, Wmkd. (191)						
372	2¢ *Half Moon* & *Clermont*	10.00	3.25	250.00	(6)	*800.00*	72,634,631
	Double transfer	14.00	4.25				
	Imperf.						
373	2¢ carmine (372)	32.50	22.50	235.00	(6)	—	216,480
	Double transfer	45.00	27.50				
	Issues of 1910-11, Wmkd. (190) #376-82: Washington (Designs of 333-38, 340)						
374	1¢ green Franklin (331), Nov. 23, 1910	5.00	.15	65.00	(6)		
a	Booklet pane of 6, Oct. 7, 1910	90.00	*75.00*				
	Double transfer	12.50	—				
	Cracked plate	—	—				
375	2¢ carmine Washington (332), Nov. 23, 1910	5.00	.15	70.00	(6)		
	2¢ lake	*150.00*					
a	Booklet pane of 6, Nov. 30, 1910	75.00	*60.00*				
	Cracked plate	—	—				
	Double transfer	10.00	—				
	Double transfer, design of 1¢	—	*1,000.00*				
376	3¢ dp. vio., type I, Jan. 16, 1911	11.50	1.00	100.00	(6)		

367

370

372

Watermark 190

We redesigned and expanded the new issues just for you! Read about the newest issues in the "Commemorative and Special" section.

397

398

399

400

Now there are more stamps than ever before and dozens of new illustrations of your favorite stamps!

	Issues of 1910-11 (continued), Wmkd. (190), Perf. 12	Un	U	PB/LP	#	FDC	Q
377	4¢ brown, Jan. 20, 1911	20.00	.30	130.00	(6)		
	Double transfer	—	—				
378	5¢ blue, Jan. 25, 1911	17.50	.30	160.00	(6)		
	Double transfer	—	—				
379	6¢ red orange, Jan. 25, 1911	25.00	.40	325.00	(6)		
380	8¢ olive green, Feb. 8, 1911	75.00	8.50	775.00	(6)		
381	10¢ yellow, Jan. 24, 1911	70.00	2.50	775.00	(6)		
382	15¢ pale ultramarine, Mar. 1, 1911	190.00	11.50	1,750.00	(6)		
	Issues of 1910, Jan. 3, Imperf.						
383	1¢ green Franklin (331)	2.25	2.00	37.50	(6)		
	Double transfer	5.75	—				
384	2¢ carmine Washington (332)	3.50	2.50	115.00	(6)		
	Dbl. transfer, design of 1¢	1,250.00					
	Double transfer	7.00	—				
	Cracked plate	17.50	—				
	Issues of 1910, Nov.1, Coil Stamps, Perf. 12 Horizontally						
385	1¢ green Franklin (331)	18.00	10.00	200.00	(2)		
386	2¢ carmine Washington (332)	32.50	12.50	375.00	(2)		
	Issues of 1910-11, Coil Stamps, Wmkd. (190), Perf. 12 Vertically						
387	1¢ green Franklin (331), Nov. 1, 1910	60.00	30.00	275.00	(2)		
388	2¢ carmine Washington (332), Nov. 1, 1910	550.00	200.00	3,750.00	(2)		
389	3¢ deep violet Washington, type I (333), Jan. 24, 1911	15,000.00	8,500.00				
	Issues of 1910-13, Coil Stamps, Perf. 8¹/₂ Horizontally						
390	1¢ green Franklin (331), Dec. 12, 1910	3.00	4.00	20.00	(2)		
	Double transfer	—	—				
391	2¢ carmine Washington (332), Dec. 23, 1910	20.00	6.75	115.00	(2)		
	Coil Stamps, Perf. 8¹/₂ Vertically #394-96: Washington (Designs of 333-35)						
392	1¢ green Franklin (331), Dec.12, 1910	12.00	14.00	85.00	(2)		
	Double transfer	—	—				
393	2¢ carmine Washington (332), Dec. 16, 1910	24.00	5.50	140.00	(2)		
394	3¢ deep violet, type I, Sept. 18, 1911	32.50	40.00	210.00	(2)		
395	4¢ brown, Apr. 15, 1912	32.50	35.00	210.00	(2)		
396	5¢ blue, Mar. 1913	32.50	35.00	210.00	(2)		
	Issues of 1913, Panama Pacific Exposition Issue, Wmkd. (190), Perf. 12						
397	1¢ Vasco Nunez de Balboa, Jan. 1	11.00	.85	110.00	(6)	3,500.00	167,398,463*
	Double transfer	17.50	2.00				
398	2¢ Pedro Miguel Locks, Panama Canal, Jan.	12.50	.30	210.00	(6)		251,856,543*
	2¢ carmine lake	400.00					
	Double transfer	35.00	2.00				
399	5¢ Golden Gate, Jan. 1	52.50	6.50	1,500.00	(6)	4,000.00	14,544,363*
400	10¢ yellow Discovery of San Francisco Bay, Jan. 1	95.00	14.00	2,000.00	(6)	—	8,484,182*
400A	10¢ orange (400), Aug.	175.00	10.50	7,750.00	(6)		
	*Includes perf. 10 printing quantities.						

	Issues of 1914-15, Perf. 10	Un	U	PB/LP	#
401	1¢ green (397), Dec. 1914	16.00	4.00	225.00	(6)
402	2¢ carmine (398), Jan. 1915	55.00	1.00	1,150.00	(6)
403	5¢ blue (399), Feb. 1915	120.00	11.00	3,250.00	(6)
404	10¢ orange (400), July 1915	825.00	42.50	10,000.00	(6)
	Issues of 1912-14, Wmkd. (190), Perf. 12				
405	1¢ green, Feb. 1912	4.00	.15	55.00	(6)
a	Vertical pair, imperf. horizontally	650.00	—		
b	Booklet pane of 6, Feb. 8, 1912	50.00	25.00		
	Cracked plate	12.00	—		
	Double transfer	5.75	—		
406	2¢ carmine, type I, Feb. 1912	3.75	.15	85.00	(6)
	2¢ lake	200.00	—		
a	Booklet pane of 6, Feb. 8, 1912	50.00	40.00		
b	Double impression	—			
	Double transfer	6.50	—		
407	7¢ black, Apr. 1914	60.00	8.00	900.00	(6)
	Imperf. #408-13: Washington (Designs of 405-6)				
408	1¢ green, Mar. 1912	.90	.50	15.00	(6)
	Double transfer	2.50	1.00		
	Cracked plate	—	—		
409	2¢ carmine, type I, Feb. 1912	1.00	.50	30.00	(6)
	Cracked plate	15.00	—		
	Coil Stamps, Perf. 8½ Horizontally				
410	1¢ green, Mar. 1912	4.50	3.00	25.00	(2)
	Double transfer	—	—		
411	2¢ carmine, type I, Mar. 1912	6.00	2.50	30.00	(2)
	Double transfer	9.00	—		
	Coil Stamps, Perf. 8½ Vertically				
412	1¢ green, Mar. 18, 1912	15.00	3.75	65.00	(2)
413	2¢ carmine, type I, Mar. 1912	24.00	.75	130.00	(2)
	Double transfer	40.00	—		
	Perf. 12				
414	8¢ Franklin, Feb. 1912	27.50	.85	325.00	(6)
415	9¢ Franklin, Apr. 1914	35.00	9.50	500.00	(6)
416	10¢ Franklin, Jan. 1912	30.00	.25	365.00	(6)
417	12¢ Franklin, Apr. 1914	30.00	3.00	350.00	(6)
	Double transfer	40.00	—		
	Triple transfer	55.00	—		
418	15¢ Franklin, Feb. 1912	55.00	2.00	475.00	(6)
	Double transfer	—	—		

405   **406**   **407**

414   **415**   **416**

417   **418**

*Make your stamp search quick and
easy! Use the improved index, now
featuring larger type.*

419
420
421

423
434

	Issues of 1912-14 (continued), Perf. 12	Un	U	PB	#
419	20¢ Franklin, Apr. 1914	125.00	9.00	1,300.00	(6)
420	30¢ Franklin, Apr. 1914	90.00	10.00	1,150.00	(6)
421	50¢ Franklin, Aug. 1914	325.00	10.00	5,750.00	(6)
	Wmkd. (191)				
422	50¢ Franklin (421), Feb. 12, 1912	175.00	9.50	3,750.00	(6)
423	$1 Franklin, Feb. 12, 1912	400.00	40.00	*8,000.00*	(6)
	Double transfer	450.00	—		
	Issues of 1914-15, Wmkd. (190), Perf.10 #424-30: Wash. (Designs of 405-06, 333-36, 407)				
424	1¢ green, Sept. 5, 1914	1.60	.15	35.00	(6)
	Cracked plate	—	—		
	Double transfer	4.25	—		
	Experimental precancel, New Orleans		—		
a	Perf. 12 x 10	*600.00*	*500.00*		
b	Perf. 10 x 12		250.00		
c	Vertical pair, imperf. horizontally	*425.00*	*250.00*		
d	Booklet pane of 6	3.00	.75		
e	Vertical pair, imperf. between and at top	—			
425	2¢ rose red, type I, Sept. 5, 1914	1.50	.15	22.50	(6)
	Cracked plate	9.00	—		
	Double transfer	—	—		
c	Perf. 10 x 12		—		
d	Perf. 12 x 10	—	*600.00*		
e	Booklet pane of 6, Jan. 6, 1914	9.00	*3.00*		
426	3¢ deep violet, type I, Sept. 18, 1914	10.00	.90	150.00	(6)
427	4¢ brown, Sept. 7, 1914	26.00	.30	475.00	(6)
	Double transfer	40.00	—		
428	5¢ blue, Sept. 14, 1914	22.50	.30	325.00	(6)
a	Perf. 12 x 10		*1,000.00*		
429	6¢ red orange, Sept. 28, 1914	35.00	.90	475.00	(6)
430	7¢ black, Sept. 10, 1914	65.00	2.50	875.00	(6)
	#431-33, 435, 437-40: Franklin (414-21, 423)				
431	8¢ pale olive green, Sept. 26, 1914	27.50	1.10	475.00	(6)
	Double impression	—			
432	9¢ salmon red, Oct. 6, 1914	37.50	5.00	650.00	(6)
433	10¢ orange yellow, Sept. 9, 1914	35.00	.20	650.00	(6)
434	11¢ Franklin, Aug. 11, 1915	16.00	5.50	225.00	(6)
435	12¢ claret brown, Sept. 10, 1914	18.00	2.75	260.00	(6)
a	12¢ copper red	19.00	2.75	290.00	(6)
	Double transfer	27.50	—		
	Triple transfer	32.50	—		
436	Not assigned				
437	15¢ gray, Sept. 16, 1914	87.50	4.50	825.00	(6)
438	20¢ ultramarine, Sept. 19, 1914	165.00	2.50	2,750.00	(6)
439	30¢ orange red, Sept. 19, 1914	190.00	10.00	3,500.00	(6)
440	50¢ violet, Dec. 10, 1915	475.00	10.00	13,500.00	(6)

Issues of 1914, Coil Stamps, Perf. 10 Horizontally #441-59: Wash. (Designs of 405-06, 333-35; Flat Press, 18½-19 x 22mm)	Un	U	PB/LB	#
441	1¢ green, Nov. 14	.55	.80	4.25	(2)
442	2¢ carmine, type I, July 22	6.00	4.50	35.00	(2)
Coil Stamps, Perf. 10 Vertically				
443	1¢ green, May 29	15.00	4.00	80.00	(2)
444	2¢ carmine, type I, Apr. 25	21.00	1.00	120.00	(2)
445	3¢ violet, type I, Dec. 18	175.00	100.00	875.00	(2)
446	4¢ brown, Oct. 2	90.00	30.00	450.00	(2)
447	5¢ blue, July 30	30.00	20.00	165.00	(2)
Issues of 1915-16, Coil Stamps, Perf. 10 Horizontally (Rotary Press, Designs 18½–19 x 22½mm)				
448	1¢ green, Dec. 12, 1915	4.25	2.25	25.00	(2)
449	2¢ red, type I, Dec. 5, 1915	1,900.00	300.00	8,500.00	(2)
450	2¢ carmine, type III, Feb. 1916	7.00	2.25	35.00	(2)
451	Not assigned				
Issues of 1914-16, Coil Stamps, Perf. 10 Vertically (Rotary Press, Designs 19½-20 x 22mm)				
452	1¢ green, Nov. 11, 1914	7.50	1.40	50.00	(2)
453	2¢ carmine rose, type I, July 3, 1914	90.00	3.25	425.00	(2)
	Cracked plate	—	—		
454	2¢ red, type II, June 1915	72.50	7.50	350.00	(2)
455	2¢ carmine, type III, Dec. 1915	7.00	.75	37.50	(2)
456	3¢ violet, type I, Feb. 2, 1916	190.00	75.00	825.00	(2)
457	4¢ brown, Feb. 18, 1916	19.00	15.00	100.00	(2)
	Cracked plate	35.00	—		
458	5¢ blue, Mar. 9, 1916	22.50	15.00	125.00	(2)
Issue of 1914, Horizontal Coil Stamp, Imperf.				
459	2¢ carmine, type I, June 30	300.00	750.00	1,250.00	(2)
Issues of 1915, Wmkd. (191), Perf. 10				
460	$1 violet black Franklin (423), Feb. 8	600.00	55.00	10,000.00	(6)
	Double transfer	650.00			
Perf. 11				
461	2¢ pale carmine red Washington (406), type I, June 17	75.00	175.00	1,000.00	(6)

Privately perforated copies of #409 have been made to resemble #461.

From 1916 to date, all postage stamps except #519 and 832b are on unwatermarked paper.

Issues of 1916-17, Unwmkd., Perf. 10 #462-69: Wash. (Designs of 405-06, 333-36, 407)				
462	1¢ green, Sept. 27, 1916	5.00	.15	125.00	(6)
	Experimental precancel, Springfield, MA, or New Orleans, LA		10.00		
a	Booklet pane of 6, Oct. 15, 1916	7.50	1.90		
463	2¢ carmine, type I, Sept. 25, 1916	3.25	.15	115.00	(6)
	Experimental precancel, Springfield, MA		22.50		
a	Booklet pane of 6, Oct. 8, 1916	62.50	20.00		
	Double transfer	5.75	—		
464	3¢ violet, type I, Nov. 11, 1916	57.50	8.00	1,200.00	(6)
	Double transfer in "CENTS"	75.00	—		
465	4¢ orange brown, Oct. 7, 1916	32.50	1.00	600.00	(6)
466	5¢ blue, Oct. 17, 1916	57.50	1.00	825.00	(6)
	Experimental precancel, Springfield, MA		150.00		
467	5¢ carmine (error in plate of 2¢)	475.00	525.00		
468	6¢ red orange, Oct. 10, 1916	70.00	5.00	1,100.00	(6)
	Experimental precancel, Springfield, MA		175.00		
469	7¢ black, Oct. 10, 1916	92.50	7.50	1,300.00	(6)
	Experimental precancel, Springfield, MA		175.00		

	Issues of 1916-17 (continued), Perf. 10	Un	U	PB/LP	#	FDC
	#470-78: Franklin (Designs of 414-16, 434, 417-21, 423)					
470	8¢ olive green, Nov. 13, 1916	42.50	3.75	500.00	(6)	
	Experimental precancel, Springfield, MA		165.00			
471	9¢ salmon red, Nov. 16, 1916	45.00	9.50	650.00	(6)	
472	10¢ orange yellow, Oct. 17, 1916	85.00	.75	1,200.00	(6)	
473	11¢ dark green, Nov. 16, 1916	25.00	11.00	300.00	(6)	
	Experimental precancel, Springfield, MA		650.00			
474	12¢ claret brown, Oct. 10, 1916	40.00	3.50	575.00	(6)	
	Double transfer	50.00	5.25			
	Triple transfer	65.00	8.50			
475	15¢ gray, Nov. 16, 1916	135.00	7.00	2,500.00	(6)	
476	20¢ light ultramarine, Dec. 5, 1916	200.00	7.50	3,250.00	(6)	
476A	30¢ orange red	3,500.00	—			
477	50¢ light violet, Mar. 2, 1917	875.00	40.00	40,000.00	(6)	
478	$1 violet black, Dec. 22, 1916	600.00	11.00	13,000.00	(6)	
	Double transfer	700.00	15.00			
479	$2 dark blue Madison (312), Mar. 22, 1917	290.00	30.00	4,000.00	(6)	
480	$5 light green Marshall (313), Mar. 22, 1917	225.00	32.50	2,750.00	(6)	
	Issues of 1916-17, Imperf.					
	#481-96: Washington (Designs of 405-06, 333-35)					
481	1¢ green, Nov. 1916	.65	.45	9.75	(6)	
	Double transfer	2.50	1.25			
482	2¢ carmine, type I, Dec. 8, 1916	1.25	1.00	20.00	(6)	
482A	2¢ deep rose, type Ia		7,500.00			
483	3¢ violet, type I, Oct. 13, 1917	9.50	6.50	110.00	(6)	
	Double transfer	16.00	—			
484	3¢ violet, type II	7.00	3.00	87.50	(6)	
	Double transfer	12.50	—			
485	5¢ carmine (error in plate of 2¢), Mar. 1917	9,000.00				
	Issues of 1916-22, Coil Stamps, Perf. 10 Horizontally					
486	1¢ green, Jan. 1918	.65	.20	3.25	(2)	
	Double transfer	2.25	—			
487	2¢ carmine, type II, Nov. 15, 1916	12.00	2.50	87.50	(2)	
488	2¢ carmine, type III, 1919	2.00	1.35	12.00	(2)	
	Cracked plate	12.00	7.50			
489	3¢ violet, type I, Oct. 10, 1917	4.00	1.00	22.50	(2)	
	Coil Stamps, Perf. 10 Vertically					
490	1¢ green, Nov. 17, 1916	.40	.15	2.50	(2)	
	Cracked plate (horizontal)	7.50	—			
	Cracked plate (vertical) retouched	9.00	—			
	Rosette crack	35.00	—			
491	2¢ carmine, type II, Nov. 17, 1916	1,500.00	450.00	7,250.00	(2)	
492	2¢ carmine, type III	6.50	.15	35.00	(2)	
493	3¢ violet, type I, July 23, 1917	13.50	2.00	90.00	(2)	
494	3¢ violet, type II, Feb. 4, 1918	7.50	1.00	50.00	(2)	
495	4¢ orange brown, Apr. 15, 1917	8.00	3.00	55.00	(2)	
	Cracked plate	25.00	—			
496	5¢ blue, Jan. 15, 1919	2.75	.90	20.00	(2)	
497	10¢ orange yellow Franklin (416), Jan. 31, 1922	16.00	9.00	100.00	(2)	2,000.00

	Issues of 1917-19, Perf. 11 #498-507: Washington (Designs of 405-06, 333-36, 407)	Un	U	PB	#	
498	1¢ green, Mar. 1917	.30	.15	13.00	(6)	
a	Vertical pair, imperf. horizontally	175.00				
b	Horizontal pair, imperf. between	75.00				
d	Double impression	150.00				
e	Booklet pane of 6, Apr. 6, 1917	1.60	.35			
f	Booklet pane of 30, Sept. 1917	750.00				
g	Perf. 10 top or bottom	500.00	—			
	Cracked plate	7.50	—			
499	2¢ rose, type I, Mar. 1917	.35	.15	14.00	(6)	
a	Vertical pair, imperf. horizontally	150.00				
b	Horizontal pair, imperf. vertically	200.00	100.00			
e	Booklet pane of 6, Mar. 31, 1917	2.75	.50			
f	Booklet pane of 30, Sept. 1917	15,000.00				
g	Double impression	125.00	—			
	Double transfer	6.00	—			
500	2¢ deep rose, type Ia	200.00	150.00	1,650.00	(6)	
	Pair, types I and Ia	1,000.00				
501	3¢ light violet, type I, Mar. 1917	8.00	.15	80.00	(6)	
b	Booklet pane of 6, Oct. 17, 1917	50.00	15.00			
d	Double impression	200.00				
502	3¢ dark violet, type II	11.00	.15	120.00	(6)	
b	Booklet pane of 6	35.00	10.00			
c	Vertical pair, imperf. horizontally	250.00	125.00			
e	Perf. 10, top or bottom	425.00	—			
503	4¢ brown, Mar. 1917	7.50	.15	110.00	(6)	
504	5¢ blue, Mar. 1917	6.50	.15	110.00	(6)	
	Double transfer	10.00	—			
505	5¢ rose (error in plate of 2¢)	350.00	400.00			
506	6¢ red orange, Mar. 1917	10.00	.20	135.00	(6)	
507	7¢ black, Mar. 1917	20.00	.85	200.00	(6)	
	#508-12, 514-18: Franklin (Designs of 414-16, 434, 417-21, 423)					
508	8¢ olive bister, Mar. 1917	9.00	.40	130.00	(6)	
c	Perf. 10 top or bottom		500.00			
509	9¢ salmon red, Mar. 1917	11.00	1.40	125.00	(6)	
510	10¢ orange yellow, Mar. 1917	13.00	.15	160.00	(6)	
511	11¢ light green, May 1917	7.00	2.00	115.00	(6)	
	Double transfer	12.50	3.00			
512	12¢ claret brown, May 1917	7.00	.30	105.00	(6)	
a	12¢ brown carmine	7.50	.35			
b	Perf. 10, top or bottom	—	450.00			
513	13¢ apple green, Jan. 10, 1919	8.50	4.75	115.00	(6)	
	13¢ deep apple green	9.75	5.25			
514	15¢ gray, May 1917	30.00	.80	425.00	(6)	
515	20¢ light ultramarine, May 1917	37.50	.20	475.00	(6)	
	20¢ deep ultramarine	39.00	.20			
b	Vertical pair, imperf. between	325.00				
516	30¢ orange red, May 1917	30.00	.60	475.00	(6)	
a	Perf. 10 top or bottom	850.00	—			
517	50¢ red violet, May 1917	60.00	.45	1,500.00	(6)	
c	Perf. 10, top or bottom		700.00			
518	$1 violet brown, May 1917	45.00	1.20	1,200.00	(6)	
b	$1 deep brown	1,000.00	600.00			

513

We redesigned and expanded the new
issues just for you! Read about the
newest issues in the "Commemorative
and Special" section.

523   524

537

*Have you noticed? We expanded the
stamp listings. They are now grouped
according to historical eras.*

	Issue of 1917, Wmkd. (191), Perf. 11	Un	U	PB	#	FDC	Q
519	2¢ carm. Washington (332), Oct. 10	225.00	*450.00*	2,000.00	(6)		
	Privately perforated copies of #344 have been made to resemble #519.						
520-22	Not assigned						
	Issues of 1918, Unwmkd.						
523	$2 Franklin, Aug. 19	600.00	200.00	*12,500.00*	(8)		
524	$5 Franklin, Aug. 19	200.00	27.50	*4,000.00*	(8)		
	Issues of 1918-20 #525-35: Washington (Designs of 405-06, 333)						
525	1¢ gray green, Dec. 1918	1.50	.35	15.00	(6)		
	1¢ Emerald	2.50	.85				
a	1¢ dark green	1.65	.75				
d	Double impression	15.00	15.00				
526	2¢ carmine, type IV, Mar. 15, 1920	21.00	2.75	160.00	(6)	800.00	
	Gash on forehead	30.00	—				
	Malformed "2" at left	27.50	5.25				
527	2¢ carmine, type V	11.50	.60	85.00	(6)		
a	Double impression	55.00	10.00				
	Line through "2" and "EN"	20.00	—				
528	2¢ carmine, type Va	6.00	.15	42.50	(6)		
c	Double impression	25.00					
528A	2¢ carmine, type VI	37.50	1.00	235.00	(6)		
d	Double impression	150.00	—				
528B	2¢ carmine, type VII	14.00	.30	100.00	(6)		
e	Double impression	55.00					
	Retouched on check	—	—				
529	3¢ violet, type III, Mar. 1918	2.25	.15	40.00	(6)		
a	Double impression	30.00	—				
b	Printed on both sides	*350.00*					
530	3¢ purple, type IV	1.00	.15	10.00	(6)		
a	Double impression	20.00	6.00				
b	Printed on both sides	250.00					
	"Blister" under "U.S."	4.00	—				
	Recut under "U.S."	4.00	—				
	Imperf.						
531	1¢ green, Jan. 1919	7.00	7.00	60.00	(6)		
532	2¢ carmine rose, type IV	35.00	25.00	225.00	(6)		
533	2¢ carmine, type V	175.00	75.00	1,300.00	(6)		
534	2¢ carmine, type Va	9.00	6.00	75.00	(6)		
534A	2¢ carmine, type VI	32.50	20.00	250.00	(6)		
534B	2¢ carmine, type VII	1,250.00	700.00	*10,000.00*	(6)		
535	3¢ violet, type IV, 1918	7.00	4.50	50.00	(6)		
a	Double impression	100.00	—				
	Issues of 1919, Perf. 12 1/2						
536	1¢ gray green Washington (405), Aug.	11.00	14.00	120.00	(6)		
a	Horizontal pair, imperf. vertically	*500.00*					
	Perf. 11						
537	3¢ Allied Victory, Mar. 3	7.50	2.75	85.00	(6)		99,585,200
a	deep red violet	*350.00*	*50.00*	*2,500.00*	(6)		
c	red violet	30.00	7.50				
	Double transfer	—	—				

	Issues of 1919 (continued), Perf. 11 x 10						
		Un	U	PB	#	FDC	Q
	#538-46: Washington (Designs of 405-06, 333; 19½-20 x 22-22¼ mm)						
538	1¢ green, June	7.50	6.00	72.50	(4)		
a	Vertical pair, imperf. horizontally	50.00	100.00	750.00	(4)		
	Double transfer	15.00	—				
539	2¢ carmine rose, type II	3,000.00	3,000.00	15,000.00	(4)		
540	2¢ carmine rose, type III, June 14	7.50	6.00	70.00	(4)		
	Double transfer	20.00	—				
a	Vertical pair, imperf. horizontally	50.00	100.00				
b	Horizontal pair, imperf. vertically	550.00					
541	3¢ violet, type II, June	22.50	20.00	265.00	(4)		
	Issue of 1920, Perf. 10 x 11 (Design 19 x 22½-22¾mm)						
542	1¢ green, May 26	6.50	.65	100.00	(6)	950.00	
	Issues of 1921, Perf. 10 (Design 19 x 22½mm)						
543	1¢ green, May	.35	.15	1.40	(4)		
a	Horizontal pair, imperf. between	550.00					
	Double transfer		—				
	Triple transfer	—	—				
	Issue of 1922, Perf. 11 (Design 19 x 22½mm)						
544	1¢ green	12,500.00	3,000.00				
	Issues of 1921 (Designs 19½-20 x 22mm)						
545	1¢ green, May	95.00	110.00	750.00	(4)		
546	2¢ carmine rose, type III, May	60.00	110.00	525.00	(4)		
a	Perf. 10 at left	—					
	Recut in hair	85.00	150.00				
	Issues of 1920, Perf. 11						
547	$2 Franklin, Nov. 1	175.00	32.50	4,000.00	(8)		
	Pilgrim Tercentenary Issue, Dec. 21						
548	1¢ The Mayflower	3.50	1.65	40.00	(6)	800.00	137,978,207
	Double transfer	—	—				
549	2¢ Landing of the Pilgrims	5.50	1.25	50.00	(6)	650.00	196,037,327
550	5¢ Signing of the Compact	35.00	10.00	400.00	(6)	—	11,321,607
	Issues of 1922-25, Perf. 11 (See also #581-91, 594-606, 622-23, 631-42, 658-79, 684-87, 692-701, 723)						
551	½¢ Nathan Hale, Apr. 4, 1925	.15	.15	4.25	(6)	15.00 (4)	
	"Cap" on fraction bar	.45	.15				
552	1¢ Franklin, Jan. 17, 1923	1.25	.15	17.50	(6)	20.00 (2)	
a	Booklet pane of 6, Aug. 11, 1923	4.50	.50				
	Double transfer	3.50	—				
553	1½¢ Harding, Mar. 19, 1925	2.25	.15	25.00	(6)	25.00 (2)	
554	2¢ Washington, Jan. 15, 1923	1.25	.15	17.50	(6)	35.00	
a	Horizontal pair, imperf. vertically	175.00					
b	Vertical pair, imperf. horizontally	500.00					
c	Booklet pane of 6, Feb. 10, 1923	5.50	1.00				
	Double transfer	2.25	.60				
555	3¢ Lincoln, Feb. 12, 1923	15.00	.85	125.00	(6)	27.50	
556	4¢ M. Washington, Jan. 15, 1923	15.00	.20	125.00	(6)	50.00	
b	Perf. 10, top or bottom	425.00	—				
557	5¢ T. Roosevelt, Oct. 27, 1922	15.00	.15	150.00	(6)	125.00	
a	Imperf. pair	1,500.00					
c	Perf. 10, top or bottom	—	500.00				
558	6¢ Garfield, Nov. 20, 1922	27.50	.75	325.00	(6)	225.00	
	Double transfer	40.00	2.00				
	Same, recut	40.00	2.00				

547

548

549

550

551

552

553

554

555

556

557

558

559

560

561

562

563

564

565

566

567

568

569

570

571

572

573

	Issues of 1922-25 (continued), Perf. 11	Un	U	PB	#	FDC	
559	7¢ McKinley, May 1, 1923	7.00	.45	50.00	(6)	140.00	
	Double transfer	—	—				
560	8¢ Grant, May 1, 1923	37.50	.35	500.00	(6)	175.00	
	Double transfer	—	—				
561	9¢ Jefferson, Jan. 15, 1923	12.00	.90	115.00	(6)	175.00	
	Double transfer	—	—				
562	10¢ Monroe, Jan. 15, 1923	16.00	.15	150.00	(6)	160.00	
a	Vertical pair, imperf. horizontally	*1,250.00*					
b	Imperf. pair	*1,250.00*					
c	Perf. 10 at top or bottom		*750.00*				
563	11¢ Hayes, Oct. 4, 1922	1.25	.25	22.50	(6)	600.00	
564	12¢ Cleveland, Mar. 20, 1923	5.50	.15	62.50	(6)	175.00	
a	Horizontal pair, imperf. vertically	*1,000.00*					
b	Imperf. pair						
565	14¢ American Indian, May 1, 1923	3.50	.65	45.00	(6)	375.00	
	Double transfer	—	—				
566	15¢ Statue of Liberty, Nov. 11, 1922	19.00	.15	225.00	(6)	500.00	
567	20¢ Golden Gate, May 1, 1923	19.00	.15	165.00	(6)	*500.00*	
a	Horizontal pair, imperf. vertically	*1,500.00*					
568	25¢ Niagara Falls, Nov. 11, 1922	17.00	.38	175.00	(6)	*675.00*	
b	Vertical pair, imperf. horizontally	*850.00*					
c	Perf. 10 at one side	—					
569	30¢ Buffalo, Mar. 20, 1923	30.00	.30	235.00	(6)	*825.00*	
	Double transfer	45.00	2.50				
570	50¢ Arlington Amphitheater, Nov. 11, 1922	50.00	.15	600.00	(6)	*1,200.00*	
571	$1 Lincoln Memorial, Feb. 12, 1923	40.00	.35	350.00	(6)	*5,500.00*	
	Double transfer	80.00	1.50				
572	$2 U.S. Capitol, Mar. 20, 1923	87.50	8.00	800.00	(6)	*11,000.00*	
573	$5 Head of Freedom, Capitol Dome, Mar. 20, 1923	140.00	12.50	2,600.00	(8)	*16,000.00*	
574	Not assigned						
	Issues of 1923-25, Imperf.						
575	1¢ green Franklin (552), Mar. 20, 1923	7.00	4.00	70.00	(6)		
576	1¹/₂¢ yel. brn. Harding (553), Apr. 4, 1925	1.50	1.50	17.00	(6)	45.00	
577	2¢ carmine Washington (554)	1.50	1.25	25.00	(6)		
	Issues of 1923, Perf. 11 x 10						
578	1¢ green Franklin (552)	70.00	110.00	600.00	(4)		
579	2¢ carmine Washington (554)	60.00	100.00	450.00	(4)		
	Recut in eye	85.00	125.00				
	Issues of 1923-26, Perf. 10 (See also #551-73, 622-23, 631-42, 658-79, 684-87, 692-701, 723)						
580	Not assigned						
581	1¢ green Franklin (552), Apr. 21, 1923	7.00	.55	75.00	(4)	*2,000.00*	
582	1¹/₂¢ brn. Harding (553), Mar. 19, 1925	3.50	.45	27.50	(4)	40.00	
	Pair with full horiz. gutter between	*135.00*					
583	2¢ carm. Wash. (554), Apr. 14, 1924	1.75	.15	17.00	(4)		
a	Booklet pane of 6, Aug. 27, 1926	75.00	*25.00*			*1,500.00*	
584	3¢ violet Lincoln (555), Aug. 1, 1925	19.00	1.75	160.00	(4)	55.00	
585	4¢ yellow brown Martha Washington (556), Mar. 1925	11.50	.30	140.00	(4)	55.00	
586	5¢ blue T. Roosevelt (557), Dec. 1924	12.00	.18	135.00	(4)	57.50	
587	6¢ red orange Garfield (558), Mar. 1925	5.50	.25	60.00	(4)	60.00	
588	7¢ black McKinley (559), May 29, 1926	8.00	4.25	67.50	(4)	70.00	

	Issues of 1923-26 (continued), Perf. 11 x 10	Un	U	PB/LP	#	FDC	Q
589	8¢ olive grn. Grant (560), May 29, 1926	17.50	2.75	150.00	(4)	72.50	
590	9¢ rose Jefferson (561), May 29, 1926	3.75	1.90	30.00	(4)	72.50	
591	10¢ orange Monroe (562), June 8, 1925	47.50	.15	350.00	(4)	95.00	
592-93	Not assigned						
	Perf. 11						
594	1¢ green Franklin (552), design 19¾ x 22¼mm	15,000.00	4,000.00				
595	2¢ carmine Washington (554), design 19¾ x 22¼mm	200.00	225.00	900.00	(4)		
596	1¢ green Franklin (552), design 19¼ x 22¾mm		27,500.00				
	Issues of 1923-29, Coil Stamps, Perf. 10 Vertically						
597	1¢ green Franklin (552), July 18, 1923	.25	.15	1.65	(2)	*550.00*	
	Gripper cracks or double transfer	2.25	1.00				
598	1½¢ brown Harding (553), Mar. 19, 1925	.60	.15	2.85	(2)	50.00	
599	2¢ carmine Washington (554), type I, Jan. 1923	.30	.15	1.65	(2)	*600.00*	
	Double transfer	1.65	1.00				
	Gripper cracks	2.00	2.00				
599A	2¢ carmine Washington (554), type II, Mar. 1929	100.00	9.50	550.00	(2)		
600	3¢ violet Lincoln (555), May 10, 1924	5.50	.15	18.50	(2)	60.00	
601	4¢ yellow brown M. Washington (556), Aug. 5, 1923	2.75	.30	17.50	(2)		
602	5¢ dark blue T. Roosevelt (557), Mar. 5, 1924	1.25	.15	7.25	(2)	82.50	
603	10¢ orange Monroe (562), Dec. 1, 1924	2.75	.15	17.50	(2)	100.00	
	Coil Stamps, Perf. 10 Horizontally						
604	1¢ yel. grn. Franklin (552), July 19, 1924	.20	.15	2.15	(2)	90.00	
605	1½¢ yel. brn. Harding (553), May 9, 1925	.25	.15	1.65	(2)	70.00	
606	2¢ carmine Washington (554), Dec. 31, 1923	.25	.15	1.25	(2)	100.00	
607-09	Not assigned						
	Issues of 1923, Harding Memorial Issue, Perf. 11						
610	2¢ blk. Harding, Sept. 1	.55	.15	18.00	(6)	30.00	1,459,487,085
a	Horizontal pair, imperf. vertically	1,100.00					
	Double transfer	1.75	.50				
	Imperf.						
611	2¢ blk. Harding (610), Nov. 15	6.50	4.25	85.00	(6)	90.00	770,000
	Perf. 10						
612	2¢ blk. Harding (610), Sept. 12	12.00	1.50	225.00	(4)	100.00	99,950,300
	Perf. 11						
613	2¢ black Harding (610)		15,000.00				
	Issues of 1924, Huguenot-Walloon Tercentary Issue, May 1						
614	1¢ Ship *Nieu Nederland*	2.50	3.00	30.00	(6)	30.00	51,378,023
615	2¢ Walloons' Landing at Fort Orange (Albany)	5.00	2.00	60.00	(6)	32.50	77,753,423
	Double transfer	12.50	3.50				
616	5¢ Huguenot Monument to Jan Ribault at Mayport, Florida	25.00	11.00	265.00	(6)	50.00	5,659,023

610

614   615   616

Have you noticed? We expanded the stamp listings. They are now grouped according to historical eras.

617

618

619

620

621

622

623

627

628

629

630

	Issues of 1925 (continued), Perf. 11	Un	U	PB	#	FDC	Q
	Issues of 1925, Lexington-Concord Issue, April 4						
617	1¢ Washington at Cambridge	2.50	2.25	40.00	(6)	27.50	15,615,000
618	2¢ "The Birth of Liberty," by Henry Sandham	5.00	3.75	67.50	(6)	30.00	26,596,600
619	5¢ "The Minute Man," by Daniel Chester French	24.00	12.50	235.00	(6)	65.00	5,348,800
	Line over head	50.00	18.50				
	Norse-American Issue, May 18						
620	2¢ Sloop *Restaurationen*	3.50	2.75	200.00	(8)	20.00	9,104,983
621	5¢ Viking Ship	14.00	10.50	650.00	(8)	30.00	1,900,983
	Issues of 1925-26 (See also #551-79, 581-91, 594-606, 631-42, 658-79, 684-87, 692-701, 723)						
622	13¢ B. Harrison, Jan. 11, 1926	12.00	.40	150.00	(6)	20.00	
623	17¢ Wilson, Dec. 28, 1925	13.00	.20	165.00	(6)	25.00	
624-26	Not assigned						
	Issues of 1926						
627	2¢ Independence Sesquicentennial Exposition, May 10	2.75	.40	35.00	(6)	10.00	307,731,900
628	5¢ John Ericsson Memorial, May 29	5.50	2.75	75.00	(6)	22.50	20,280,500
629	2¢ Battle of White Plains, Oct. 18	1.75	1.50	35.00	(6)	6.25	40,639,485
a	Vertical pair, imperf. between	—					
	International Philatelic Exhibition Souvenir Sheet, Oct. 18						
630	2¢ Battle of White Plains, sheet of 25 with salvage inscription (629)	350.00	375.00			1,400.00	107,398
	Dot over first "S" of "States"	375.00	400.00				
	Imperf. (See also #551-79, 581-91, 594-606, 622-23, 658-79, 684-87, 692-701, 723)						
631	1¹/₂¢ yellow brown Harding (553), Aug. 27	1.75	1.60	42.50	(4)	30.00	
	Issues of 1926-34, Perf. 11 x 10¹/₂ (See also #551-73, 575-79, 581-91, 594-606, 622-23, 631-42, 684-87, 692-701, 723)						
632	1¢ green Franklin (552), June 10, 1927	.15	.15	1.65	(4)	45.00	
a	Booklet pane of 6, Nov. 2, 1927	4.50	.25			3,000.00	
b	Vertical pair, imperf. between	200.00	125.00				
	Pair with full vertical gutter between	150.00	—				
	Cracked plate	—	—				
633	1¹/₂¢ yellow brown Harding (553), May 17, 1927	1.60	.15	50.00	(4)	45.00	
634	2¢ carmine Washington (554), type I, Dec. 10, 1926	.15	.15	1.00	(4)	47.50	
	Pair with full vertical gutter between	200.00					
b	2¢ carmine lake, type I	—	—	—			
c	Horizontal pair, imperf. between	2,000.00					
d	Booklet pane of 6, Feb. 25, 1927	1.25	.15				
634A	2¢ carmine Washington (554), type II, Dec. 1928	300.00	12.50	1,550.00	(4)		
	Pair with full vertical or horizontal gutter between	1,000.00					
635	3¢ violet Lincoln (555), Feb. 3, 1927	.35	.15	5.00	(4)	47.50	
a	3¢ bright violet Lincoln, Feb. 7, 1934	.25	.15	3.25	(4)	25.00	
	Gripper cracks	3.25	2.00				
636	4¢ yellow brown Martha Washington (556), May 17, 1927	2.00	.15	60.00	(4)	50.00	
	Pair with full vertical gutter between	200.00					
637	5¢ dark blue Theodore Roosevelt (557), Mar. 24, 1927	1.90	.15	12.00	(4)	50.00	
	Pair with full vertical gutter between	275.00					

	Issues of 1926-34 (continued), Perf. 11 x 10½	Un	U	PB/LB	#	FDC	Q
638	6¢ red orange Garfield (558), July 27, 1927	2.00	.15	12.00	(4)	57.50	
	Pair with full vert. gutter between	200.00					
639	7¢ black McKinley (559), Mar. 24, 1927	2.00	.15	21.00	(4)	57.50	
a	Vertical pair, imperf. between	150.00	80.00				
640	8¢ olive green Grant (560), June 10, 1927	2.00	.15	12.00	(4)	62.50	
641	9¢ orange red Jefferson (561), 1931	2.00	.15	12.00	(4)	72.50	
642	10¢ orange Monroe (562), Feb. 3, 1927	3.25	.15	23.50	(4)	90.00	
	Double transfer	—	—				
	Issues of 1927, Perf. 11						
643	2¢ Vermont Sesquicentennial, Aug. 3	1.25	.75	35.00	(6)	5.00	39,974,900
644	2¢ Burgoyne Campaign, Aug. 3	3.00	1.90	35.00	(6)	12.50	25,628,450
	Issues of 1928						
645	2¢ Valley Forge, May 26	.90	.35	22.50	(6)	4.00	101,330,328
	Perf. 11 x 10½						
646	2¢ Battle of Monmouth/ Molly Pitcher, Oct. 20	.95	.95	25.00	(4)	15.00	9,779,896
	Wide spacing, vertical pair	20.00	—				
	Hawaii Sesquicentennial Issue, Aug. 13						
647	2¢ Washington (554)	3.75	3.75	90.00	(4)	15.00	5,519,897
	Wide spacing, vertical pair	75.00					
648	5¢ Theodore Roosevelt (557)	11.00	11.00	225.00	(4)	22.50	1,459,897
	Aeronautics Conference Issue, Dec. 12, Perf. 11						
649	2¢ Wright Airplane	1.00	.75	11.50	(6)	7.00	51,342,273
650	5¢ Globe and Airplane	4.50	3.00	50.00	(6)	10.00	10,319,700
	Plate flaw, "prairie dog"	27.50	12.50				
	Issues of 1929						
651	2¢ George Rogers Clark, Feb. 25	.55	.40	8.50	(6)	6.00	16,684,674
	Double transfer	4.00	2.00				
652	Not assigned						
	Perf. 11 x 10½						
653	½¢ olive brown Nathan Hale (551), May 25	.15	.15	1.00	(4)	25.00	
	Electric Light's Golden Jubilee Issue, June 5, Perf. 11						
654	2¢ Thomas Edison's First Lamp	.60	.60	25.00	(6)	10.00	31,679,200
	Perf. 11 x 10½						
655	2¢ carmine rose (654), June 11	.55	.15	30.00	(4)	80.00	210,119,474
	Coil Stamp, Perf. 10 Vertically						
656	2¢ carmine rose (654), June 11	11.50	1.25	50.00	(2)	90.00	133,530,000
	Perf. 11						
657	2¢ Sullivan Expedition, June 17	.60	.50	24.00	(6)	4.00	51,451,880
	2¢ lake	50.00	—				

643   644   645

646   647   648

649   650

651

654   657

658

669

680

681

682

683

684

685

Issues of 1929 (continued), Perf. 11 x 10½		Un	U	PB/LP	#	FDC	Q
#658-68 overprinted "Kans.," May 1, Perf. 11 x 10½ (See also #551-73, 575-79, 581-91, 594-606, 622-23, 631-42, 684-87, 692-701, 723)							
658	1¢ Franklin	1.50	1.35	25.00	(4)	35.00	13,390,000
a	Vertical pair, one without overprint	300.00					
659	1½¢ brown Harding (553)	2.25	1.90	35.00	(4)	35.00	8,240,000
	Wide spacing, pair	65.00					
660	2¢ carmine Washington (554)	2.75	.75	30.00	(4)	35.00	87,410,000
661	3¢ violet Lincoln (555)	12.50	10.00	115.00	(4)	37.50	2,540,000
662	4¢ yellow brown Martha Washington (556)	12.50	6.00	120.00	(4)	40.00	2,290,000
663	5¢ deep blue T. Roosevelt (557)	9.00	6.50	92.50	(4)	40.00	2,700,000
664	6¢ red orange Garfield (558)	19.00	12.00	275.00	(4)	50.00	1,450,000
665	7¢ black McKinley (559)	18.00	18.00	350.00	(4)	50.00	1,320,000
666	8¢ olive green Grant (560)	60.00	50.00	525.00	(4)	95.00	1,530,000
667	9¢ light rose Jefferson (561)	9.00	7.50	110.00	(4)	95.00	1,130,000
668	10¢ orange yel. Monroe (562)	15.00	8.00	200.00	(4)	100.00	2,860,000
	#669-79 overprinted "Nebr.," May 1						
669	1¢ Franklin	2.25	1.50	30.00	(4)	35.00	8,220,000
a	Vertical pair, one without overprint	275.00					
670	1½¢ brown Harding (553)	2.00	1.65	32.50	(4)	35.00	8,990,000
671	2¢ carmine Washington (554)	2.00	.85	25.00	(4)	35.00	73,220,000
672	3¢ violet Lincoln (555)	8.50	7.50	87.50	(4)	40.00	2,110,000
673	4¢ yellow brown Martha Washington (556)	13.00	9.50	140.00	(4)	47.50	1,600,000
	Wide spacing, pair	110.00					
674	5¢ deep blue T. Roosevelt (557)	11.00	9.50	150.00	(4)	47.50	1,860,000
675	6¢ red orange Garfield (558)	27.50	15.00	300.00	(4)	70.00	980,000
676	7¢ black McKinley (559)	15.00	11.50	180.00	(4)	75.00	850,000
677	8¢ olive green Grant (560)	20.00	16.00	275.00	(4)	75.00	1,480,000
678	9¢ light rose Jefferson (561)	24.00	18.00	350.00	(4)	85.00	530,000
679	10¢ orange yel. Monroe (562)	70.00	14.00	750.00	(4)	95.00	1,890,000
	Warning: Excellent forgeries of the Kansas and Nebraska overprints exist.						
	Perf. 11						
680	2¢ Battle of Fallen Timbers, Sept. 14	.65	.65	21.00	(6)	3.50	29,338,274
681	2¢ Ohio River Canalization, Oct. 19	.50	.50	16.00	(6)	3.50	32,680,900
	Issues of 1930						
682	2¢ Mass. Bay Colony, Apr. 8	.50	.38	20.00	(6)	3.50	74,000,774
683	2¢ Carolina-Charleston, Apr. 10	1.00	.90	35.00	(6)	3.50	25,215,574
	Perf. 11 x 10½						
684	1½¢ Warren G. Harding, Dec. 1	.25	.15	1.40	(4)	4.50	
	Pair with full horizontal gutter between	175.00					
	Pair with full vert. gutter between —						
685	4¢ William H. Taft, June 4	.75	.15	9.00	(4)	6.00	
	Gouge on right "4"	2.00	.60				
	Recut right "4"	2.00	.65				
	Pair with full horizontal gutter between	—					
	Coil Stamps, Perf. 10 Vertically						
686	1½¢ brn. Harding (684), Dec. 1	1.50	.15	5.00	(2)	5.00	
687	4¢ brown Taft (685), Sept. 18	2.75	.38	10.00	(2)	20.00	

	Issues of 1930 (continued), Perf. 11	Un	U	PB	#	FDC	Q
688	2¢ Battle of Braddock's Field, July 9	.85	.75	28.50	(6)	4.00	25,609,470
689	2¢ General von Steuben, Sept. 17	.45	.45	17.00	(6)	4.00	66,487,000
a	Imperf. pair	2,500.00		12,000.00	(6)		
	Issues of 1931						
690	2¢ General Pulaski, Jan. 16	.20	.15	10.00	(6)	4.00	96,559,400
691	Not assigned						
	Perf. 11 x 10¹/₂ (See also #551-73, 575-79, 581-91, 594-606, 622-23, 631-42, 658-79, 684-87, 723)						
692	11¢ light bl. Hayes (563), Sept. 4	2.00	.15	10.50	(4)	100.00	
	Retouched forehead	6.50	1.00				
693	12¢ brown violet Cleveland (564), Aug. 25	4.00	.15	17.50	(4)	100.00	
694	13¢ yellow green Harrison (622), Sept. 4	1.75	.15	11.50	(4)	100.00	
695	14¢ dark blue American Indian (565), Sept. 8	2.75	.22	13.50	(4)	100.00	
696	15¢ gray Statue of Liberty (566), Aug. 27	6.50	.15	30.00	(4)	125.00	
	Perf. 10¹/₂ x 11						
697	17¢ black Wilson (623), July 25	3.50	.15	16.50	(4)	400.00	
698	20¢ carmine rose Golden Gate (567), Sept. 8	7.75	.15	35.00	(4)	325.00	
	Double transfer	20.00	—				
699	25¢ blue green Niagara Falls (568), July 25	7.25	.15	35.00	(4)	450.00	
700	30¢ brown Buffalo (569), Sept. 8	11.50	.15	60.00	(4)	325.00	
	Cracked plate	22.50	.85				
701	50¢ lilac Arlington Amphitheater (570), Sept. 4	35.00	.15	185.00	(4)	450.00	
	Perf. 11						
702	2¢ Red Cross, May 21	.15	.15	1.60	(4)	3.00	99,074,600
	Red cross omitted	—					
703	2¢ Yorktown, Oct. 19	.35	.25	2.25	(4)	3.50	25,006,400
a	2¢ lake and black	4.00	.65				
b	2¢ dark lake and black	350.00		1,750.00	(4)		
c	Pair, imperf. vertically	4,000.00					
	Issues of 1932, Washington Bicentennial Issue, Jan. 1, Perf. 11 x 10¹/₂						
704	¹/₂¢ Portrait by Charles W. Peale	.15	.15	3.00	(4)	5.00 (4)	87,969,700
	Broken circle	.60	.15				
705	1¢ Bust by Jean Antoine Houdon	.15	.15	4.00	(4)	4.00 (2)	1,265,555,100
706	1¹/₂¢ Portrait by Charles W. Peale	.32	.15	13.00	(4)	4.00 (2)	304,926,800
707	2¢ Portrait by Gilbert Stuart	.15	.15	1.50	(4)	4.00	4,222,198,300
	Gripper cracks	1.50	.50				
708	3¢ Portrait by Charles W. Peale	.40	.15	10.50	(4)	4.00	456,198,500
709	4¢ Portrait by Charles P. Polk	.22	.15	4.25	(4)	4.00	151,201,300
	Broken bottom frame line	1.50	.50				
710	5¢ Portrait by Charles W. Peale	1.40	.15	14.50	(4)	4.00	170,565,100
	Cracked plate	5.00	1.00				
711	6¢ Portrait by John Trumbull	2.75	.15	50.00	(4)	4.00	111,739,400
712	7¢ Portrait by John Trumbull	.22	.15	4.25	(4)	4.00	83,257,400
713	8¢ Portrait by Charles B.J.F. Saint Memin	2.50	.50	50.00	(4)	4.50	96,506,100
	Pair, full vert. gutter between	—					
714	9¢ Portrait by W. Williams	2.00	.15	30.00	(4)	4.50	75,709,200
715	10¢ Portrait by Gilbert Stuart	8.50	.15	95.00	(4)	4.50	147,216,000

688 **689** **690**

702 **703**

704 **705** **706**

707 **708** **709**

710 **711** **712**

713 **714** **715**

716

717

718

719

720

724

725

726

727

728

729

730

731

732

733

734

118

	Issues of 1932 (continued), Perf. 11	Un	U	PB/LP	#	FDC	Q
	Olympic Winter Games Issue, Jan. 25						
716	2¢ Ski Jumper	.35	.16	10.00	(6)	6.00	51,102,800
	Recut	3.50	1.50				
	Colored "snowball"	25.00	5.00				
	Perf. 11 x 10¹/₂						
717	2¢ Arbor Day, Apr. 22	.15	.15	6.50	(4)	4.00	100,869,300
	Olympic Summer Games Issue, June 15						
718	3¢ Runner at Starting Mark	1.25	.15	9.50	(4)	6.00	168,885,300
	Gripper cracks	4.00	.75				
719	5¢ Myron's Discobolus	2.00	.20	18.00	(4)	8.00	53,376,100
	Gripper cracks	4.00	1.00				
720	3¢ Washington, June 16	.15	.15	1.20	(4)	7.50	
	Pair with full vertical or horizontal gutter between	200.00					
b	Booklet pane of 6, July 25	27.50	5.00			100.00	
c	Vertical pair, imperf. between	300.00	250.00				
	Recut lines on nose	2.00	.75				
	Coil Stamp, Perf. 10 Vertically						
721	3¢ deep violet (720), June 24	2.25	.15	8.25	(2)	15.00	
	Recut lines around eyes	—	—				
	Coil Stamp, Perf. 10 Horizontally						
722	3¢ deep violet (720), Oct. 12	1.25	.30	5.00	(2)	15.00	
	Coil Stamp, Perf. 10 Vertically (See also #551-73, 575-79, 581-91, 594-606, 622-23, 631-42, 684-87, 692-701)						
723	6¢ deep orange Garfield (558), Aug. 18	8.50	.25	42.50	(2)	15.00	
	Perf. 11						
724	3¢ William Penn, Oct. 24	.25	.15	8.00	(6)	3.25	49,949,000
a	Vertical pair, imperf. horizontally	—					
725	3¢ Daniel Webster, Oct. 24	.30	.24	16.50	(6)	3.25	49,538,500
	Issues of 1933						
726	3¢ Georgia Settlement, Feb. 12	.25	.18	10.00	(6)	3.25	61,719,200
	Perf. 10¹/₂ x 11						
727	3¢ Peace of 1783, Apr. 19	.15	.15	4.00	(4)	3.50	73,382,400
	Century of Progress Issue, May 25						
728	1¢ Restoration of Fort Dearborn	.15	.15	2.00	(4)	3.00	348,266,800
	Gripper cracks	2.00	—				
729	3¢ Federal Building at Chicago	.15	.15	2.00	(4)	3.00	480,239,300
	American Philatelic Society Issue Souvenir Sheets, Aug. 25, Without Gum, Imperf.						
730	1¢ sheet of 25 (728)	24.00	24.00			100.00	456,704
a	Single stamp from sheet	.65	.35			3.25 (3)	11,417,600
731	3¢ sheet of 25 (729)	22.50	22.50			100.00	441,172
a	Single stamp from sheet	.50	.35			3.25	11,029,300
	Perf. 10¹/₂ x 11						
732	3¢ NRA, Aug. 15	.15	.15	1.50	(4)	3.25	1,978,707,300
	Gripper cracks	1.50	—				
	Recut at right	2.00					
	Perf. 11						
733	3¢ Byrd Antarctic Expedition II, Oct. 9	.40	.48	15.00	(6)	7.00	5,735,944
	Double transfer	2.50	1.00				
734	5¢ Kosciuszko, Oct. 13	.50	.22	27.50	(6)	4.50	45,137,700
a	Horizontal pair, imperf. vertically	2,000.00					

	Issues of 1934, Imperf.	Un	U	PB	#	FDC	Q
	National Stamp Exhibition Issue Souvenir Sheet, Feb. 10, Without Gum						
735	3¢ sheet of 6 (733)	12.50	10.00			40.00	811,404
a	Single stamp from sheet	2.00	1.65			5.00	4,868,424
	Perf. 11						
736	3¢ Maryland Tercentary, Mar. 23	.15	.15	7.50	(6)	1.60	46,258,300
	Double transfer	—	—				
	Mothers of America Issue, May 2, Perf. 11 x 10½						
737	3¢ Portrait of his Mother, by James A. McNeill Whistler	.15	.15	1.00	(4)	1.60	193,239,100
	Perf. 11						
738	3¢ deep violet (737)	.15	.15	4.25	(6)	1.60	15,432,200
739	3¢ Wisconsin Tercentary, July 7	.15	.15	3.00	(6)	1.10	64,525,400
a	Vertical pair, imperf. horizontally	250.00					
b	Horizontal pair, imperf. vertically	325.00					
	National Parks Issue, Unwmkd.						
740	1¢ El Capitan, Yosemite (California), July 16	.15	.15	1.00	(6)	2.25	84,896,350
	Recut	1.50	.50				
a	Vertical pair, imperf. horizontally, with gum	450.00					
741	2¢ Grand Canyon (Ariz.), July 24	.15	.15	1.25	(6)	2.25	74,400,200
a	Vertical pair, imperf. horizontally, with gum	300.00					
b	Horizontal pair, imperf. vertically, with gum	300.00					
	Double transfer	1.25	—				
742	3¢ Mirror Lake, Mt. Rainier (Washington), Aug. 3	.15	.15	1.75	(6)	2.50	95,089,000
a	Vertical pair, imperf. horizontally, with gum	350.00					
743	4¢ Cliff Palace, Mesa Verde (Colorado), Sept. 25	.35	.32	7.00	(6)	2.25	19,178,650
a	Vertical pair, imperf. horizontally, with gum	500.00					
744	5¢ Old Faithful, Yellowstone (Wyoming), July 30	.60	.55	8.75	(6)	2.25	30,980,100
a	Horizontal pair, imperf. with gum	400.00					
745	6¢ Crater Lake (Oregon), Sept. 5	1.00	.75	15.00	(6)	3.00	16,923,350
746	7¢ Great Head, Acadia Park (Maine), Oct. 2	.55	.65	10.00	(6)	3.00	15,988,250
a	Horizontal pair, imperf. vertically, with gum	550.00					
747	8¢ Great White Throne, Zion Park (Utah), Sept. 18	1.40	1.65	15.00	(6)	3.25	15,288,700
748	9¢ Mt. Rockwell and Two Medicine Lake, Glacier National Park (Montana), Aug. 27	1.50	.55	15.00	(6)	3.50	17,472,600
749	10¢ Great Smoky Mountains (North Carolina), Oct. 8	2.75	.90	25.00	(6)	6.00	18,874,300
	American Philatelic Society Issue Souvenir Sheet, Aug. 28, Imperf.						
750	3¢ sheet of 6 (742)	27.50	25.00			40.00	511,391
a	Single stamp from sheet	3.25	3.00			3.25	3,068,346
	Trans-Mississippi Philatelic Exposition Issue Souvenir Sheet, Oct. 10						
751	1¢ sheet of 6 (740)	12.00	12.00			35.00	793,551
a	Single stamp from sheet	1.35	1.50			3.25 (3)	4,761,306

735

736

737

739

740

741

742

744

743

745

746

747

748

749

750

751

Examples of Special Printing Position Blocks

Gutter Block 752

Centerline Block 754

Line Block 756

Arrow Block 763

Cross-Gutter Block 768

	Issues of 1935, Special Printing (#752-71), March 15, Without Gum, Perf. 10½ x 11	Un	U	PB	#	FDC	Q
752	3¢ violet Peace of 1783 (727)	.15	.15	11.00	(4)	5.00	3,274,556
	Perf. 11						
753	3¢ blue Byrd Expedition II (733)	.40	.40	15.00	(6)	6.00	2,040,760
	Imperf.						
754	3¢ dp. vio. Whistler's Mother (737)	.50	.50	16.50	(6)	6.00	2,389,288
755	3¢ deep violet Wisconsin (739)	.50	.50	16.50	(6)	6.00	2,294,948
756	1¢ green Yosemite (740)	.20	.20	3.65	(6)	6.00	3,217,636
757	2¢ red Grand Canyon (741)	.22	.22	4.50	(6)	6.00	2,746,640
	Double transfer	—					
758	3¢ deep violet Mt. Rainier (742)	.45	.40	12.50	(6)	6.00	2,168,088
759	4¢ brown Mesa Verde (743)	.90	.90	16.50	(6)	6.50	1,822,684
760	5¢ blue Yellowstone (744)	1.40	1.25	18.50	(6)	6.50	1,724,576
	Double transfer	—					
761	6¢ dark blue Crater Lake (745)	2.25	2.00	30.00	(6)	6.50	1,647,696
762	7¢ black Acadia (746)	1.40	1.25	25.00	(6)	6.50	1,682,948
	Double transfer	—					
763	8¢ sage green Zion (747)	1.50	1.40	30.00	(6)	7.50	1,638,644
764	9¢ red orange Glacier (748)	1.75	1.50	32.50	(6)	7.50	1,625,224
765	10¢ gray black Smoky Mts. (749)	3.50	3.00	41.50	(6)	7.50	1,644,900
766	1¢ yellow grn. (728), pane of 25	24.00	24.00			250.00	98,712
a	Single stamp from pane	.65	.35			5.50	2,467,800
767	3¢ violet (729), pane of 25	22.50	22.50			250.00	85,914
a	Single stamp from pane	.50	.35			5.50 (3)	2,147,850
768	3¢ dark blue (733), pane of 6	18.00	12.50			250.00	267,200
a	Single stamp from pane	2.50	2.00			6.50	1,603,200
769	1¢ green (740), pane of 6	12.00	9.00			250.00	279,960
a	Single stamp from pane	1.75	1.50			4.00	1,679,760
770	3¢ deep violet (742), pane of 6	27.50	22.50			250.00	215,920
a	Single stamp from pane	3.00	3.00			5.00	1,295,520
771	16¢ dark blue Great Seal of U.S.	2.00	2.00	43.50	(6)	12.50	1,370,560
	For perforate variety, see #CE2.						

A number of position pieces can be collected from the panes or sheets of the 1935 Special Printing issues, including horizontal and vertical gutter (#752, 766-70) and line (#753-65, 771) blocks of four (HG/L and VG/L), arrow-and-guideline blocks of four (AGL) and crossed-gutter or centerline blocks of four (CG/L). Pairs sell for half the price of blocks of four.

	HG/L	VG/L	AGL	CG/L		HG/L	VG/L	AGL	CG/L
752	9.00	15.00		35.00	762	6.00	6.00	6.50	10.00
753	3.50	37.50	40.00	42.50	763	6.50	6.50	7.00	11.00
754	2.10	2.10	2.25	5.00	764	7.50	7.50	8.00	21.00
755	2.10	2.10	2.25	5.00	765	14.50	14.50	15.00	21.50
756	.90	.90	1.00	2.35	766	8.50	9.75		11.50
757	.95	.95	1.00	2.75	767	7.50	8.75		11.50
758	1.95	1.95	2.00	4.00	768	12.00	13.00		15.00
759	3.75	3.75	4.00	5.50	769	11.00	11.00		12.00
760	6.50	6.50	7.00	11.00	770	20.00	20.00		21.50
761	9.25	9.25	9.50	14.50	771	8.75	8.75	10.00	36.50

	Issues of 1935 (continued), Perf. 11 x 10½	Un	U	PB	#	FDC	Q
	Beginning with #772, unused values are for never-hinged stamps.						
772	3¢ Connecticut Settlement, Apr. 26	.15	.15	1.40	(4)	8.00	70,726,800
	Defect in cent design	1.00	.25				
773	3¢ California Pacific International Exposition, May 29	.15	.15	1.40	(4)	8.00	100,839,600
	Pair with full vertical gutter between	—					
	Perf. 11						
774	3¢ Boulder Dam, Sept. 30	.15	.15	1.85	(6)	10.00	73,610,650
	Perf. 11 x 10½						
775	3¢ Michigan Statehood, Nov. 1	.15	.15	1.40	(4)	8.00	75,823,900
	Issues of 1936						
776	3¢ Republic of Texas Independence, Mar. 2	.15	.15	1.40	(4)	17.50	124,324,500
	Perf. 10½ x 11						
777	3¢ Rhode Island Settlement, May 4	.15	.15	1.40	(4)	8.00	67,127,650
	Pair with full gutter between	200.00					
	Third International Philatelic Exhibition Issue Souvenir Sheet, May 9, Imperf.						
778	Sheet of 4 different stamps (#772, 773, 775 and 776)	1.75	1.75			13.00	2,809,039
a-d	Single stamp from sheet	.40	.30				2,809,039
779-81	Not assigned						
	Perf. 11 x 10½						
782	3¢ Arkansas Statehood, June 15	.15	.15	1.40	(4)	8.00	72,992,650
783	3¢ Oregon Territory, July 14	.15	.15	1.40	(4)	8.50	74,407,450
	Double transfer	1.00	.50				
784	3¢ Susan B. Anthony, Aug. 26	.15	.15	.75	(4)	5.00	269,522,200
	Period missing after "B"	.75	.25				

SUSAN B. ANTHONY

Who was the first woman featured on an American coin?

Women's rights leader Susan B. Anthony was the first "actual" woman to be pictured on a U.S. coin in general circulation. (A fictional woman, representing "Liberty," graced many coins, beginning in 1794 with a set of half-dollar coins.) The Anthony $1 coins were minted in 1979 and 1980.

Anthony formed the Women's State Temperance Society of N.Y.— created to abolish alcoholic beverages — in 1852 after she wasn't allowed to speak in other temperance groups because she was a woman. A recognized leader, she later published a weekly journal, *The Revolution*, demanding equal rights for women, and fought for women's voting rights. Anthony died in 1906, 14 years before the 19th Amendment gave U.S. women the right to vote. **(#784)**

772

773

774

775

776

777

778

782

783

784

785

786

787

788

789

790

791

792

793

794

795

796

798

799

800

801

802

Issues of 1936-37, Perf. 11 x 10½	Un	U	PB	#	FDC	Q
Army Issue						
785 1¢ George Washington, Nathanael Green and Mount Vernon, Dec. 15, 1936	.15	.15	.85	(4)	5.00	105,196,150
Pair with full vertical gutter between	—					
786 2¢ Andrew Jackson, Winfield Scott and The Hermitage, Jan. 15, 1937	.15	.15	.85	(4)	5.00	93,848,500
787 3¢ Generals Sherman, Grant and Sheridan, Feb. 18, 1937	.15	.15	1.10	(4)	5.00	87,741,150
788 4¢ Generals Robert E. Lee and "Stonewall" Jackson and Stratford Hall, Mar. 23, 1937	.30	.15	8.00	(4)	5.50	35,794,150
789 5¢ U.S. Military Academy at West Point, May 26, 1937	.60	.15	8.50	(4)	5.50	36,839,250
Navy Issue						
790 1¢ John Paul Jones, John Barry, *Bon Homme Richard* and *Lexington*, Dec. 15, 1936	.15	.15	.85	(4)	5.00	104,773,450
791 2¢ Stephen Decatur, Thomas Macdonough and *Saratoga*, Jan. 15, 1937	.15	.15	.80	(4)	5.00	92,054,550
792 3¢ David G. Farragut and David D. Porter, *Hartford* and *Powhatan*, Feb. 18, 1937	.15	.15	1.00	(4)	5.00	93,291,650
793 4¢ Admirals William T. Sampson, George Dewey and Winfield S. Schley, Mar. 23, 1937	.30	.15	8.00	(4)	5.50	34,552,950
794 5¢ Seal of U.S. Naval Academy and Naval Cadets, May 26, 1937	.60	.15	8.50	(4)	5.50	36,819,050
Issues of 1937						
795 3¢ Northwest Territory Ordinance, July 13	.15	.15	1.10	(4)	6.00	84,825,250
Perf. 11						
796 5¢ Virginia Dare, Aug. 18	.20	.18	7.00	(6)	7.00	25,040,400
Society of Philatelic Americans Issue Souvenir Sheet, Aug. 26, Imperf.						
797 10¢ blue green (749)	.60	.40			6.00	5,277,445
Perf. 11 x 10½						
798 3¢ Constitution Sesquicentennial, Sept. 17	.15	.15	1.00	(4)	6.50	99,882,300
Territorial Issues, Perf. 10½ x 11						
799 3¢ Hawaii, Oct. 18	.15	.15	1.25	(4)	7.00	78,454,450
Perf. 11 x 10½						
800 3¢ Alaska, Nov. 12	.15	.15	1.25	(4)	7.00	77,004,200
Pair with full gutter between	—					
801 3¢ Puerto Rico, Nov. 25	.15	.15	1.25	(4)	7.00	81,292,450
802 3¢ Virgin Islands, Dec. 15	.15	.15	1.25	(4)	7.00	76,474,550
Pair with full vertical gutter between	275.00					

Minimum value listed for a stamp is 15 cents; for a First Day Cover (FDC), $1.00. This minimum represents a fair-market price for having a dealer locate and provide a single stamp or cover from his or her stock. Dealers may charge less per stamp or cover for a group of such stamps or covers, or less for a single stamp or cover.

	Issues of 1938-54, Perf. 11 x 10½	Un	U	PB	#	FDC
	Presidential Issue (#804b, 806b, 807a issued in 1939, 832b in 1951, 832c in 1954, rest in 1938; see also 839-51)					
803	½¢ Benjamin Franklin, May 19	.15	.15	.35	(4)	1.75
804	1¢ George Washington, Apr. 25	.15	.15	.35	(4)	2.00
b	Booklet pane of 6, Jan. 27, 1939	1.50	.20			15.00
	Pair with full vertical gutter between	125.00	—			
805	1½¢ Martha Washington, May 5	.15	.15	.30	(4)	2.00
b	Horizontal pair, imperf. between	150.00	25.00			
	Pair with full horizontal gutter between	150.00				
806	2¢ John Adams, June 3	.15	.15	.35	(4)	2.00
b	Booklet pane of 6, Jan. 27, 1939	3.50	.50			15.00
	Recut at top of head	3.00	1.50			
807	3¢ Thomas Jefferson, June 16	.15	.15	.35	(4)	2.00
a	Booklet pane of 6, Jan. 27, 1939	6.50	.50			18.00
b	Horizontal pair, imperf. between	650.00	—			
c	Imperf. pair	2,500.00				
808	4¢ James Madison, July 1	.60	.15	4.00	(4)	2.00
809	4½¢ The White House, July 11	.15	.15	1.60	(4)	2.00
810	5¢ James Monroe, July 21	.22	.15	1.25	(4)	2.00
811	6¢ John Quincy Adams, July 28	.25	.15	1.75	(4)	2.00
812	7¢ Andrew Jackson, Aug. 4	.28	.15	1.75	(4)	2.00
813	8¢ Martin Van Buren, Aug. 11	.30	.15	1.75	(4)	2.00
814	9¢ William H. Harrison, Aug. 18	.38	.15	1.90	(4)	3.00
	Pair with full vertical gutter between	—				
815	10¢ John Tyler, Sept. 2	.28	.15	1.40	(4)	3.00
816	11¢ James K. Polk, Sept. 8	.65	.15	3.25	(4)	3.00
817	12¢ Zachary Taylor, Sept. 14	1.00	.15	4.50	(4)	3.00
818	13¢ Millard Fillmore, Sept. 22	1.25	.15	6.75	(4)	3.00
819	14¢ Franklin Pierce, Oct. 6	.90	.15	4.50	(4)	3.00
820	15¢ James Buchanan, Oct. 13	.50	.15	2.50	(4)	3.00
821	16¢ Abraham Lincoln, Oct. 20	.90	.25	4.50	(4)	5.00
822	17¢ Andrew Johnson, Oct. 27	.85	.15	4.25	(4)	5.00
823	18¢ Ulysses S. Grant, Nov. 3	1.50	.15	7.50	(4)	5.00
824	19¢ Rutherford B. Hayes, Nov. 10	1.25	.35	6.25	(4)	5.00
825	20¢ James A. Garfield, Nov. 10	.70	.15	3.50	(4)	5.00
826	21¢ Chester A. Arthur, Nov. 22	1.25	.15	7.50	(4)	5.00
827	22¢ Grover Cleveland, Nov. 22	1.00	.40	9.50	(4)	5.00
828	24¢ Benjamin Harrison, Dec. 2	3.50	.18	18.75	(4)	5.00
829	25¢ William McKinley, Dec. 2	.80	.15	4.00	(4)	6.00
830	30¢ Theodore Roosevelt, Dec. 8	4.50	.15	24.00	(4)	7.50
831	50¢ William Howard Taft, Dec. 8	7.00	.15	37.50	(4)	10.00

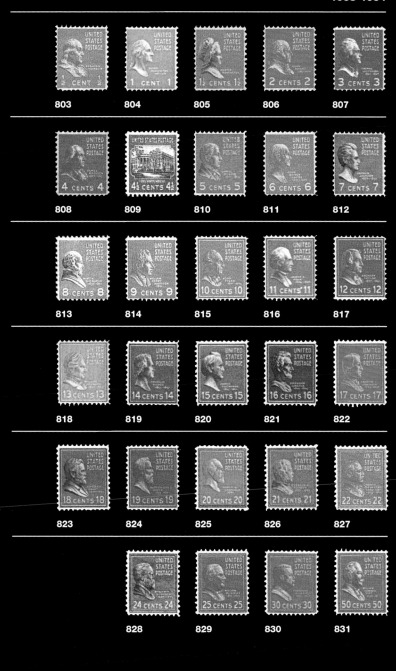

832   833   834

835   837   838

836

852   853   854

855   856

858

857

	Issues of 1938-54, Perf. 11	Un	U	PB/LP	#	FDC	Q
832	$1 Woodrow Wilson, Aug. 29	7.00	.15	35.00	(4)	45.00	
a	Vertical pair, imperf. horizontally	1,750.00					
	Wmkd. USIR						
b	$1 purple and black, 1951	300.00	70.00	1,850.00	(4)		
	Unwmkd.						
c	$1 red violet and black, Aug. 31, 1954	6.00	.15	30.00	(4)	25.00	
d	As "c," vert. pair, imperf. horiz.	1,000.00					
e	Vertical pair, imperf. between	2,500.00					
f	As "c," vert. pair, imperf. between	7,000.00					
833	$2 Warren G. Harding, Sept. 29	21.00	3.75	110.00	(4)	90.00	
834	$5 Calvin Coolidge, Nov. 17	95.00	3.00	425.00	(4)	140.00	
a	$5 red, brown and black	2,000.00	1,250.00				
	Issues of 1938, Perf. 11 x 10¹/₂						
835	3¢ Constitution Ratification, June 21	.22	.15	3.50	(4)	6.50	73,043,650
	Perf. 11						
836	3¢ Swedish-Finnish Tercentary, June 27	.15	.15	2.75	(6)	6.00	58,564,368
	Perf. 11 x 10¹/₂						
837	3¢ Northwest Territory Sesquicentennial, July 15	.15	.15	8.00	(4)	6.00	65,939,500
838	3¢ Iowa Territorial Centennial, Aug. 24	.15	.15	4.50	(4)	6.00	47,064,300
	Pair with full vertical gutter between	—					
	Issues of 1939, Coil Stamps, Jan. 20, Perf. 10 Vertically						
839	1¢ green Washington (804)	.20	.15	.90	(2)	5.00	
840	1¹/₂¢ bister brn. Martha Washington (805)	.24	.15	.95	(2)	5.00	
841	2¢ rose carmine, John Adams (806)	.24	.15	1.25	(2)	5.00	
842	3¢ deep violet Jefferson (807)	.42	.15	1.50	(2)	5.00	
	Gripper cracks	—					
	Thin, translucent paper	2.00	—				
843	4¢ red violet Madison (808)	6.00	.35	22.50	(2)	5.00	
844	4¹/₂¢ dark gray White House (809)	.50	.35	3.25	(2)	5.00	
845	5¢ bright blue Monroe (810)	4.50	.30	20.00	(2)	5.00	
846	6¢ red orange John Quincy Adams (811)	1.10	.15	7.00	(2)	7.00	
847	10¢ brown red Tyler (815)	10.00	.40	35.00	(2)	9.00	
	Coil Stamps, Jan. 27, Perf. 10 Horizontally						
848	1¢ green Washington (804)	.55	.15	2.00	(2)	5.00	
849	1¹/₂¢ bister brn. Martha Washington (805)	1.10	.30	3.00	(2)	5.00	
850	2¢ rose carmine John Adams (806)	2.00	.40	6.00	(2)	5.00	
851	3¢ deep violet Jefferson (807)	1.90	.35	5.00	(2)	6.00	
	Perf. 10¹/₂ x 11						
852	3¢ Golden Gate Exposition, Feb. 18	.15	.15	1.40	(4)	6.00	114,439,600
853	3¢ New York World's Fair, Apr. 1	.15	.15	1.90	(4)	8.00	101,699,550
	Perf. 11						
854	3¢ Washington's Inauguration, Apr. 30	.40	.15	3.50	(6)	6.00	72,764,550
	Perf. 11 x 10¹/₂						
855	3¢ Baseball, June 12	1.25	.15	6.75	(4)	25.00	81,269,600
	Perf. 11						
856	3¢ Panama Canal, Aug. 15	.18	.15	3.00	(6)	5.00	67,813,350
	Perf. 10¹/₂ x 11						
857	3¢ Printing, Sept. 25	.15	.15	1.00	(4)	5.00	71,394,750
	Perf. 11 x 10¹/₂						
858	3¢ 50th Anniversary of Statehood (Montana, North Dakota, South Dakota, Washington), Nov. 2	.15	.15	1.25	(4)	5.00	66,835,000

	Issues of 1940, Perf. 10¹/₂ x 11	Un	U	PB	#	FDC	Q
	Famous Americans Issue						
	Authors						
859	1¢ Washington Irving, Jan. 29	.15	.15	.90	(4)	1.50	56,348,320
860	2¢ James Fenimore Cooper, Jan. 29	.15	.15	.90	(4)	1.50	53,177,110
861	3¢ Ralph Waldo Emerson, Feb. 5	.15	.15	1.25	(4)	1.50	53,260,270
862	5¢ Louisa May Alcott, Feb. 5	.28	.20	8.50	(4)	2.25	22,104,950
863	10¢ Samuel L. Clemens (Mark Twain), Feb. 13	1.50	1.35	35.00	(4)	3.75	13,201,270
	Poets						
864	1¢ Henry W. Longfellow, Feb. 16	.15	.15	1.65	(4)	1.50	51,603,580
865	2¢ John Greenleaf Whittier, Feb. 16	.15	.15	1.75	(4)	1.50	52,100,510
866	3¢ James Russell Lowell, Feb. 20	.15	.15	2.00	(4)	1.50	51,666,580
867	5¢ Walt Whitman, Feb. 20	.32	.18	9.00	(4)	4.00	22,207,780
868	10¢ James Whitcomb Riley, Feb. 24	1.65	1.40	35.00	(4)	6.00	11,835,530
	Educators						
869	1¢ Horace Mann, Mar. 14	.15	.15	1.90	(4)	1.50	52,471,160
870	2¢ Mark Hopkins, Mar. 14	.15	.15	1.00	(4)	1.50	52,366,440
871	3¢ Charles W. Eliot, Mar. 28	.15	.15	2.00	(4)	1.50	51,636,270
872	5¢ Frances E. Willard, Mar. 28	.38	.25	9.50	(4)	4.00	20,729,030
873	10¢ Booker T. Washington, Apr. 7	1.10	1.25	25.00	(4)	6.00	14,125,580
	Scientists						
874	1¢ John James Audubon, Apr. 8	.15	.15	.90	(4)	1.50	59,409,000
875	2¢ Dr. Crawford W. Long, Apr. 8	.15	.15	.75	(4)	1.50	57,888,600
876	3¢ Luther Burbank, Apr. 17	.15	.15	1.00	(4)	2.00	58,273,180
877	5¢ Dr. Walter Reed, Apr. 17	.25	.15	5.75	(4)	2.50	23,779,000
878	10¢ Jane Addams, Apr. 26	1.00	.95	22.50	(4)	5.00	15,112,580
	Composers						
879	1¢ Stephen Collins Foster, May 3	.15	.15	.90	(4)	1.50	57,322,790
880	2¢ John Philip Sousa, May 3	.15	.15	.90	(4)	1.50	58,281,580
881	3¢ Victor Herbert, May 13	.15	.15	1.10	(4)	1.50	56,398,790
882	5¢ Edward A. MacDowell, May 13	.40	.22	8.75	(4)	2.50	21,147,000
883	10¢ Ethelbert Nevin, June 10	3.50	1.35	32.50	(4)	5.00	13,328,000
	Artists						
884	1¢ Gilbert Charles Stuart, Sept. 5	.15	.15	1.00	(4)	1.50	54,389,510
885	2¢ James A. McNeill Whistler, Sept. 5	.15	.15	.90	(4)	1.50	53,636,580
886	3¢ Augustus Saint-Gaudens, Sept. 16	.15	.15	.90	(4)	1.50	55,313,230
887	5¢ Daniel Chester French, Sept. 16	.48	.22	8.00	(4)	1.75	21,720,580
888	10¢ Frederic Remington, Sept. 30	1.75	1.40	30.00	(4)	5.00	13,600,580
	Inventors						
889	1¢ Eli Whitney, Oct. 7	.15	.15	1.75	(4)	1.50	47,599,580
890	2¢ Samuel F.B. Morse, Oct. 7	.15	.15	.90	(4)	1.50	53,766,510
891	3¢ Cyrus Hall McCormick, Oct. 14	.25	.15	1.65	(4)	1.50	54,193,580
892	5¢ Elias Howe, Oct. 14	1.00	.32	13.00	(4)	3.00	20,264,580
893	10¢ Alexander Graham Bell, Oct. 28	10.00	2.25	70.00	(4)	7.50	13,726,580

Minimum value listed for a stamp is 15 cents; for a First Day Cover (FDC), $1.00. This minimum represents a fair-market price for having a dealer locate and provide a single stamp or cover from his or her stock. Dealers may charge less per stamp or cover for a group of such stamps or covers, or less for a single stamp or cover.

859 860 861 862 863

864 865 866 867 868

869 870 871 872 873

874 875 876 877 878

879 880 881 882 883

884 885 886 887 888

889 890 891 892 893

894

895

896

897

898

899

900

901

902

903

904

905

906

907

908

	Issues of 1940 (continued), Perf. 11 x 10½						
		Un	U	PB	#	FDC	Q
894	3¢ Pony Express, Apr. 3	.25	.15	3.00	(4)	5.00	46,497,400
	Perf. 10½ x 11						
895	3¢ Pan American Union, Apr. 14	.20	.15	2.75	(4)	4.50	47,700,000
	Perf. 11 x 10½						
896	3¢ Idaho Statehood, July 3	.15	.15	1.75	(4)	4.50	50,618,150
	Perf. 10½ x 11						
897	3¢ Wyoming Statehood, July 10	.15	.15	1.50	(4)	4.50	50,034,400
	Perf. 11 x 10½						
898	3¢ Coronado Expedition, Sept. 7	.15	.15	1.50	(4)	4.50	60,943,700
	National Defense Issue, Oct. 16						
899	1¢ Statue of Liberty	.15	.15	.45	(4)	4.25	
a	Vertical pair, imperf. between	500.00	—				
b	Horizontal pair, imperf. between	40.00	—				
	Pair with full vertical gutter between	200.00					
	Cracked plate	3.00					
	Gripper cracks	3.00					
900	2¢ 90mm Anti-aircraft Gun	.15	.15	.50	(4)	4.25	
a	Horizontal pair, imperf. between	40.00	—				
	Pair with full vertical gutter between	275.00					
901	3¢ Torch of Enlightenment	.15	.15	.60	(4)	4.25	
a	Horizontal pair, imperf. between	30.00	—				
	Pair with full vertical gutter between	—					
	Perf. 10½ x 11						
902	3¢ Thirteenth Amendment, Oct. 20	.16	.15	3.00	(4)	5.00	44,389,550
	Issue of 1941, Perf. 11 x 10½						
903	3¢ Vermont Statehood, Mar. 4	.15	.15	1.75	(4)	6.00	54,574,550
	Issues of 1942						
904	3¢ Kentucky Statehood, June 1	.15	.15	1.10	(4)	4.00	63,558,400
905	3¢ Win the War, July 4	.15	.15	.40	(4)	3.75	
b	3¢ purple	20.00	8.00				
	Pair with full vertical or horizontal gutter between	175.00					
906	5¢ Chinese Resistance, July 7	.22	.16	9.50	(4)	6.00	21,272,800
	Issues of 1943						
907	2¢ Allied Nations, Jan. 14	.15	.15	.35	(4)	3.50	1,671,564,200
	Pair with full vertical or horizontal gutter between	225.00					
908	1¢ Four Freedoms, Feb. 12	.15	.15	.50	(4)	3.50	1,227,334,200

How much did it cost to use the Pony Express?

The pony express system was set up to offer an express mail service between St. Joseph, Mo., and Sacramento, Ca. Using a set of fast horses at posts stationed 10 to 15 miles apart, William H. Russell's Missouri freighting firm initially charged $5 to send half an ounce of mail. The price later dropped to $1 per half ounce — about the price of a steak dinner in those days — and the service shut down in 1861 because of competition from the new transcontinental telegraph. **(#894)**

Issues of 1943-44, Perf. 12	Un	U	PB	#	FDC	Q
Overrun Countries Issue (#921 issued in 1944, rest in 1943)						
909 — 5¢ Poland, June 22	.18	.15	6.00*	(4)	5.00	19,999,646
910 — 5¢ Czechoslovakia, July 12	.18	.15	3.00*	(4)	4.00	19,999,646
911 — 5¢ Norway, July 27	.15	.15	1.50*	(4)	4.00	19,999,646
912 — 5¢ Luxembourg, Aug. 10	.15	.15	1.40*	(4)	4.00	19,999,646
913 — 5¢ Netherlands, Aug. 24	.15	.15	1.40*	(4)	4.00	19,999,646
914 — 5¢ Belgium, Sept. 14	.15	.15	1.25*	(4)	4.00	19,999,646
915 — 5¢ France, Sept. 28	.15	.15	1.40*	(4)	4.00	19,999,646
916 — 5¢ Greece, Oct. 12	.38	.25	13.00*	(4)	4.00	14,999,646
917 — 5¢ Yugoslavia, Oct. 26	.28	.15	6.50*	(4)	4.00	14,999,646
918 — 5¢ Albania, Nov. 9	.18	.15	6.00*	(4)	4.00	14,999,646
919 — 5¢ Austria, Nov. 23	.18	.15	4.00*	(4)	4.00	14,999,646
920 — 5¢ Denmark, Dec. 7	.18	.15	5.75*	(4)	4.00	14,999,646
921 — 5¢ Korea, Nov. 2, 1944	.15	.15	5.00*	(4)	5.00	14,999,646
"KORPA" plate flaw	17.50	12.50				
*Instead of plate numbers, the selvage is inscribed with the name of the country.						
Issues of 1944, Perf. 11 x 10½						
922 — 3¢ Transcontinental Railroad, May 10	.22	.15	1.50	(4)	5.00	61,303,000
923 — 3¢ Steamship, May 22	.15	.15	1.25	(4)	4.00	61,001,450
924 — 3¢ Telegraph, May 24	.15	.15	.90	(4)	3.50	60,605,000
925 — 3¢ Philippines, Sept. 27	.15	.15	1.10	(4)	3.50	50,129,350
926 — 3¢ Motion Pictures, Oct. 31	.15	.15	.90	(4)	3.50	53,479,400

How was the first motion picture made?

The first successful photographs of motion were taken in 1877 and 1878 by British photographer Eadward Muybridge. He set up 12 (and later 24) cameras in a row to photograph a horse as it ran by. Each camera had a string attached to its shutter, and as the horse broke the string, the camera took a picture. Muybridge completed a series of photos with the horse in motion.

The first projection movies — allowing people to view a single film at the same time — were created in 1894, and in 1896 Thomas Edison presented the first U.S. screening of projected motion pictures in a New York City music hall. **(#926)**

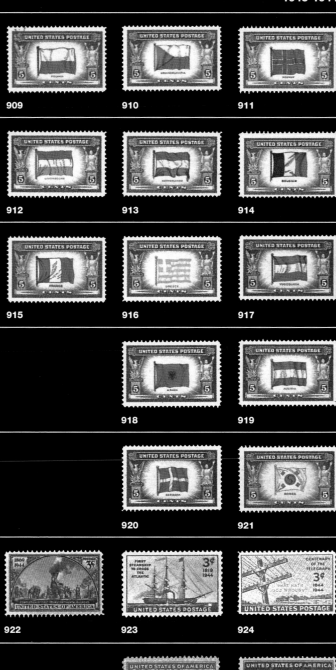

909   910   911

912   913   914

915   916   917

918   919

920   921

922   923   924

925   926

927

928

929

930

931

932

933

934

935

936

937

938

939

940

941

942

943

944

945

946

947

	Issues of 1945 (continued), Perf. 11 x 10¹/₂	Un	U	PB	#	FDC	Q
927	3¢ Florida Statehood, Mar. 3	.15	.15	.55	(4)	3.50	61,617,350
928	5¢ United Nations Conference, Apr. 25	.15	.15	.45	(4)	4.00	75,500,000
	Perf. 10¹/₂ x 11						
929	3¢ Iwo Jima (Marines), July 11	.15	.15	.38	(4)	6.75	137,321,000
	Issues of 1945-46, Franklin D. Roosevelt Issue, Perf. 11 x 10¹/₂						
930	1¢ Roosevelt and Hyde Park Residence, July 26, 1945	.15	.15	.16	(4)	2.50	128,140,000
931	2¢ Roosevelt and "The Little White House" at Warm Springs, Ga., Aug. 24, 1945	.15	.15	.24	(4)	2.50	67,255,000
932	3¢ Roosevelt and White House, June 27, 1945	.15	.15	.28	(4)	2.50	133,870,000
933	5¢ Roosevelt, Map of Western Hemisphere and Four Freedoms, Jan. 30, 1946	.15	.15	.40	(4)	3.00	76,455,400
934	3¢ Army, Sept. 28	.15	.15	.30	(4)	4.75	128,357,750
935	3¢ Navy, Oct. 27	.15	.15	.30	(4)	4.75	135,863,000
936	3¢ Coast Guard, Nov. 10	.15	.15	.30	(4)	4.75	111,616,700
937	3¢ Alfred E. Smith, Nov. 26	.15	.15	.30	(4)	2.50	308,587,700
	Pair with full vertical gutter between	—					
938	3¢ Texas Statehood, Dec. 29	.15	.15	.30	(4)	4.00	170,640,000
	Issues of 1946						
939	3¢ Merchant Marine, Feb. 26	.15	.15	.30	(4)	4.75	135,927,000
940	3¢ Veterans of World War II, May 9	.15	.15	.30	(4)	1.75	260,339,100
941	3¢ Tennessee Statehood, June 1	.15	.15	.30	(4)	1.50	132,274,500
942	3¢ Iowa Statehood, Aug. 3	.15	.15	.30	(4)	1.50	132,430,000
943	3¢ Smithsonian Institution, Aug. 10	.15	.15	.30	(4)	1.50	139,209,500
944	3¢ Kearny Expedition, Oct. 16	.15	.15	.30	(4)	1.50	114,684,450
	Issues of 1947, Perf. 10¹/₂ x 11						
945	3¢ Thomas A. Edison, Feb. 11	.15	.15	.30	(4)	2.00	156,540,510
	Perf. 11 x 10¹/₂						
946	3¢ Joseph Pulitzer, Apr. 10	.15	.15	.30	(4)	1.50	120,452,600
947	3¢ Postage Stamps Centenary, May 17	.15	.15	.30	(4)	1.50	127,104,300

Which famous publisher was rejected from three armies?

The armed services of Austria, France and Great Britain each rejected Hungarian-born Joseph Pulitzer before he was recruited by the United States to fight with the Union Army in the Civil War. After serving with the Union, he settled in St. Louis and began a career in the newspaper business. He eventually bought two St. Louis newspapers, merged them into the *St. Louis Post-Dispatch*, and also bought the *New York World*. He revived the *World* and it soon had the largest circulation nationwide. **(#946)**

Add Stamps Automatically

- Automatic shipment of new stamps, stationery and/or philatelic products you want via mail order
- Quality guaranteed

Convenient and Complete

Armchair collectors need never leave the comfort of home to use the U.S. Postal Service's Standing Order Service subscription program. Sign up once, make an advance deposit, and all postal items you desire will be shipped to you automatically each quarter.

Guaranteed Quality

Subscribers to the Standing Order Service receive mint-condition postal items of exceptional quality—the best available centering, color and printing registration. If you are not completely satisfied, return the item within 30 days for a full refund or replacement.

All products are sold at face value—there are no markups, extra fees or shipping and handling charges. Just make an advance deposit based on the items and quantities you plan to select. You will be notified when you need to replenish your deposit account.

For Information

Send in the postage-paid request card in this book or write to:

**U.S. POSTAL SERVICE GUIDE
STANDING ORDER SUBSCRIPTION SERVICE
PHILATELIC FULFILLMENT SERVICE CENTER
PO BOX 449980
KANSAS CITY MO 64144-9980**

	Issues of 1947 (continued), Imperf.	Un	U	PB	#	FDC	Q
	Centenary International Philatelic Exhibition Issue Souvenir Sheet, May 19						
948	Souvenir sheet of 2 stamps (#1-2)	.60	.45			2.00	10,299,600
a	5¢ single stamp from sheet	.25	.20				
b	10¢ single stamp from sheet	.30	.25				
	Perf. 11 x 10¹/₂						
949	3¢ Doctors, June 9	.15	.15	.30	(4)	1.00	132,902,000
950	3¢ Utah Settlement, July 24	.15	.15	.30	(4)	1.00	131,968,000
951	3¢ U.S. Frigate Constitution, Oct. 21	.15	.15	.30	(4)	1.50	131,488,000
	Perf. 10¹/₂ x 11						
952	3¢ Everglades National Park, Dec. 5	.15	.15	.30	(4)	1.00	122,362,000
	Issues of 1948, Perf. 10¹/₂ x 11						
953	3¢ Dr. George Washington Carver, Jan. 5	.15	.15	.30	(4)	1.00	121,548,000
	Perf. 11 x 10¹/₂						
954	3¢ California Gold, Jan. 24	.15	.15	.30	(4)	1.00	131,109,500
955	3¢ Mississippi Territory, Apr. 7	.15	.15	.30	(4)	1.00	122,650,500
956	3¢ Four Chaplains, May 28	.15	.15	.30	(4)	1.00	121,953,500
957	3¢ Wisconsin Statehood, May 29	.15	.15	.30	(4)	1.00	115,250,000
958	5¢ Swedish Pioneer, June 4	.15	.15	.45	(4)	1.00	64,198,500
959	3¢ Progress of Women, July 19	.15	.15	.30	(4)	1.00	117,642,500
	Perf. 10¹/₂ x 11						
960	3¢ William Allen White, July 31	.15	.15	.30	(4)	1.00	77,649,600
	Perf. 11 x 10¹/₂						
961	3¢ U.S.-Canada Friendship, Aug. 2	.15	.15	.30	(4)	1.00	113,474,500
962	3¢ Francis Scott Key, Aug. 9	.15	.15	.30	(4)	1.00	120,868,500
963	3¢ Salute to Youth, Aug. 11	.15	.15	.30	(4)	1.00	77,800,500
964	3¢ Oregon Territory, Aug. 14	.15	.15	.30	(4)	1.00	52,214,000
	Perf. 10¹/₂ x 11						
965	3¢ Harlan F. Stone, Aug. 25	.15	.15	.60	(4)	1.00	53,958,100
966	3¢ Palomar Mountain Observatory, Aug. 30	.15	.15	1.10	(4)	1.50	61,120,100
a	Vertical pair, imperf. between	500.00					
	Perf. 11 x 10¹/₂						
967	3¢ Clara Barton, Sept. 7	.15	.15	.30	(4)	.90	57,823,000

DR. GEORGE WASHINGTON CARVER

How did the peanut become world-famous?

In his early twenties George Washington Carver had hoped to be a painter, before he pursued a degree in agriculture. He later began researching the peanut and preached its usefulness throughout the country. Carver eventually made over 300 products from the annual vine, including a face powder, printer's ink, soap and — of course — peanut butter. He received awards from London's Royal Society of Arts and the National Association for the Advancement of Colored People, and was also the recipient of science's Theodore Roosevelt Medal. **(#953)**

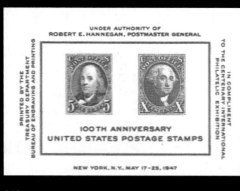

948

949

950

951

952

953

954

955

956

957

958

959

960

961

962

963

964

965

966

967

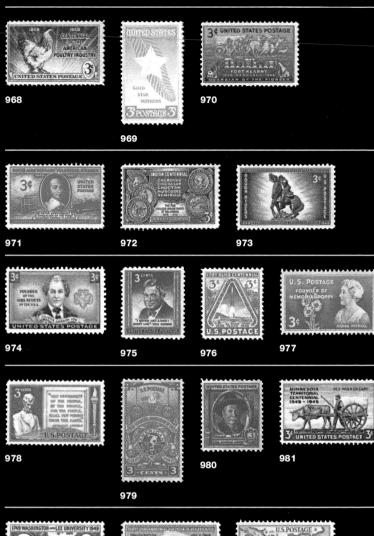

968

969

970

971

972

973

974

975

976

977

978

979

980

981

982

983

984

985

986

987

988

	Issues of 1948 (continued), Perf. 11 x 10¹/²	Un	U	PB	#	FDC	Q
968	3¢ Poultry Industry, Sept. 9	.15	.15	.35	(4)	.90	52,975,000
	Perf. 10¹/² x 11						
969	3¢ Gold Star Mothers, Sept. 21	.15	.15	.35	(4)	1.00	77,149,000
	Perf. 11 x 10¹/²						
970	3¢ Fort Kearny, Sept. 22	.15	.15	.35	(4)	1.00	58,332,000
971	3¢ Volunteer Firemen, Oct. 4	.15	.15	.35	(4)	1.50	56,228,000
972	3¢ Indian Centennial, Oct. 15	.15	.15	.35	(4)	1.00	57,832,000
973	3¢ Rough Riders, Oct. 27	.15	.15	.35	(4)	1.00	53,875,000
974	3¢ Juliette Gordon Low, Oct. 29	.15	.15	.35	(4)	1.00	63,834,000
	Perf. 10¹/² x 11						
975	3¢ Will Rogers, Nov. 4	.15	.15	.40	(4)	1.00	67,162,200
976	3¢ Fort Bliss, Nov. 5	.15	.15	1.25	(4)	1.00	64,561,000
	Perf. 11 x 10¹/²						
977	3¢ Moina Michael, Nov. 9	.15	.15	.35	(4)	1.00	64,079,500
978	3¢ Gettysburg Address, Nov. 19	.15	.15	.35	(4)	1.00	63,388,000
	Perf. 10¹/² x 11						
979	3¢ American Turners, Nov. 20	.15	.15	.35	(4)	1.00	62,285,000
980	3¢ Joel Chandler Harris, Dec. 9	.15	.15	.55	(4)	1.00	57,492,600
	Issues of 1949, Perf. 11 x 10¹/²						
981	3¢ Minnesota Territory, Mar. 3	.15	.15	.30	(4)	1.00	99,190,000
982	3¢ Washington and Lee University, Apr. 12	.15	.15	.30	(4)	1.00	104,790,000
983	3¢ Puerto Rico Election, Apr. 27	.15	.15	.30	(4)	1.00	108,805,000
984	3¢ Annapolis Tercentary, May 23	.15	.15	.30	(4)	1.00	107,340,000
985	3¢ Grand Army of the Republic, Aug. 29	.15	.15	.30	(4)	1.00	117,020,000
	Perf. 10¹/² x 11						
986	3¢ Edgar Allan Poe, Oct. 7	.15	.15	.45	(4)	1.00	122,633,000
	Thin outer frame line at top, inner frame line missing	6.00					
	Issues of 1950, Perf. 11 x 10¹/²						
987	3¢ American Bankers Association, Jan. 3	.15	.15	.30	(4)	1.00	130,960,000
	Perf. 10¹/² x 11						
988	3¢ Samuel Gompers, Jan. 27	.15	.15	.30	(4)	1.00	128,478,000

Why do people celebrate Poppy Week?

Poppy Week, the week ending on the Saturday before Memorial Day, is a memorial to all men and women who have served in the U.S. armed services. Thanks to Moina Michael, the American Legion and the Veterans of Foreign Wars, poppies were sold to aid child victims of war in France and Belgium. The memorial poppy's popularity spread, and poppies were then commonly sold to aid veterans in the early 1920s. **(#977)**

	Issues of 1950 (continued), Perf. 10½ x 11, 11 x 10½						
		Un	U	PB	#	FDC	Q
	National Capital Sesquicentennial Issue						
989	3¢ Statue of Freedom on Capitol Dome, Apr. 20	.15	.15	.30	(4)	1.00	132,090,000
990	3¢ Executive Mansion, June 12	.15	.15	.38	(4)	1.00	130,050,000
991	3¢ Supreme Court, Aug. 2	.15	.15	.30	(4)	1.00	131,350,000
992	3¢ U.S. Capitol, Nov. 22	.15	.15	.38	(4)	1.00	129,980,000
	Gripper cracks	1.00	.50				
	Perf. 11 x 10½						
993	3¢ Railroad Engineers, Apr. 29	.15	.15	.30	(4)	1.00	122,315,000
994	3¢ Kansas City, MO, June 3	.15	.15	.30	(4)	1.00	122,170,000
995	3¢ Boy Scouts, June 30	.15	.15	.35	(4)	3.00	131,635,000
996	3¢ Indiana Territory, July 4	.15	.15	.30	(4)	1.00	121,860,000
997	3¢ California Statehood, Sept. 9	.15	.15	.30	(4)	1.00	121,120,000
	Issues of 1951						
998	3¢ United Confederate Veterans, May 30	.15	.15	.30	(4)	1.00	119,120,000
999	3¢ Nevada Settlement, July 14	.15	.15	.30	(4)	1.00	112,125,000
1000	3¢ Landing of Cadillac, July 24	.15	.15	.30	(4)	1.00	114,140,000
1001	3¢ Colorado Statehood, Aug. 1	.15	.15	.30	(4)	1.00	114,490,000
1002	3¢ American Chemical Society, Sept. 4	.15	.15	.30	(4)	1.00	117,200,000
1003	3¢ Battle of Brooklyn, Dec. 10	.15	.15	.30	(4)	1.00	116,130,000
	Issues of 1952						
1004	3¢ Betsy Ross, Jan. 2	.15	.15	.35	(4)	1.00	116,175,000
1005	3¢ 4-H Club, Jan. 15	.15	.15	.30	(4)	1.00	115,945,000
1006	3¢ B&O Railroad, Feb. 28	.15	.15	.35	(4)	1.25	112,540,000
1007	3¢ American Automobile Association, Mar. 4	.15	.15	.30	(4)	1.00	117,415,000

Who ruled Motown but never heard of an automobile?

Detroit, Michigan — the auto capital of the world, also known as Motown (Motortown) — was founded by France's Antoine de la Mothe Cadillac in 1701. Cadillac, who originally was the head of France's huge Mackinac (Michigan) fur-trading post, received funding for a new colony after France abandoned its posts in 1697. Joined by many colonists, Cadillac landed at and ruled what would later be known as Detroit in 1701. **(#1000)**

989

990

991

992

993

994

995

996

997

998

999

1000

1001

1002

1003

1004

1005

1006

1007

1008

1009

1010

1011

1012

1013

1014

1015

1016

1017

1018

1019

1020

1021

1022

1023

1024

1025

1026

1027

1028

1029

	Issues of 1952 (continued), Perf. 11 x 10½	Un	U	PB	#	FDC	Q
1008	3¢ NATO, Apr. 4	.15	.15	.30	(4)	1.00	2,899,580,000
1009	3¢ Grand Coulee Dam, May 15	.15	.15	.30	(4)	1.00	114,540,000
1010	3¢ Arrival of Lafayette, June 13	.15	.15	.30	(4)	1.00	113,135,000
	Perf. 10½ x 11						
1011	3¢ Mt. Rushmore Memorial, Aug. 11	.15	.15	.35	(4)	1.00	116,255,000
	Perf. 11 x 10½						
1012	3¢ Engineering, Sept. 6	.15	.15	.30	(4)	1.00	113,860,000
1013	3¢ Service Women, Sept. 11	.15	.15	.30	(4)	1.00	124,260,000
1014	3¢ Gutenberg Bible, Sept. 30	.15	.15	.30	(4)	1.00	115,735,000
1015	3¢ Newspaper Boys, Oct. 4	.15	.15	.30	(4)	1.00	115,430,000
1016	3¢ International Red Cross, Nov. 21	.15	.15	.30	(4)	1.00	136,220,000
	Issues of 1953						
1017	3¢ National Guard, Feb. 23	.15	.15	.35	(4)	1.00	114,894,600
1018	3¢ Ohio Statehood, Mar. 2	.15	.15	.35	(4)	1.00	118,706,000
1019	3¢ Washington Territory, Mar. 2	.15	.15	.30	(4)	1.00	114,190,000
1020	3¢ Louisiana Purchase, Apr. 30	.15	.15	.30	(4)	1.00	113,990,000
1021	5¢ Opening of Japan, July 14	.15	.15	.90	(4)	1.00	89,289,600
1022	3¢ American Bar Association, Aug. 24	.15	.15	.30	(4)	1.00	114,865,000
1023	3¢ Sagamore Hill, Sept. 14	.15	.15	.30	(4)	1.00	115,780,000
1024	3¢ Future Farmers, Oct. 13	.15	.15	.30	(4)	1.00	115,244,600
1025	3¢ Trucking Industry, Oct. 27	.15	.15	.30	(4)	1.00	123,709,600
1026	3¢ General George S. Patton, Nov. 11	.15	.15	.40	(4)	1.75	114,798,600
1027	3¢ New York City, Nov. 20	.15	.15	.35	(4)	1.00	115,759,600
1028	3¢ Gadsden Purchase, Dec. 30	.15	.15	.30	(4)	1.00	116,134,600
	Issue of 1954						
1029	3¢ Columbia University, Jan. 4	.15	.15	.30	(4)	1.00	118,540,000

How can you become your own boss at age 12?

Millions of American kids have become their own bosses as news carriers — a popular job among young teens for decades. In 1952 the U.S. Post Office Department honored newspaper boys with a commemorative stamp. The torch on the right symbolizes the carriers' spirit of enterprise. The homes along the bottom represent the communities these carriers work in, and on the left, of course, is the reliable newspaper boy. Today, of course, such a stamp undoubtedly would have to honor all newspaper carriers, both boys and girls. **(#1015)**

	Issues of 1954-67 (continued), Perf. 11 x 10½	Un	U	PB	#	FDC
	Liberty Issue					
1030	½¢ Franklin, Oct. 20, 1954	.15	.15	.25	(4)	1.00
1031	1¢ Washington, Aug. 26, 1954	.15	.15	.20	(4)	1.00
	Pair with full vertical or horizontal gutter between	150.00				
b	Wet printing	.15	.15	.20		
	Perf. 10½ x 11					
1031A	1¼¢ Palace of the Governors, June 17, 1960	.15	.15	.45	(4)	1.00
1032	1½¢ Mt. Vernon, Feb. 22, 1956	.15	.15	2.00	(4)	1.00
	Perf. 11 x 10½					
1033	2¢ Jefferson, Sept. 15, 1954	.15	.15	.22	(4)	1.00
	Pair with full vertical or horizontal gutter between	—				
1034	2½¢ Bunker Hill, June 17, 1959	.15	.15	.50	(4)	1.00
1035	3¢ Statue of Liberty, June 24, 1954	.15	.15	.30	(4)	1.00
a	Booklet pane of 6, June 30, 1954	4.00	.50			5.00
b	Tagged, July 6, 1966	.25	.25	5.00	(4)	15.00
c	Imperf. pair	1,500.00				
d	Horizontal pair, imperf. between	—				
e	Wet printing	.15	.15	.30		
f	As "a," dry printing	4.75	.60			
1036	4¢ Lincoln, Nov. 19, 1954	.15	.15	.35	(4)	1.00
a	Booklet pane of 6, July 31, 1958	2.25	.50			4.00
b	Tagged, Nov. 2, 1963	.48	.40	6.50	(4)	50.00
	Perf. 10½ x 11					
1037	4½¢ The Hermitage, Mar. 16, 1959	.15	.15	.65	(4)	1.00
	Perf. 11 x 10½					
1038	5¢ James Monroe, Dec. 2, 1954	.15	.15	.50	(4)	1.00
	Pair with full vertical gutter between	200.00				
1039	6¢ T. Roosevelt, Nov. 18, 1955	.25	.15	1.10	(4)	1.00
a	Wet printing	.42	.15			
1040	7¢ Wilson, Jan. 10, 1956	.20	.15	1.00	(4)	1.00
	Perf. 11					
1041	8¢ Statue of Liberty, Apr. 9, 1954	.24	.15	2.25	(4)	1.00
a	Carmine double impression	650.00				
1042	8¢ Statue of Liberty, redrawn, Mar. 22, 1958	.20	.15	.95	(4)	1.00
	Perf. 11 x 10½					
1042A	8¢ Gen. John J. Pershing, Nov. 17, 1961	.22	.15	.95	(4)	1.00
	Perf. 10½ x 11					
1043	9¢ The Alamo, June 14, 1956	.28	.15	1.40	(4)	1.50
1044	10¢ Independence Hall, July 4, 1956	.22	.15	1.10	(4)	1.00
b	Tagged, July 6, 1966	2.00	1.00	20.00	(4)	15.00
	Perf. 11					
1044A	11¢ Statue of Liberty, June 15, 1961	.28	.15	1.25	(4)	1.00
c	Tagged, Jan. 11, 1967	2.00	1.60	35.00	(4)	22.50

1030   **1031**

1031A

1032

1033   **1034**

1035   **1036**

1037

1038   **1039**   **1040**

1041   **1042**   **1042A**

1043   **1044**

1044A

1045 **1046**

1047

1048 **1049**

1050 **1051**

1052 **1053**

	Issues of 1954-67 (continued), Perf. 11 x 10½	Un	U	PB/LP	#	FDC
1045	12¢ Benjamin Harrison, June 6, 1959	.32	.15	1.50	(4)	1.00
a	Tagged, 1968	.45	.15	3.00	(4)	25.00
1046	15¢ John Jay, Dec. 12, 1958	.90	.15	3.00	(4)	1.00
a	Tagged, July 6, 1966	1.00	.35	7.50	(4)	20.00
	Perf. 10½ x 11					
1047	20¢ Monticello, Apr. 13, 1956	.45	.15	1.80	(4)	1.20
	Perf. 11 x 10½					
1048	25¢ Paul Revere, Apr. 18, 1958	1.40	.15	5.60	(4)	1.30
1049	30¢ Robert E. Lee, Sept. 21, 1955	.90	.15	5.65	(4)	1.50
a	Wet printing	1.75	.15	5.65	(4)	
1050	40¢ John Marshall, Sept. 24, 1955	1.90	.15	8.00	(4)	1.75
a	Wet printing	2.50	.25	8.00	(4)	
1051	50¢ Susan B. Anthony, Aug. 25, 1955	1.50	.15	6.75	(4)	6.00
a	Wet printing	2.50	.15	6.75	(4)	
1052	$1 Patrick Henry, Oct. 7, 1955	5.00	.15	24.00	(4)	10.00
a	Wet printing	6.50	.15	24.00	(4)	
	Perf. 11					
1053	$5 Alexander Hamilton, Mar. 19, 1956	75.00	6.75	325.00	(4)	55.00
	Issues of 1954-73, Coil Stamps, Perf. 10 Vertically					
1054	1¢ dark green Washington (1031), Oct. 8, 1954	.18	.15	.75	(2)	1.00
b	Imperf. pair	2,000.00	—			
c	Wet printing	.35	.16			
	Coil Stamp, Perf. 10 Horizontally					
1054A	1¼¢ turquoise Palace of the Governors (1031A), June 17, 1960	.15	.15	2.25	(2)	1.00
	Coil Stamps, Perf. 10 Vertically					
1055	2¢ rose carmine Jefferson (1033), Oct. 22, 1954	.15	.15	.75	(2)	1.00
a	Tagged, May 6, 1968	.15	.15			11.00
b	Imperf. pair (Bureau precanceled)		450.00			
c	As "a," imperf. pair	525.00				
d	Wet printing	.20	.15			
1056	2½¢ gray blue Bunker Hill (1034), Sept. 9, 1959	.25	.25	3.50	(2)	2.00
1057	3¢ deep violet Statue of Liberty (1035), July 20, 1954	.15	.15	.55	(2)	1.00
a	Imperf. pair	1,350.00	—	1,650.00	(2)	
b	Tagged, Oct. 1966	.50	.50	65.00		
c	Wet printing	.24	.15			
1058	4¢ red violet Lincoln (1036), July 31, 1958	.15	.15	.60	(2)	1.00
a	Imperf. pair	90.00	70.00	200.00	(2)	
b	Wet printing (Bureau precanceled)		.50			
	Coil Stamp, Perf. 10 Horizontally					
1059	4½¢ blue green The Hermitage (1037), May 1, 1959	1.50	1.20	14.00	(2)	1.75
	Coil Stamp, Perf. 10 Vertically					
1059A	25¢ green Revere (1048), Feb. 25, 1965	.50	.30	1.75	(2)	1.25
b	Tagged, Apr. 3, 1973	.55	.20			14.00
	Dull finish gum	.55				
c	Imperf. pair	40.00		75.00	(2)	

	Issues of 1954, Perf. 11 x 10½	Un	U	PB	#	FDC	Q
1060	3¢ Nebraska Territory, May 7	.15	.15	.30	(4)	1.00	115,810,000
1061	3¢ Kansas Territory, May 31	.15	.15	.30	(4)	1.00	113,603,700
	Perf. 10½ x 11						
1062	3¢ George Eastman, July 12	.15	.15	.35	(4)	1.00	128,002,000
	Perf. 11 x 10½						
1063	3¢ Lewis and Clark Expedition, July 28	.15	.15	.35	(4)	1.00	116,078,150
	Issues of 1955, Perf. 10½ x 11						
1064	3¢ Pennsylvania Academy of the Fine Arts, Jan. 15	.15	.15	.30	(4)	1.00	116,139,800
	Perf. 11 x 10½						
1065	3¢ Land-Grant Colleges, Feb. 12	.15	.15	.30	(4)	1.00	120,484,800
1066	8¢ Rotary International, Feb. 23	.16	.15	.85	(4)	1.75	53,854,750
1067	3¢ Armed Forces Reserve, May 21	.15	.15	.30	(4)	1.00	176,075,000
	Perf. 10½ x 11						
1068	3¢ New Hampshire, June 21	.15	.15	.35	(4)	1.00	125,944,400
	Perf. 11 x 10½						
1069	3¢ Soo Locks, June 28	.15	.15	.30	(4)	1.00	122,284,600
1070	3¢ Atoms for Peace, July 28	.15	.15	.35	(4)	1.00	133,638,850
1071	3¢ Fort Ticonderoga, Sept. 18	.15	.15	.35	(4)	1.00	118,664,600
1072	3¢ Andrew W. Mellon, Dec. 20	.15	.15	.30	(4)	1.00	112,434,000

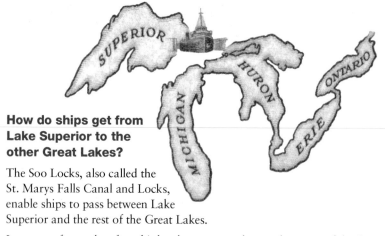

How do ships get from Lake Superior to the other Great Lakes?

The Soo Locks, also called the St. Marys Falls Canal and Locks, enable ships to pass between Lake Superior and the rest of the Great Lakes.

Long ago, fur traders found it hard to manage the rough waters of the St. Marys River, which runs between lakes Superior and Huron. A canal and lock built in 1798 were destroyed by American troops in the war of 1812. Michigan obtained a federal grant to construct a new lock in 1855, and today there are five sets of locks on the St. Marys. **(#1069)**

1060

1061

1062

1063

1064

1065

1066

1067

1068

1069

1070

1071

1072

155

1956

1073

1074

1075

1076

1077

1078

1079

1080

1081

1082

1083

1084

1085

	Issues of 1956, Perf. 10¹/₂ x 11	Un	U	PB/LP	#	FDC	Q
1073	3¢ Benjamin Franklin, Jan. 17	.15	.15	.30	(4)	1.00	129,384,550
	Perf. 11 x 10¹/₂						
1074	3¢ Booker T. Washington, Apr. 5	.15	.15	.30	(4)	1.00	121,184,600
	Fifth International Philatelic Exhibition Issues Souvenir Sheet, Imperf.						
1075	Sheet of 2 stamps (1035, 1041), Apr. 28	2.25	2.00			5.00	2,900,731
a	3¢ (1035), single stamp from sheet	.90	.80				
b	8¢ (1041), single stamp from sheet	1.25	1.00				
	Perf. 11 x 10¹/₂						
1076	3¢ New York Coliseum and Columbus Monument, Apr. 30	.15	.15	.30	(4)	1.00	119,784,200
	Wildlife Conservation Issue						
1077	3¢ Wild Turkey, May 5	.15	.15	.35	(4)	1.10	123,159,400
1078	3¢ Pronghorn Antelope, June 22	.15	.15	.35	(4)	1.10	123,138,800
1079	3¢ King Salmon, Nov. 9	.15	.15	.35	(4)	1.10	109,275,000
	Perf. 10¹/₂ x 11						
1080	3¢ Pure Food and Drug Laws, June 27	.15	.15	.30	(4)	1.00	112,932,200
	Perf. 11 x 10¹/₂						
1081	3¢ Wheatland, Aug. 5	.15	.15	.30	(4)	1.00	125,475,000
	Perf. 10¹/₂ x 11						
1082	3¢ Labor Day, Sept. 3	.15	.15	.30	(4)	1.00	117,855,000
	Perf. 11 x 10¹/₂						
1083	3¢ Nassau Hall, Sept. 22	.15	.15	.30	(4)	1.00	122,100,000
	Perf. 10¹/₂ x 11						
1084	3¢ Devils Tower, Sept. 24	.15	.15	.30	(4)	1.00	118,180,000
	Pair with full horizontal gutter between	—					
	Perf. 11 x 10¹/₂						
1085	3¢ Children's Stamp, Dec. 15	.15	.15	.30	(4)	1.00	100,975,000

When did we start celebrating Labor Day?

Labor Day, the holiday that honors all working people, is usually celebrated on the first Monday in September throughout the United States, Puerto Rico and Canada. The first Labor Day parade took place in New York City in 1882. The first state to make Labor Day a legal holiday in 1887 was Oregon. President Grover Cleveland made Labor Day a national holiday in 1894. **(#1082)**

LABOR
IS LIFE
CARLYLE

	Issues of 1957, Perf. 11 x 10½	Un	U	PB	#	FDC	Q
1086	3¢ Alexander Hamilton, Jan. 11	.15	.15	.30	(4)	1.00	115,299,450
	Perf. 10½ x 11						
1087	3¢ Polio, Jan. 15	.15	.15	.30	(4)	1.00	186,949,600
	Perf. 11 x 10½						
1088	3¢ Coast and Geodetic Survey, Feb. 11	.15	.15	.30	(4)	1.00	115,235,000
1089	3¢ American Institute of Architects, Feb. 23	.15	.15	.30	(4)	1.00	106,647,500
	Perf. 10½ x 11						
1090	3¢ Steel Industry, May 22	.15	.15	.30	(4)	1.00	112,010,000
	Perf. 11 x 10½						
1091	3¢ International Naval Review-Jamestown Festival, June 10	.15	.15	.30	(4)	1.00	118,470,000
1092	3¢ Oklahoma Statehood, June 14	.15	.15	.35	(4)	1.00	102,230,000
1093	3¢ School Teachers, July 1	.15	.15	.30	(4)	1.00	102,410,000
	Perf. 11						
1094	4¢ Flag, July 4	.15	.15	.35	(4)	1.00	84,054,400
	Perf. 10½ x 11						
1095	3¢ Shipbuilding, Aug. 15	.15	.15	.30	(4)	1.00	126,266,000
	Champion of Liberty Issue, Ramon Magsaysay, Aug. 31, Perf. 11						
1096	8¢ Bust of Magsaysay on Medal	.16	.15	.70	(4)	1.00	39,489,600
	Plate block of 4, ultramarine P# omitted	—					
	Perf. 10½ x 11						
1097	3¢ Lafayette, Sept. 6	.15	.15	.30	(4)	1.00	122,990,000
	Perf. 11						
1098	3¢ Wildlife Conservation, Nov. 22	.15	.15	.35	(4)	1.00	174,372,800
	Perf. 10½ x 11						
1099	3¢ Religious Freedom, Dec. 27	.15	.15	.30	(4)	1.00	114,365,000
	Issues of 1958						
1100	3¢ Gardening-Horticulture, Mar. 15	.15	.15	.30	(4)	1.00	122,765,200
1101-03	Not assigned						
	Perf. 11 x 10½						
1104	3¢ Brussels Universal and International Exhibition, Apr. 17	.15	.15	.30	(4)	1.00	113,660,200
1105	3¢ James Monroe, Apr. 28	.15	.15	.30	(4)	1.00	120,196,580
1106	3¢ Minnesota Statehood, May 11	.15	.15	.30	(4)	1.00	120,805,200
	Perf. 11						
1107	3¢ International Geophysical Year, May 31	.15	.15	.35	(4)	1.00	125,815,200
	Perf. 11 x 10½						
1108	3¢ Gunston Hall, June 12	.15	.15	.30	(4)	1.00	108,415,200

Minimum value listed for a stamp is 15 cents; for a First Day Cover (FDC), $1.00. This minimum represents a fair-market price for having a dealer locate and provide a single stamp or cover from his or her stock. Dealers may charge less per stamp or cover for a group of such stamps or covers, or less for a single stamp or cover.

1086

1087

1088

1089

1090

1091

1092

1093

1094

1095

1096

1097

1098

1099

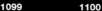

1100

1104

1105

1106

1107

1108

1109

1110

1111

1112

1113

1114

1115

1116

1117

1118

1119

1120

1121

1122

1123

1124

1125

1126

1127

1128

1129

1130

1131

	Issues of 1958 (continued), Perf. 10¹/₂ x 11	Un	U	PB	#	FDC	Q
1109	3¢ Mackinac Bridge, June 25	.15	.15	.30	(4)	1.00	107,195,200
	Champion of Liberty Issue, Simon Bolivar, July 24						
1110	4¢ Bust of Bolivar on Medal	.15	.15	.35	(4)	1.00	115,745,280
	Perf. 11						
1111	8¢ Bust of Bolivar on Medal	.16	.15	1.40	(4)	1.00	39,743,670
	Plate block of four, ocher P# only	—					
	Perf. 11 x 10¹/₂						
1112	4¢ Atlantic Cable, Aug. 15	.15	.15	.40	(4)	1.00	114,570,200
	Issues of 1958-59, Lincoln Sesquicentennial Issue, Perf. 10¹/₂ x 11						
1113	1¢ Portrait by George Healy, Feb. 12, 1959	.15	.15	.25	(4)	1.00	120,400,200
1114	3¢ Sculptured Head by Gutzon Borglum, Feb. 27, 1959	.15	.15	.30	(4)	1.00	91,160,200
	Perf. 11 x 10¹/₂						
1115	**4¢ Lincoln and Stephen Douglas Debating, by Joseph Boggs Beale,** Aug. 27, 1958	.15	.15	.40	(4)	1.00	114,860,200
1116	4¢ Statue in Lincoln Memorial by Daniel Chester French, May 30, 1959	.15	.15	.40	(4)	1.00	126,500,000
	Champion of Liberty Issue, Lajos Kossuth, Sept. 19, Perf. 10¹/₂ x 11						
1117	4¢ Bust of Kossuth on Medal	.15	.15	.40	(4)	1.00	120,561,280
	Perf. 11						
1118	8¢ Bust of Kossuth on Medal	.16	.15	1.25	(4)	1.00	44,064,580
	Perf. 10¹/₂ x 11						
1119	4¢ Freedom of the Press, Sept. 22	.15	.15	.40	(4)	1.00	118,390,200
	Perf. 11 x 10¹/₂						
1120	4¢ Overland Mail, Oct. 10	.15	.15	.40	(4)	1.00	125,770,200
	Perf. 10¹/₂ x 11						
1121	4¢ Noah Webster, Oct. 16	.15	.15	.40	(4)	1.00	114,114,280
	Perf. 11						
1122	4¢ Forest Conservation, Oct. 27	.15	.15	.40	(4)	1.00	156,600,200
	Perf. 11 x 10¹/₂						
1123	4¢ Fort Duquesne, Nov. 25	.15	.15	.40	(4)	1.00	124,200,200
	Issues of 1959						
1124	4¢ Oregon Statehood, Feb. 14	.15	.15	.40	(4)	1.00	120,740,200
	Champion of Liberty Issue, José de San Martin, Feb. 25, Perf. 10¹/₂ x 11						
1125	4¢ Bust of San Martin on Medal	.15	.15	.40	(4)	1.00	133,623,280
a	Horizontal pair, imperf. between	1,250.00					
	Perf. 11						
1126	8¢ Bust of San Martin on Medal	.16	.15	.80	(4)	1.00	45,568,000
	Perf. 10¹/₂ x 11						
1127	4¢ NATO, Apr. 1	.15	.15	.40	(4)	1.00	122,493,280
	Perf. 11 x 10¹/₂						
1128	4¢ Arctic Explorations, Apr. 6	.15	.15	.40	(4)	1.00	131,260,200
1129	8¢ World Peace Through World Trade, Apr. 20	.16	.15	.75	(4)	1.00	47,125,200
1130	4¢ Silver Centennial, June 8	.15	.15	.40	(4)	1.00	123,105,000
	Perf. 11						
1131	4¢ St. Lawrence Seaway, June 26	.15	.15	.40	(4)	1.00	126,105,050
	Pair with full horizontal gutter between	—					

	Issues of 1959 (continued), Perf. 11	Un	U	PB	#	FDC	Q
1132	4¢ 49-Star Flag, July 4	.15	.15	.40	(4)	1.00	209,170,000
1133	4¢ Soil Conservation, Aug. 26	.15	.15	.40	(4)	1.00	120,835,000
	Perf. 10¹/₂ x 11						
1134	4¢ Petroleum Industry, Aug. 27	.15	.15	.40	(4)	1.00	115,715,000
	Perf. 11 x 10¹/₂						
1135	4¢ Dental Health, Sept. 14	.15	.15	.40	(4)	1.00	118,445,000
	Champion of Liberty Issue, Ernst Reuter, Sept. 29, Perf. 10¹/₂ x 11						
1136	4¢ Bust of Reuter on Medal	.15	.15	.40	(4)	1.00	111,685,000
	Perf. 11						
1137	8¢ Bust of Reuter on Medal	.16	.15	.80	(4)	1.00	43,099,210
	Perf. 10¹/₂ x 11						
1138	4¢ Dr. Ephraim McDowell, Dec. 3	.15	.15	.40	(4)	1.00	115,444,000
a	Vertical pair, imperf. between	400.00					
b	Vertical pair, imperf. horizontally	275.00					
	Issues of 1960-61, American Credo Issue, Perf. 11						
1139	4¢ Quotation from Washington's Farewell Address, Jan. 20, 1960	.15	.15	.40	(4)	1.00	126,470,000
1140	4¢ Benjamin Franklin Quotation, Mar. 31, 1960	.15	.15	.40	(4)	1.00	124,560,000
1141	4¢ Thomas Jefferson Quotation, May 18, 1960	.15	.15	.45	(4)	1.00	115,455,000
1142	4¢ Francis Scott Key Quotation, Sept. 14, 1960	.15	.15	.45	(4)	1.00	122,060,000
1143	4¢ Abraham Lincoln Quotation, Nov. 19, 1960	.15	.15	.48	(4)	1.00	120,540,000
	Pair with full horizontal gutter between	—					
1144	4¢ Patrick Henry Quotation, Jan. 11, 1961	.15	.15	.50	(4)	1.00	113,075,000
	Issues of 1960						
1145	4¢ Boy Scouts, Feb. 8	.15	.15	.40	(4)	1.75	139,325,000
	Olympic Winter Games Issue, Feb. 18, Perf. 10¹/₂ x 11						
1146	4¢ Olympic Rings and Snowflake	.15	.15	.40	(4)	1.00	124,445,000
	Champion of Liberty Issue, Thomas G. Masaryk, Mar. 7						
1147	4¢ Bust of Masaryk on Medal	.15	.15	.35	(4)	1.00	113,792,100
a	Vertical pair, imperf. between	3,250.00					
	Perf. 11						
1148	8¢ Bust of Masaryk on Medal	.16	.15	1.00	(4)	1.00	44,215,500
a	Horizontal pair, imperf. between	—					
	Perf. 11 x 10¹/₂						
1149	4¢ World Refugee Year, Apr. 7	.15	.15	.40	(4)	1.00	113,195,000
	Perf. 11						
1150	4¢ Water Conservation, Apr. 18	.15	.15	.40	(4)	1.00	121,805,000
	Perf. 10¹/₂ x 11						
1151	4¢ SEATO, May 31	.15	.15	.40	(4)	1.00	115,353,000
a	Vertical pair, imperf. between	150.00					

1132

1133

1134

1135

1136

1137

1138

1139

1140

1141

1142

1143

1144

1145

1147

1148

1146

152

1153

1154

1155

156

1157

1158

1159

1160

161

1162

1163

1164

165

1166

1167

1168

1169

	Issues of 1960 (continued), Perf. 11 x 10½	Un	U	PB	#	FDC	Q
1152	4¢ American Woman, June 2	.15	.15	.40	(4)	1.00	111,080,000
	Perf. 11						
1153	4¢ 50-Star Flag, July 4	.15	.15	.40	(4)	1.00	153,025,000
	Perf. 11 x 10½						
1154	4¢ Pony Express, July 19	.15	.15	.40	(4)	1.00	119,665,000
	Perf. 10½ x 11						
1155	4¢ Employ the Handicapped, Aug. 28	.15	.15	.40	(4)	1.00	117,855,000
1156	4¢ 5th World Forestry Congress, Aug. 29	.15	.15	.40	(4)	1.00	118,185,000
	Perf. 11						
1157	4¢ Mexican Independence, Sept. 16	.15	.15	.40	(4)	1.00	112,260,000
1158	4¢ U.S.-Japan Treaty, Sept. 28	.15	.15	.40	(4)	1.00	125,010,000
	Champion of Liberty Issue, Ignacy Jan Paderewski, Oct. 8, Perf. 10½ x 11						
1159	4¢ Bust of Paderewski on Medal	.15	.15	.40	(4)	1.00	119,798,000
	Perf. 11						
1160	8¢ Bust of Paderewski on Medal	.16	.15	1.10	(4)	1.00	42,696,050
	Perf. 10½ x 11						
1161	4¢ Sen. Robert A. Taft Memorial, Oct. 10	.15	.15	.40	(4)	1.00	106,610,000
	Perf. 11 x 10½						
1162	4¢ Wheels of Freedom, Oct. 15	.15	.15	.40	(4)	1.00	109,695,000
	Perf. 11						
1163	4¢ Boys' Clubs of America, Oct. 18	.15	.15	.40	(4)	1.00	123,690,000
1164	4¢ First Automated Post Office, Oct. 20	.15	.15	.40	(4)	1.00	123,970,000
	Champion of Liberty Issue, Gustaf Mannerheim, Oct. 26, Perf. 10½ x 11						
1165	4¢ Bust of Mannerheim on Medal	.15	.15	.40	(4)	1.00	124,796,000
	Perf. 11						
1166	8¢ Bust of Mannerheim on Medal	.16	.15	.80	(4)	1.00	42,076,720
1167	4¢ Camp Fire Girls, Nov. 1	.15	.15	.40	(4)	1.00	116,210,000
	Champion of Liberty Issue, Giusseppe Garibaldi, Nov. 2, Perf. 10½ x 11						
1168	4¢ Bust of Garibaldi on Medal	.15	.15	.40	(4)	1.00	126,252,000
	Perf. 11						
1169	8¢ Bust of Garibaldi on Medal	.16	.15	.80	(4)	1.00	42,746,200
	Perf. 10½ x 11						
1170	4¢ Sen. Walter F. George Memorial, Nov. 5	.15	.15	.40	(4)	1.00	124,117,000
1171	4¢ Andrew Carnegie, Nov. 25	.15	.15	.40	(4)	1.00	119,840,000
1172	4¢ John Foster Dulles Memorial, Dec. 6	.15	.15	.40	(4)	1.00	117,187,000
	Perf. 11 x 10½						
1173	4¢ Echo I-Communications for Peace, Dec. 15	.18	.15	.75	(4)	2.00	124,390,000

What's a *wohelo*?

Camp Fire Girls, founded for girls in 1910 by Luther and Charlotte Gulick, was created to foster child development, group camping, outdoor programs and social action. Now known as Camp Fire Inc., the organization teaches that life's enjoyment grows out of *wo*rk, *he*alth and *lo*ve — the three words which make up Camp Fire's watchword: *wohelo*. **(#1167)**

	Issues of 1961, Perf. 10¹/₂ x 11	Un	U	PB	#	FDC	Q
	Champion of Liberty Issue, Mahatma Gandhi, Jan. 26						
1174	4¢ Bust of Gandhi on Medal	.15	.15	.40	(4)	1.00	112,966,000
	Perf. 11						
1175	8¢ Bust of Gandhi on Medal	.16	.15	1.00	(4)	1.00	41,644,400
1176	4¢ Range Conservation, Feb. 2	.15	.15	.40	(4)	1.00	110,850,000
	Perf. 10¹/₂ x 11						
1177	4¢ Horace Greeley, Feb. 3	.15	.15	.40	(4)	1.00	98,616,000
	Issues of 1961-65, Civil War Centennial Issue, Perf. 11 x 10¹/₂						
1178	4¢ Fort Sumter, Apr. 12, 1961	.16	.15	.60	(4)	1.25	101,125,000
1179	4¢ Shiloh, Apr. 7, 1962	.15	.15	.48	(4)	1.25	124,865,000
	Perf. 11						
1180	5¢ Gettysburg, July 1, 1963	.15	.15	.55	(4)	1.25	79,905,000
1181	5¢ The Wilderness, May 5, 1964	.15	.15	.55	(4)	1.25	125,410,000
1182	5¢ Appomattox, Apr. 9, 1965	.25	.15	1.15	(4)	1.25	112,845,000
a	Horizontal pair, imperf. vertically	4,500.00					
1183	4¢ Kansas Statehood, May 10	.15	.15	.40	(4)	1.00	106,210,000
	Perf. 11 x 10¹/₂						
1184	4¢ Sen. George W. Norris, July 11	.15	.15	.40	(4)	1.00	110,810,000
1185	4¢ Naval Aviation, Aug. 20	.15	.15	.40	(4)	1.00	116,995,000
	Pair with full vertical gutter between	150.00					
	Perf. 10¹/₂ x 11						
1186	4¢ Workmen's Compensation, Sept. 4	.15	.15	.40	(4)	1.00	121,015,000
	With plate # inverted			.60	(4)		
	Perf. 11						
1187	4¢ Frederic Remington, Oct. 4	.15	.15	.40	(4)	1.00	111,600,000
	Perf. 10¹/₂ x 11						
1188	4¢ Republic of China, Oct. 10	.15	.15	.40	(4)	1.00	110,620,000
1189	4¢ Naismith-Basketball, Nov. 6	.15	.15	.40	(4)	2.00	109,110,000
	Perf. 11						
1190	4¢ Nursing, Dec. 28	.15	.15	.40	(4)	1.00	145,350,000
	Issues of 1962						
1191	4¢ New Mexico Statehood, Jan. 6	.15	.15	.40	(4)	1.00	112,870,000
1192	4¢ Arizona Statehood, Feb. 14	.15	.15	.40	(4)	1.00	121,820,000
1193	4¢ Project Mercury, Feb. 20	.15	.15	.40	(4)	3.00	289,240,000
1194	4¢ Malaria Eradication, Mar. 30	.15	.15	.40	(4)	1.00	120,155,000
	Perf. 10¹/₂ x 11						
1195	4¢ Charles Evans Hughes, Apr. 11	.15	.15	.40	(4)	1.00	124,595,000

How did *Satyagraha* motivate Gandhi?

Mohandas Gandhi, who fought for Indian rights in South Africa and helped free India from British control, believed in a way of life called "Satyagraha," which was his word for a way of life involving courage, nonviolence and truth. Gandhi constantly developed these principles in order to lead a life that was based more on behavior than on achievements. Gandhi promoted tolerance for all creeds and religions. He was assassinated in 1948. **(#1175)**

1174

1175

1176

1177

1178

1179

1180

1181

1182

1183

1184

1185

1186

1187

1188

1189

1190

1191

1192

1193

1194

1195

167

1196

1197

1198

1199

1200

1201

1202

1203

1204

1205

1206

1207

1208

1209

1213

1230

1231

1232

1233

1234

1235

	Issues of 1962 (continued), Perf. 11	Un	U	PB/LP	#	FDC	Q
1196	4¢ Seattle World's Fair, Apr. 25	.15	.15	.40	(4)	1.00	147,310,000
1197	4¢ Louisiana Statehood, Apr. 30	.15	.15	.40	(4)	1.00	118,690,000
	Perf. 11 x 10¹/₂						
1198	4¢ Homestead Act, May 20	.15	.15	.40	(4)	1.00	122,730,000
1199	4¢ Girl Scout Jubilee, July 24	.15	.15	.40	(4)	1.00	126,515,000
	Pair with full vertical gutter between *250.00*						
1200	4¢ Sen. Brien McMahon, July 28	.15	.15	.40	(4)	1.00	130,960,000
1201	4¢ Apprenticeship, Aug. 31	.15	.15	.40	(4)	1.00	120,055,000
	Perf. 11						
1202	4¢ Sam Rayburn, Sept. 16	.15	.15	.40	(4)	1.00	120,715,000
1203	4¢ Dag Hammarskjold, Oct. 23	.15	.15	.40	(4)	1.00	121,440,000
1204	4¢ black, brown and yellow (yellow inverted), Dag Hammarskjold, special printing, Nov. 16	.15	.15	1.25	(4)	6.00	40,270,000
	Christmas Issue, Nov. 1						
1205	4¢ Wreath and Candles	.15	.15	.40	(4)	1.00	861,970,000
1206	4¢ Higher Education, Nov. 14	.15	.15	.40	(4)	1.00	120,035,000
1207	4¢ Winslow Homer, Dec. 15	.15	.15	.48	(4)	1.00	117,870,000
a	Horizontal pair, imperf. between *6,750.00*						
	Issue of 1963-66						
1208	5¢ Flag over White House, Jan. 9, 1963	.15	.15	.50	(4)	1.00	
a	Tagged, Aug. 25, 1966	.16	.15	.80	(4)	11.50	
b	Horizontal pair, imperf. between *1,500.00*						
	Pair with full horizontal gutter between	—					
	Issues of 1962-66, Perf. 11 x 10¹/₂						
1209	1¢ Andrew Jackson, Mar. 22, 1963	.15	.15	.20	(4)	1.00	
a	Tagged, July 6, 1966	.15	.15	.30	(4)	5.75	
b	Horizontal pair, imperf. between, tagged —						
1210-12	Not assigned						
1213	5¢ George Washington, Nov. 23, 1962	.15	.15	.45	(4)	1.00	
a	Booklet pane of 5 + label	2.75	*1.50*			4.00	
b	Tagged, Oct. 28, 1963	.50	.22	3.00	(4)	5.75	
c	As "a," tagged	1.75	*1.50*				
1214-24	Not assigned						
	Coil Stamps, Perf. 10 Vertically						
1225	1¢ green Jackson (1209), May 31, 1963	.15	.15	1.75	(2)	1.00	
a	Tagged, July 6, 1966	.15	.15	5.75	(2)	5.00	
1226-28	Not assigned						
1229	5¢ dark blue gray Washington (1213), Nov. 23, 1962	1.00	.15	3.50	(2)	1.00	
a	Tagged, Oct. 28, 1963	1.25	.15			20.00	
b	Imperf. pair	*375.00*		*1,150.00*	(2)		
	Issues of 1963, Perf. 11						
1230	5¢ Carolina Charter, Apr. 6	.15	.15	.50	(4)	1.00	129,945,000
1231	5¢ Food for Peace-Freedom from Hunger, June 4	.15	.15	.50	(4)	1.00	135,620,000
1232	5¢ West Virginia Statehood, June 20	.15	.15	.50	(4)	1.00	137,540,000
1233	5¢ Emancipation Proclamation, Aug. 16	.15	.15	.50	(4)	1.00	132,435,000
1234	5¢ Alliance for Progress, Aug. 17	.15	.15	.50	(4)	1.00	135,520,000
	Perf. 10¹/₂ x 11						
1235	5¢ Cordell Hull, Oct. 5	.15	.15	.50	(4)	1.00	131,420,000

	Issues of 1963 (continued), Perf. 11 x 10½	Un	U	PB	#	FDC	Q
1236	5¢ Eleanor Roosevelt, Oct. 11	.15	.15	.50	(4)	1.00	133,170,000
	Perf. 11						
1237	5¢ The Sciences, Oct. 14	.15	.15	.50	(4)	1.00	130,195,000
1238	5¢ City Mail Delivery, Oct. 26	.15	.15	.50	(4)	1.00	128,450,000
1239	5¢ International Red Cross, Oct. 29	.15	.15	.50	(4)	1.00	118,665,000
	Christmas Issue, Nov. 1						
1240	5¢ National Christmas Tree and White House	.15	.15	.50	(4)	1.00	1,291,250,000
a	Tagged, Nov. 2	.65	.40	5.00	(4)	60.00	
	Pair with full horizontal gutter between	—					
1241	5¢ John James Audubon, Dec. 7 (See also #C71)	.15	.15	.50	(4)	1.00	175,175,000
	Issues of 1964, Perf. 10½ x 11						
1242	5¢ Sam Houston, Jan. 10	.15	.15	.50	(4)	1.00	125,995,000
	Perf. 11						
1243	5¢ Charles M. Russell, Mar. 19	.15	.15	.50	(4)	1.00	128,025,000
	Perf. 11 x 10½						
1244	5¢ New York World's Fair, Apr. 22	.15	.15	.50	(4)	1.00	145,700,000
	Perf. 11						
1245	5¢ John Muir, Apr. 29	.15	.15	.50	(4)	1.00	120,310,000
	Perf. 11 x 10½						
1246	5¢ President John Fitzgerald Kennedy Memorial, May 29	.15	.15	.50	(4)	1.00	511,750,000
	Perf. 10½ x 11						
1247	5¢ New Jersey Settlement, June 15	.15	.15	.50	(4)	1.00	123,845,000
	Perf. 11						
1248	5¢ Nevada Statehood, July 22	.15	.15	.50	(4)	1.00	122,825,000
1249	5¢ Register and Vote, Aug. 1	.15	.15	.50	(4)	1.00	453,090,000
	Perf. 10½ x 11						
1250	5¢ Shakespeare, Aug. 14	.15	.15	.50	(4)	1.00	123,245,000
1251	5¢ Doctors William and Charles Mayo, Sept. 11	.15	.15	.50	(4)	1.00	123,355,000
	Perf. 11						
1252	5¢ American Music, Oct. 15	.15	.15	.50	(4)	1.00	126,970,000
a	Blue omitted	1,250.00					
1253	5¢ Homemakers, Oct. 26	.15	.15	.50	(4)	1.00	121,250,000

Who were the Mayo brothers?

Brothers William James and Charles Horace Mayo established the world-famous Mayo Foundation and Mayo Graduate School of Medicine in Rochester, Minn. Their medical center, the Mayo Clinic, has treated about 4 million patients since 1907. William became famous for his treatment of gallstones, cancer and stomach operations, and Charles was known for reducing the death rate in goiter surgery. **(#1251)**

1236

1237

1238

1239

1240

1241

1242

1243

1244

1245

1246

1247

1248

1249

1250

1251

1252

1253

1254 1255 1257b
1256 1257

1258

1259

1260

1261

1262

1263

1264

1265

1266

1267 1268

1269

1270

1271

1272

1273

1274

1275

1276

	Issues of 1964 (continued), Perf. 11	Un	U	PB	#	FDC	Q
	Christmas Issue, Nov. 9						
1254	5¢ Holly	.35	.15			1.00	351,940,000
1255	5¢ Mistletoe	.35	.15			1.00	351,940,000
1256	5¢ Poinsettia	.35	.15			1.00	351,940,000
1257	5¢ Sprig of Conifer	.35	.15			1.00	351,940,000
b	Block of four, #1254-57	1.50	1.25	1.50	(4)	3.00	
c	As "b," tagged, Nov. 10	4.25	2.00			57.50	
	Perf. 10¹/₂ x 11						
1258	5¢ Verrazano-Narrows Bridge, Nov. 21	.15	.15	.50	(4)	1.00	120,005,000
	Perf. 11						
1259	5¢ Fine Arts, Dec. 2	.15	.15	.50	(4)	1.00	125,800,000
	Perf. 10¹/₂ x 11						
1260	5¢ Amateur Radio, Dec. 15	.15	.15	.50	(4)	1.00	122,230,000
	Issues of 1965, Perf. 11						
1261	5¢ Battle of New Orleans, Jan. 8	.15	.15	.50	(4)	1.00	115,695,000
1262	5¢ Physical Fitness-Sokol, Feb. 15	.15	.15	.50	(4)	1.00	115,095,000
1263	5¢ Crusade Against Cancer, Apr. 1	.15	.15	.50	(4)	1.00	119,560,000
	Perf. 10¹/₂ x 11						
1264	5¢ Winston Churchill Memorial, May 13	.15	.15	.50	(4)	1.00	125,180,000
	Perf. 11						
1265	5¢ Magna Carta, June 15	.15	.15	.50	(4)	1.00	120,135,000
	Corner block of four, black PB# omitted	—					
1266	5¢ International Cooperation Year—United Nations, June 26	.15	.15	.50	(4)	1.00	115,405,000
1267	5¢ Salvation Army, July 2	.15	.15	.50	(4)	1.00	115,855,000
	Perf. 10¹/₂ x 11						
1268	5¢ Dante Alighieri, July 17	.15	.15	.50	(4)	1.00	115,340,000
1269	5¢ President Herbert Hoover Memorial, Aug. 10	.15	.15	.50	(4)	1.00	114,840,000
	Perf. 11						
1270	5¢ Robert Fulton, Aug. 19	.15	.15	.50	(4)	1.00	116,140,000
1271	5¢ Florida Settlement, Aug. 28	.15	.15	.50	(4)	1.00	116,900,000
a	Yellow omitted	550.00					
1272	5¢ Traffic Safety, Sept. 3	.15	.15	.50	(4)	1.00	114,085,000
1273	5¢ John Singleton Copley, Sept. 17	.15	.15	.50	(4)	1.00	114,880,000
1274	11¢ International Telecommunication Union, Oct. 6	.32	.16	5.75	(4)	1.00	26,995,000
1275	5¢ Adlai E. Stevenson Memorial, Oct. 23	.15	.15	.50	(4)	1.00	128,495,000
	Christmas Issue, Nov. 2						
1276	5¢ Angel with Trumpet (1840 Weather Vane)	.15	.15	.50	(4)	1.00	1,139,930,000
a	Tagged, Nov. 15	.75	.25	7.50	(4)	42.50	
1277	Not assigned						

The stamp listings contain a number of "a," "b," "c," etc. additions which include recognized varieties and errors. These listings are as complete as space permits.

	Issues of 1965-78, Perf. 11 x 10½, 10½ x 11 (See also #1299, 1303-05C)					
		Un	U	PB	#	FDC
	Prominent Americans Issue					
1278	1¢ Jefferson, Jan. 12, 1968	.15	.15	.20	(4)	1.00
a	Booklet pane of 8	1.00	.25			2.50
b	Bklt. pane of 4 + 2 labels, May 10, 1971	.75	.20			12.50
c	Untagged (Bureau precanceled)		.15			
1279	1¼¢ Albert Gallatin, Jan. 30, 1967	.15	.15	10.00	(4)	1.00
1280	2¢ Frank Lloyd Wright, Jan. 8, 1968	.15	.15	.25	(4)	1.00
a	Booklet pane of 5 + label	1.20	.40			4.00
b	Untagged (Bureau precanceled)		.15			
c	Booklet pane of 6, May 7, 1971	1.00	.35			15.00
	Pair with full vertical gutter between	—				
1281	3¢ Francis Parkman, Sept. 16, 1967	.15	.15	.30	(4)	1.00
a	Untagged (Bureau precanceled)		.15			
1282	4¢ Lincoln, Nov. 19, 1965	.15	.15	.38	(4)	1.00
a	Tagged, Dec. 1, 1965	.15	.15	.38	(4)	20.00
	Pair with full horizontal gutter between	—				
1283	5¢ Washington, Feb. 22, 1966	.15	.15	.50	(4)	1.00
a	Tagged, Feb. 23, 1966	.15	.15	.50	(4)	22.50
1283B	5¢ redrawn, Nov. 17, 1967	.15	.15	.50	(4)	1.00
	Dull finish gum	.20		1.00	(4)	
d	Untagged (Bureau precanceled)		.15			
1284	6¢ Roosevelt, Jan. 29, 1966	.15	.15	.60	(4)	1.00
a	Tagged, Dec. 29, 1966	.15	.15	.80	(4)	20.00
b	Booklet pane of 8, Dec. 28, 1967	1.50	.50			3.00
c	Booklet pane of 5 + label, Jan. 9, 1968	1.25	.50			100.00
1285	8¢ Albert Einstein, Mar. 14, 1966	.20	.15	.85	(4)	1.50
a	Tagged, July 6, 1966	.16	.15	.75	(4)	14.00
1286	10¢ Jackson, Mar. 15, 1967	.20	.15	1.00	(4)	1.00
b	Untagged (Bureau precanceled)		.20			
1286A	12¢ Henry Ford, July 30, 1968	.25	.15	1.00	(4)	1.00
c	Untagged (Bureau precanceled)		.25			
1287	13¢ John F. Kennedy, May 29, 1967	.25	.15	1.20	(4)	1.50
a	Untagged (Bureau precanceled)		.25			
1288	15¢ Oliver Wendell Holmes, Mar. 8, 1968	.30	.15	1.25	(4)	1.00
a	Untagged (Bureau precanceled)		.30			
	Booklet Stamp, Perf. 10					
1288B	15¢ dark rose claret Holmes (1288), Single from booklet	.28	.15			1.00
c	Booklet pane of 8, June 14, 1978	2.75	1.25			3.00
e	As "c," vert. imperf. between	—				
	Perf. 11 x 10½, 10½ x 11					
1289	20¢ George C. Marshall, Oct. 24, 1967	.42	.15	1.90	(4)	1.00
a	Tagged, Apr. 3, 1973	.40	.15	1.75	(4)	12.50
1290	25¢ Frederick Douglass, Feb. 14, 1967	.55	.15	2.25	(4)	1.25
a	Tagged, Apr. 3, 1973	.55	.15	2.00	(4)	14.00
1291	30¢ John Dewey, Oct. 21, 1968	.65	.15	3.00	(4)	1.25
a	Tagged, Apr. 3, 1973	.60	.15	2.75	(4)	14.00
1292	40¢ Thomas Paine, Jan. 29, 1968	.85	.15	3.25	(4)	1.60
a	Tagged, Apr. 3, 1973	.75	.15	3.00	(4)	15.00
1293	50¢ Lucy Stone, Aug. 13, 1968	1.00	.15	4.50	(4)	3.25
a	Tagged, Apr. 3, 1973	.85	.15	3.75	(4)	20.00
1294	$1 Eugene O'Neill, Oct. 16, 1967	2.50	.15	10.00	(4)	7.50
a	Tagged, Apr. 3, 1973	2.00	.15	8.00	(4)	22.50

1278

1279

1280

1281

1282

1283

1283B

1284

1285

1286

1286A

1287

1291

1288

1289

1290

1292

1293

1294

175

1295

1305

1306

1307

1308

1309

1310

1311

1312

1313

1314

	Issues of 1965-78 (continued), Perf. 11 x 10½, 10½ x 11	Un	U	PB/LP	#	FDC	Q
1295	$5 John Bassett Moore, Dec. 3, 1966	12.50	2.00	50.00	(4)	40.00	
a	Tagged, Apr. 3, 1973	8.50	2.00	35.00	(4)	65.00	
1296	Not assigned						
	Issues of 1966-81, Coil Stamps, Perf. 10 Horizontally						
1297	3¢ violet Parkman (1281), Nov. 4, 1975	.15	.15	.45	(2)	1.00	
a	Imperf. pair	30.00		25.00	(2)		
b	Untagged (Bureau precanceled)		.15				
c	As "b," imperf. pair		6.00	25.00	(2)		
1298	6¢ Roosevelt (1284), Dec. 28, 1967	.15	.15	1.25	(2)	1.00	
a	Imperf. pair	2,000.00					
	Coil Stamps, Perf. 10 Vertically (See also #1279-96)						
1299	1¢ green Jefferson (1278), Jan. 12, 1968	.15	.15	.20	(2)	1.00	
a	Untagged (Bureau precanceled)		.15				
b	Imperf. pair	30.00	—	65.00	(2)		
1300-02	Not assigned						
1303	4¢ blk. Lincoln (1282), May 28, 1966	.15	.15	.75	(2)	1.00	
a	Untagged (Bureau precanceled)		.15				
b	Imperf. pair	800.00		1,500.00	(2)		
1304	5¢ bl. Washington (1283), Sept. 8, 1966	.15	.15	.40	(2)	1.00	
a	Untagged (Bureau precanceled)		.15				
b	Imperf. pair	150.00		900.00	(2)		
e	As "a," imperf. pair		450.00				
1304C	5¢ redrawn (1283B), 1981	.15	.15	.60	(2)		
d	Imperf. pair	—					
1305	6¢ gray brown Roosevelt, Feb. 28, 1968	.15	.15	.55	(2)	1.00	
a	Imperf. pair	70.00		120.00	(2)		
b	Untagged (Bureau precanceled)		.20				
1305E	15¢ rose claret Holmes (1288), June 14, 1978	.25	.15	1.25	(2)	1.00	
	Dull finish gum	.60					
f	Untagged (Bureau precanceled)		.30				
g	Imperf. pair	25.00		90.00	(2)		
h	Pair, imperf. between	200.00		600.00	(2)		
1305C	$1 dull purple Eugene O'Neill (1294), Jan. 12, 1973	1.50	.20	5.00	(2)	5.00	
d	Imperf. pair	2,250.00		4,000.00	(2)		
	Issues of 1966, Perf. 11						
1306	5¢ Migratory Bird Treaty, Mar. 16	.15	.15	.50	(4)	1.00	116,835,000
1307	5¢ Humane Treatment of Animals, Apr. 9	.15	.15	.50	(4)	1.00	117,470,000
1308	5¢ Indiana Statehood, Apr. 16	.15	.15	.50	(4)	1.00	123,770,000
1309	5¢ American Circus, May 2	.20	.15	.50	(4)	2.50	131,270,000
	Sixth International Philatelic Exhibition Issue						
1310	5¢ Stamped Cover, May 21	.15	.15	.50	(4)	1.00	122,285,000
	Souvenir Sheet, Imperf.						
1311	5¢ Stamped Cover (1310) and Washington, D.C., Scene, May 23	.15	.15			1.00	14,680,000
	Perf. 11						
1312	5¢ The Bill of Rights, July 1	.15	.15	.50	(4)	1.00	114,160,000
	Perf. 10½ x 11						
1313	5¢ Poland's Millennium, July 30	.15	.15	.50	(4)	1.00	128,475,000
	Perf. 11						
1314	5¢ National Park Service, Aug. 25	.15	.15	.50	(4)	1.00	119,535,000
a	Tagged, Aug. 26	.30	.25	2.00	(4)	20.00	

	Issues of 1966 (continued), Perf. 11	Un	U	PB	#	FDC	Q
1315	5¢ Marine Corps Reserve, Aug. 29	.15	.15	.50	(4)	1.00	125,110,000
a	Tagged	.30	.20	2.00	(4)	20.00	
b	Black and bister omitted	—					
1316	5¢ General Federation of Women's Clubs, Sept. 12	.15	.15	.50	(4)	1.00	114,853,200
a	Tagged, Sept. 13	.30	.20	2.00	(4)	22.50	
	American Folklore Issue, Johnny Appleseed, Sept. 24						
1317	5¢ Appleseed Carrying Shovel and Seed Sack, Apple in Background	.15	.15	.50	(4)	1.00	124,290,000
a	Tagged, Sept. 26	.30	.20	2.00	(4)	22.50	
1318	5¢ Beautification of America, Oct. 5	.15	.15	.50	(4)	1.00	128,460,000
a	Tagged	.30	.20	1.50	(4)	20.00	
1319	5¢ Great River Road, Oct. 21	.15	.15	.50	(4)	1.00	127,585,000
a	Tagged, Oct. 22	.30	.20	2.00	(4)	22.50	
1320	5¢ Savings Bond-Servicemen, Oct. 26	.15	.15	.50	(4)	1.00	115,875,000
a	Tagged, Oct. 27	.30	.20	2.00	(4)	22.50	
b	Red, dark bl. and blk. omitted	4,750.00					
c	Dark blue omitted	8,000.00					
	Christmas Issue, Nov. 1						
1321	5¢ Madonna and Child, by Hans Memling	.15	.15	.50	(4)	1.00	1,173,547,400
a	Tagged, Nov. 2	.30	.20	1.90	(4)	9.50	
1322	5¢ Mary Cassatt, Nov. 17	.15	.15	.60	(4)	1.00	114,015,000
a	Tagged	.30	.25	2.00	(4)	20.00	
	Issues of 1967						
1323	5¢ National Grange, Apr. 17	.15	.15	.50	(4)	1.00	121,105,000
a	Tagging omitted	3.50					
1324	5¢ Canada, May 25	.15	.15	.50	(4)	1.00	132,045,000
1325	5¢ Erie Canal, July 4	.15	.15	.50	(4)	1.00	118,780,000
1326	5¢ Search for Peace— Lions International, July 5	.15	.15	.50	(4)	1.00	121,985,000
1327	5¢ Henry David Thoreau, July 12	.15	.15	.50	(4)	1.00	111,850,000
1328	5¢ Nebraska Statehood, July 29	.15	.15	.50	(4)	1.00	117,225,000
a	Tagging omitted	4.00					
1329	5¢ Voice of America, Aug. 1	.15	.15	.50	(4)	1.00	111,515,000
	American Folklore Issue, Davy Crockett, Aug. 17						
1330	5¢ Davy Crockett with Rifle and Scrub Pine	.15	.15	.50	(4)	1.00	114,270,000
a	Vertical pair, imperf. between	6,000.00					
b	Green omitted	—					
c	Black and green omitted	—					
d	Yellow and green omitted	—					
	Accomplishments in Space Issue, Sept. 29						
1331	5¢ Space-Walking Astronaut	.55	.15			1.10	60,432,500
a	Attached pair, #1331-32	1.25	1.25	3.50	(4)	8.00	
1332	5¢ Gemini 4 Capsule and Earth	.55	.15	3.00	(4)		60,432,500
1333	5¢ Urban Planning, Oct. 2	.15	.15	.50	(4)	1.00	110,675,000
1334	5¢ Finland Independence, Oct. 6	.15	.15	.50	(4)	1.00	110,670,000

Minimum value listed for a stamp is 15 cents; for a First Day Cover (FDC), $1.00. This minimum represents a fair-market price for having a dealer locate and provide a single stamp or cover from his or her stock. Dealers may charge less per stamp or cover for a group of such stamps or covers, or less for a single stamp or cover.

1315

1316

1317

1318

1319

1320

1321

1322

1323

1324

1325

1326

1327

1328

1329

1330

1331   1332   1331a

1333

1334

1335

1336

1337

1338

1339

1340

1341

1342

1343

1344

1345

1346

1347

1348

1349

1350

1351

1352

1353

1354

1355

	Issues of 1967 (continued), Perf. 12	Un	U	PB	#	FDC	Q
1335	5¢ Thomas Eakins, Nov. 2	.15	.15	.50	(4)	1.00	113,825,000
	Christmas Issue, Nov. 6, Perf. 11						
1336	5¢ Madonna and Child, by Hans Memling	.15	.15	.45	(4)	1.00	1,208,700,000
1337	5¢ Mississippi Statehood, Dec. 11	.15	.15	.50	(4)	1.00	113,330,000
	Issues of 1968-1971						
1338	6¢ Flag over White House (design 19 x 22mm), Jan. 24, 1968	.15	.15	.45	(4)	1.00	
k	Vertical pair, imperf. between	500.00					
	Coil Stamp, Perf. 10 Vertically						
1338A	6¢ dark blue, red and green (1338), May 30, 1969	.15	.15	.28		1.00	
b	Imperf. pair	450.00					
	Perf. 11 x 10½						
1338D	6¢ dark blue, red and green (1338, design 18¼ x 21mm), Aug. 7, 1970	.15	.15	2.60	(20)	1.00	
e	Horizontal pair, imperf. between	100.00					
1338F	8¢ dark blue, red and slate green (1338), May 10, 1971	.16	.15	3.50	(20)	1.00	
i	Imperf., vertical pair	40.00					
j	Horizontal pair, imperf. between	40.00					
	Coil Stamp, Perf. 10 Vertically						
1338G	8¢ dark blue, red and slate green (1338), May 10, 1971	.18	.15	.36		1.00	
h	Imperf. pair	55.00					
	Issues of 1968, Perf. 11						
1339	6¢ Illinois Statehood, Feb. 12	.15	.15	.50	(4)	1.00	141,350,000
1340	6¢ HemisFair '68, Mar. 30	.15	.15	.50	(4)	1.00	144,345,000
a	White omitted	1,400.00					
1341	$1 Airlift, Apr. 4	2.65	1.25	12.50	(4)	6.50	
	Pair with full horizontal gutter between		—				
1342	6¢ Support Our Youth-Elks, May 1	.15	.15	.50	(4)	1.00	147,120,000
1343	6¢ Law and Order, May 17	.15	.15	.50	(4)	1.00	130,125,000
1344	6¢ Register and Vote, June 27	.15	.15	.50	(4)	1.00	158,700,000
	Historic Flag Issue, July 4						
1345	6¢ Ft. Moultrie Flag, 1776	.50	.25			3.00	22,804,000
1346	6¢ U.S. Flag, 1795-1818 (Ft. McHenry Flag)	.35	.25			3.00	22,804,000
1347	6¢ Washington's Cruisers Flag, 1775	.30	.25			3.00	22,804,000
1348	6¢ Bennington Flag, 1777	.30	.25			3.00	22,804,000
1349	6¢ Rhode Island Flag, 1775	.30	.25			3.00	22,804,000
1350	6¢ First Stars and Stripes, 1777	.30	.25			3.00	22,804,000
1351	6¢ Bunker Hill Flag, 1775	.30	.25			3.00	22,804,000
1352	6¢ Grand Union Flag, 1776	.30	.25			3.00	22,804,000
1353	6¢ Philadelphia Light Horse Flag, 1775	.30	.25			3.00	22,804,000
1354	6¢ First Navy Jack, 1775	.30	.25			3.00	22,804,000
a	Strip of 10, #1345-54	3.25	3.00	6.75	(20)	15.00	
	Perf. 12						
1355	6¢ Walt Disney, Sept. 11	.16	.15	.70	(4)	2.50	153,015,000
a	Ocher omitted	700.00	—				
b	Vertical pair, imperf. horizontally	750.00					
c	Imperf. pair	600.00					
d	Black omitted	2,100.00					
e	Horizontal pair, imperf. between	4,750.00					
f	Blue omitted	2,100.00					

	Issues of 1968 (continued), Perf. 11	Un	U	PB	#	FDC	Q
1356	6¢ Father Marquette, Sept. 20	.15	.15	.50	(4)	1.00	132,560,000
	American Folklore Issue, Daniel Boone, Sept. 26						
1357	6¢ Pennsylvania Rifle, Powder Horn, Tomahawk, Pipe and Knife	.15	.15	.50	(4)	1.00	130,385,000
a	Tagging omitted	—					
1358	6¢ Arkansas River Navigation, Oct. 1	.15	.15	.50	(4)	1.00	132,265,000
1359	6¢ Leif Erikson, Oct. 9	.15	.15	.50	(4)	1.00	128,710,000
	Perf. 11 x 10¹/₂						
1360	6¢ Cherokee Strip, Oct. 15	.15	.15	.55	(4)	1.00	124,775,000
a	Tagging omitted	4.50					
	Perf. 11						
1361	6¢ John Trumbull, Oct. 18	.15	.15	.60	(4)	1.00	128,295,000
1362	6¢ Waterfowl Conservation, Oct. 24	.15	.15	.70	(4)	1.00	142,245,000
a	Vertical pair, imperf. between	550.00					
b	Red and dark blue omitted	1,400.00					
	Christmas Issue, Nov. 1						
1363	6¢ Angel Gabriel, from "The Annunciation," by Jan Van Eyck	.15	.15	2.00	(10)	1.00	1,410,580,000
a	Untagged, Nov. 2	.15	.15	2.00	(10)	6.50	
b	Imperf. pair tagged	250.00					
c	Light yellow omitted	120.00					
d	Imperf. pair (untagged)	325.00					
1364	6¢ American Indian, Nov. 4	.16	.15	.70	(4)	1.00	125,100,000
	Issues of 1969, Beautification of America Issue, Jan. 16						
1365	6¢ Capitol, Azaleas and Tulips	.40	.15			1.00	48,142,500
1366	6¢ Washington Monument, Potomac River and Daffodils	.40	.15			1.00	48,142,500
1367	6¢ Poppies and Lupines along Highway	.40	.15			1.00	48,142,500
1368	6¢ Blooming Crabapple Trees Lining Avenue	.40	.15	2.25	(4)	1.00	48,142,500
a	Block of 4, #1365-68	1.85	1.50	2.25	(4)	4.00	
b	As "a," tagging omitted	—					
1369	6¢ American Legion, Mar. 15	.15	.15	.50	(4)	1.00	148,770,000
	American Folklore Issue, Grandma Moses, May 1						
1370	6¢ "July Fourth," by Grandma Moses	.15	.15	.50	(4)	1.00	139,475,000
a	Horizontal pair, imperf. between	225.00					
b	Black and Prussian blue omitted	1,000.00					
1371	6¢ Apollo 8, May 5	.15	.15	.65	(4)	3.00	187,165,000
a	Imperf. pair	—					
1372	6¢ W.C. Handy, May 17	.15	.15	.50	(4)	1.00	125,555,000
a	Tagging omitted	4.50					
1373	6¢ California Settlement, July 16	.15	.15	.50	(4)	1.00	144,425,000
1374	6¢ John Wesley Powell, Aug. 1	.15	.15	.50	(4)	1.00	135,875,000
1375	6¢ Alabama Statehood, Aug. 2	.15	.15	.50	(4)	1.00	151,110,000

1356 1357 1358

1359 1360 1361 1362

1363 1364 1365 1366 1368a

1367 1368

1369 1370 1371 1372

1376 1377 1379a
1378 1379
1380

1381 1382
1383

1384
1385 1386

1384 Precancel

1391

	Issues of 1969 (continued), Perf. 11	Un	U	PB	#	FDC	Q
	Botanical Congress Issue, Aug. 23						
1376	6¢ Douglas Fir (Northwest)	.75	.15			1.00	39,798,750
1377	6¢ Lady's Slipper (Northeast)	.75	.15			1.00	39,798,750
1378	6¢ Ocotillo (Southwest)	.75	.15			1.00	39,798,750
1379	6¢ Franklinia (Southeast)	.75	.15			1.00	39,798,750
a	Block of 4, #1376-79	3.00	3.00	3.75	(4)	5.00	
	Perf. 10¹/₂ x 11						
1380	6¢ Dartmouth College Case, Sept. 22	.15	.15	.50	(4)	1.00	129,540,000
	Perf. 11						
1381	6¢ Professional Baseball, Sept. 24	.55	.15	2.70	(4)	6.00	130,925,000
a	Black omitted	1,100.00					
1382	6¢ College Football, Sept. 26	.15	.15	.80	(4)	3.00	139,055,000
1383	6¢ Dwight D. Eisenhower, Oct. 14	.15	.15	.50	(4)	1.00	150,611,200
	Christmas Issue, Nov. 3, Perf. 11 x 10¹/₂						
1384	6¢ Winter Sunday in Norway, Maine	.15	.15	1.40	(10)	1.00	1,709,795,000
	Precanceled	.50	.15				
b	Imperf. pair	1,250.00					
c	Light green omitted	25.00					
d	Light green and yellow omitted	1,000.00	—				
e	Yellow omitted	—					
f	Tagging omitted	1.50					
	Precanceled versions issued on an experimental basis in four cities whose names appear on the stamps: Atlanta, GA; Baltimore, MD; Memphis, TN; and New Haven, CT.						
	Perf. 11						
1385	6¢ Hope for the Crippled, Nov. 20	.15	.15	.50	(4)	1.00	127,545,000
1386	6¢ William M. Harnett, Dec. 3	.15	.15	.50	(4)	1.00	145,788,800
	Issues of 1970, Natural History Issue, May 6						
1387	6¢ American Bald Eagle	.15	.15			1.50	50,448,550
1388	6¢ African Elephant Herd	.15	.15			1.50	50,448,550
1389	6¢ Tlingit Chief in Haida Ceremonial Canoe	.15	.15			1.50	50,448,550
1390	6¢ Brontosaurus, Stegosaurus and Allosaurus from Jurassic Period	.15	.15			1.50	50,448,550
a	Block of 4, #1387-90	.50	.50	.65	(4)	4.00	
1391	6¢ Maine Statehood, July 9	.15	.15	.50	(4)	1.00	171,850,000
	Perf. 11 x 10¹/₂						
1392	6¢ Wildlife Conservation, July 20	.15	.15	.50	(4)	1.00	142,205,000

Where were earmuffs invented?

The first pair of earmuffs was patented in 1877 by Chester Greenwood of Farmington, in chilly Maine. He actually invented his first pair in 1873 at the age of 15, and went on to mass-produce them in his own factory. The town of Farmington, formerly  referred to as "Earmuff Capital of the World," still observes a Chester Greenwood Day each year. **(#1391)**

185

	Issues of 1970-74, Perf. 11 x 10½	Un	U	PB/LP	#	FDC	Q
1393	6¢ Eisenhower, Aug. 6, 1970	.15	.15	.50	(4)	1.00	
a	Booklet pane of 8	1.25	*.50*			3.00	
b	Booklet pane of 5 + label	1.25	*.50*			1.50	
c	Untagged (Bureau precanceled)		.15				
	Perf. 10½ x 11						
1393D	7¢ Franklin, Oct. 20, 1972	.15	.15	.60	(4)	1.00	
e	Untagged (Bureau precanceled)		.15				
	Perf. 11						
1394	8¢ Eisenhower, May 10, 1971	.16	.15	.60	(4)	1.00	
	Pair with full vertical gutter between	—					
	Perf. 11 x 10½						
1395	8¢ deep claret Eisenhower (1394), Single from booklet	.18	.15			1.00	
a	Booklet pane of 8, May 10, 1971	1.80	*1.25*			3.00	
b	Booklet pane of 6, May 10, 1971	1.25	*.75*			3.00	
c	Booklet pane of 4 + 2 labels, Jan. 28, 1972	1.65	*.50*			2.25	
d	Booklet pane of 7 + label, Jan. 28, 1972	1.75	*1.00*			2.00	
1396	8¢ U.S. Postal Service, July 1, 1971	.15	.15	2.00	(12)	1.00	
1397	14¢ Fiorello H. LaGuardia, Apr. 24, 1972	.25	.15	1.15	(4)	1.00	
a	Untagged (Bureau precanceled)		.25				
1398	16¢ Ernie Pyle, May 7, 1971	.28	.15	1.25	(4)	1.00	
a	Untagged (Bureau precanceled)		.35				
1399	18¢ Dr. Elizabeth Blackwell, Jan. 23, 1974	.32	.15	1.40	(4)	1.00	
1400	21¢ Amadeo P. Giannini, June 27, 1973	.32	.15	1.50	(4)	1.00	
	Coil Stamps, Perf. 10 Vertically						
1401	6¢ dark blue gray Eisenhower (1393), Aug. 6, 1970	.15	.15	.50	(2)	1.00	
a	Untagged (Bureau precanceled)		.15				
b	Imperf. pair	*1,500.00*		—	(2)		
1402	8¢ deep claret Eisenhower (1394), May 10, 1971	.15	.15	.45	(2)	1.00	
a	Imperf. pair	45.00		70.00	(2)		
b	Untagged (Bureau precanceled)		.15				
c	Pair, imperf. between	*6,250.00*					
1403-04	Not assigned						
	Issues of 1970, Perf. 11						
1405	6¢ Edgar Lee Masters, Aug. 22	.15	.15	.50	(4)	1.00	137,660,000
a	Tagging omitted	7.50					
1406	6¢ Woman Suffrage, Aug. 26	.15	.15	.50	(4)	1.00	135,125,000
1407	6¢ South Carolina Settlement, Sept. 12	.15	.15	.50	(4)	1.00	135,895,000
1408	6¢ Stone Mountain Memorial, Sept. 19	.15	.15	.50	(4)	1.00	132,675,000
1409	6¢ Ft. Snelling, Oct. 17	.15	.15	.50	(4)	1.00	134,795,000
*	**Anti-Pollution Issue, Oct. 28, Perf. 11 x 10½**						
1410	6¢ Save Our Soil— Globe and Wheat Field	.22	.15			1.25	40,400,000
1411	6¢ Save Our Cities— Globe and City Playground	.22	.15			1.25	40,400,000
1412	6¢ Save Our Water— Globe and Bluegill Fish	.22	.15			1.25	40,400,000
1413	6¢ Save Our Air— Globe and Seagull	.22	.15			1.25	40,400,000
a	Block of 4, #1410-13	1.00	1.00	2.50	(10)	3.00	

1393

1393D

1394

1396

1397

1398

1399

1400

1405

1406

1407

1408

1409

1410   1411   1413a
1412   1413

187

1414

1414a

Christmas 6 U.S.

Christmas 6 U.S.

Christmas 6 U.S.

Christmas 6 U.S.

1415   1416   1418b
1417   1418

UNITED NATIONS 25th Anniversary
1419

1420

1421

1422   1421a

AMERICA'S WOOL

DOUGLAS MacARTHUR

1425

1426

1423   1424

1427   1428   1430a
1429   1430

	Issues of 1970 (continued), Perf. 10½ x 11	Un	U	PB	#	FDC	Q
	Christmas Issue, Nov. 5						
1414	6¢ Nativity, by Lorenzo Lotto	.15	.15	1.15	(8)	1.40	638,730,000*
a	Precanceled	.15	.15	1.90	(8)		358,245,000
b	Black omitted	650.00					
c	As "a," blue omitted	1,500.00					

#1414a-18a were furnished to 68 cities. Unused prices are for copies with gum and used prices are for copies with or without gum but with an additional cancellation. *Includes #1414a.

	Perf. 11 x 10½	Un	U	PB	#	FDC	Q
1415	6¢ Tin and Cast-iron Locomotive	.40	.15			1.40	122,313,750
a	Precanceled	.90	.15				109,912,500
b	Black omitted	2,500.00					
1416	6¢ Toy Horse on Wheels	.40	.15			1.40	122,313,750
a	Precanceled	.90	.15				109,912,500
b	Black omitted	2,500.00					
c	Imperf. pair		4,000.00				
1417	6¢ Mechanical Tricycle	.40	.15			1.40	122,313,750
a	Precanceled	.90	.15				109,912,500
b	Black omitted	2,500.00					
1418	6¢ Doll Carriage	.40	.15	3.75	(8)	1.40	122,313,750
a	Precanceled	.90	.15	3.75	(8)		109,912,500
b	Block of 4, #1415-18	1.90	1.75	3.75	(8)	3.50	
c	Block of 4, #1415a-18a	3.75	3.50	9.00	(8)		
d	Black omitted	2,500.00					
	Perf. 11						
1419	6¢ United Nations, Nov. 20	.15	.15	.50	(4)	1.00	127,610,000
	Pair with full horizontal gutter between	—					
1420	6¢ Landing of the Pilgrims, Nov. 21	.15	.15	.50	(4)	1.00	129,785,000
a	Orange and yellow omitted	1,200.00					
	Disabled American Veterans and Servicemen Issue, Nov. 24						
1421	6¢ Disabled American Veterans Emblem	.15	.15			1.00	67,190,000
a	Attached pair, #1421-22	.25	.25	1.00	(4)	1.25	
1422	6¢ U.S. Servicemen	.15	.15			1.00	67,190,000
	Issues of 1971						
1423	6¢ American Wool Industry, Jan. 19	.15	.15	.50	(4)	1.00	136,305,000
a	Tagging omitted	3.50	—				
1424	6¢ Gen. Douglas MacArthur, Jan. 26	.15	.15	.50	(4)	1.00	134,840,000
1425	6¢ Blood Donor, Mar. 12	.15	.15	.50	(4)	1.00	130,975,000
a	Tagging omitted	4.50					
	Perf. 11 x 10½						
1426	8¢ Missouri Statehood, May 8	.15	.15	2.00	(12)	1.00	161,235,000
	Wildlife Conservation Issue, June 12, Perf. 11						
1427	8¢ Trout	.16	.15			1.25	43,920,000
1428	8¢ Alligator	.16	.15			1.25	43,920,000
1429	8¢ Polar Bear	.16	.15			1.25	43,920,000
1430	8¢ California Condor	.16	.15			1.25	43,920,000
a	Block of 4, #1427-30	.65	.65	.75	(4)	3.00	
b	As "a," light green and dark green omitted from #1427-28	3,500.00					
c	As "a," red omitted from #1427, 1429-30	9,000.00					

	Issues of 1971 (continued), Perf. 11	Un	U	PB	#	FDC	Q
1431	8¢ Antarctic Treaty, June 23	.15	.15	.70	(4)	1.00	138,700,000
a	Tagging omitted	4.00					
	American Revolution Bicentennial Issue, July 4						
1432	8¢ Bicentennial Commission Emblem	.16	.15	.85	(4)	1.00	138,165,000
a	Gray and black omitted	650.00					
b	Gray omitted	1,100.00					
1433	8¢ John Sloan, Aug. 2	.15	.15	.70	(4)	1.00	152,125,000
a	Tagging omitted	—					
	Space Achievement Decade Issue, Aug. 2						
1434	8¢ Earth, Sun and Landing Craft on Moon	.15	.15				88,147,500
a	Attached pair, #1434-35	.30	.25	.70	(4)	2.50	
b	As "a," blue and red omitted	1,500.00					
1435	8¢ Lunar Rover and Astronauts	.15	.15				88,147,500
a	Tagging omitted	6.00					
1436	8¢ Emily Dickinson, Aug. 28	.15	.15	.70	(4)	1.00	142,845,000
a	Black and olive omitted	950.00					
b	Pale rose omitted	7,500.00					
1437	8¢ San Juan, Puerto Rico, Sept. 12	.15	.15	.70	(4)	1.00	148,755,000
a	Tagging omitted	5.00					
	Perf. 10½ x 11						
1438	8¢ Prevent Drug Abuse, Oct. 4	.15	.15	1.00	(6)	1.00	139,080,000
1439	8¢ CARE, Oct. 27	.15	.15	1.25	(8)	1.00	130,755,000
a	Black omitted	4,500.00					
b	Tagging omitted	2.50					
	Historic Preservation Issue, Oct. 29, Perf. 11						
1440	8¢ Decatur House, Washington, D.C.	.16	.15			1.25	42,552,000
1441	8¢ Whaling Ship *Charles W. Morgan*, Mystic, Connecticut	.16	.15			1.25	42,552,000
1442	8¢ Cable Car, San Francisco	.16	.15			1.25	42,552,000
1443	8¢ San Xavier del Bac Mission, Tucson, Arizona	.16	.15			1.25	42,552,000
a	Block of 4, #1440-43	.65	.65	.75	(4)	3.00	
b	As "a," black brown omitted	2,400.00					
c	As "a," ocher omitted	—					
	Christmas Issue, Nov. 10, Perf. 10½ x 11						
1444	8¢ Adoration of the Shepherds, by Giorgione	.15	.15	2.00	(12)	1.00	1,074,350,000
a	Gold omitted	600.00					
1445	8¢ Partridge in a Pear Tree	.15	.15	2.00	(12)	1.00	979,540,000
	Issues of 1972, Perf. 11						
1446	8¢ Sidney Lanier, Feb. 3	.15	.15	.70	(4)	1.00	137,355,000
	Perf. 10½ x 11						
1447	8¢ Peace Corps, Feb. 11	.15	.15	1.00	(6)	1.00	150,400,000

The stamp listings contain a number of "a," "b," "c," etc. additions which include recognized varieties and errors. These listings are as complete as space permits.

1431

1433

1432

UNITED STATES IN SPACE··· A DECADE OF ACHIEVEMENT

1434 **1435** **1434a**

1436 **1437** **1438** **1439**

HISTORIC PRESERVATION   HISTORIC PRESERVATION

HISTORIC PRESERVATION   HISTORIC PRESERVATION

1440 **1441** **1443a**

1442 **1443**

448
450

1449
1451

1451a

1452

Old Faithful, Yellowstone

1453

454

1455

1456
1458

1457
1459

1459a

460

1461

1462

463

	Issues of 1972 (continued), Perf. 11	Un	U	PB	#	FDC	Q
	National Parks Centennial Issue, Cape Hatteras, Apr. 5 (See also #C84)						
1448	2¢ Ship at Sea	.15	.15				43,182,500
1449	2¢ Cape Hatteras Lighthouse	.15	.15				43,182,500
1450	2¢ Laughing Gulls on Driftwood	.15	.15				43,182,500
1451	2¢ Laughing Gulls and Dune	.15	.15				43,182,500
a	Block of 4, #1448-51	.20	.20	.45	(4)	1.25	
b	As "a," black omitted	2,750.00					
	Wolf Trap Farm, June 26						
1452	6¢ Performance at Shouse Pavilion	.15	.15	.55	(4)	1.00	104,090,000
1453	8¢ Old Faithful, Yellowstone, Mar. 1	.15	.15	.70	(4)	1.00	164,096,000
a	Tagging omitted	10.00					
	Mount McKinley, July 28						
1454	15¢ View of Mount McKinley in Alaska	.30	.18	1.30	(4)	1.00	53,920,000

Note: Beginning with this National Parks Centennial issue, the USPS began to offer stamp collectors first day cancellations affixed to 8" x 10½" souvenir pages. The pages are similar to the stamp announcements that have appeared on Post Office bulletin boards beginning with Scott #1132.

1455	8¢ Family Planning, Mar. 18	.15	.15	.70	(4)	1.00	153,025,000
a	Yellow omitted	—					
b	Dark brown and olive omitted	—					
	American Bicentennial Issue, Colonial American Craftsmen, July 4, Perf. 11 x 10½						
1456	8¢ Glassblower	.16	.15			1.00	50,472,500
1457	8¢ Silversmith	.16	.15			1.00	50,472,500
1458	8¢ Wigmaker	.16	.15			1.00	50,472,500
1459	8¢ Hatter	.16	.15			1.00	50,472,500
a	Block of 4, #1456-59	.65	.65	.75	(4)	2.50	
	Olympic Games Issue, Aug. 17 (See also #C85)						
1460	8¢ Bicycling and Olympic Rings	.15	.15	1.25	(10)	1.00	67,335,000
	Plate flaw (broken red ring)	7.50					
1461	8¢ Bobsledding and Olympic Rings	.15	.15	1.60	(10)	1.00	179,675,000
1462	15¢ Running and Olympic Rings	.28	.18	3.00	(10)	1.00	46,340,000
1463	8¢ Parent Teachers Association, Sept. 15	.15	.15	.70	(4)	1.00	180,155,000
	Wildlife Conservation Issue, Sept. 20, Perf. 11						
1464	8¢ Fur Seals	.16	.15			1.50	49,591,200
1465	8¢ Cardinal	.16	.15			1.50	49,591,200
1466	8¢ Brown Pelican	.16	.15			1.50	49,591,200
1467	8¢ Bighorn Sheep	.16	.15			1.50	49,591,200
a	Block of 4, #1464-67	.65	.65	.75	(4)	3.00	
b	As "a," brown omitted	3,750.00					
c	As "a," green and blue omitted	—					

Note: With this Wildlife Conservation issue the USPS introduced the "American Commemorative Series" Stamp Panels. Each panel contains a block of four mint stamps with text and background illustrations.

	Issues of 1972 (continued), Perf. 11 x 10½	Un	U	PB	#	FDC	Q
1468	8¢ Mail Order Business, Sept. 27	.15	.15	1.90	(12)	1.00	185,490,000
	Perf. 10½ x 11						
1469	8¢ Osteopathic Medicine, Oct. 9	.15	.15	1.00	(6)	1.00	162,335,000
	American Folklore Issue, Tom Sawyer, Oct. 13, Perf. 11						
1470	8¢ Tom Sawyer Whitewashing a Fence, by Norman Rockwell	.15	.15	.70	(4)	1.00	162,789,950
a	Horizontal pair, imperf. between	4,500.00					
b	Red and black omitted	2,000.00					
c	Yellow and tan omitted	1,850.00					
	Christmas Issue, Nov. 9, Perf. 10½ x 11						
1471	8¢ Angels from "Mary, Queen of Heaven," by the Master of the St. Lucy Legend	.15	.15	1.90	(12)	1.00	1,003,475,000
a	Pink omitted	250.00					
b	Black omitted	4,000.00					
1472	8¢ Santa Claus	.15	.15	1.90	(12)	1.00	1,017,025,000
	Perf. 11						
1473	8¢ Pharmacy, Nov. 10	.15	.15	.70	(4)	1.00	165,895,000
a	Blue and orange omitted	1,000.00					
b	Blue omitted	2,000.00					
c	Orange omitted	2,000.00					
1474	8¢ Stamp Collecting, Nov. 17	.15	.15	.65	(4)	1.00	166,508,000
a	Black omitted	1,000.00					
	Issues of 1973, Perf. 11 x 10½						
1475	8¢ Love, Jan. 26	.15	.15	1.00	(6)	1.00	320,055,000
	American Bicentennial Issue, Communications in Colonial Times, Perf. 11						
1476	8¢ Printer and Patriots Examining Pamphlet, Feb. 16	.15	.15	.65	(4)	1.00	166,005,000
1477	8¢ Posting a Broadside, Apr. 13	.15	.15	.65	(4)	1.00	163,050,000
	Pair with full horizontal gutter between	—					
1478	8¢ Postrider, June 22	.15	.15	.65	(4)	1.00	159,005,000
1479	8¢ Drummer, Sept. 28	.15	.15	.70	(4)	1.00	147,295,000
	Boston Tea Party, July 4						
1480	8¢ British Merchantman	.15	.15			1.00	49,068,750
1481	8¢ British Three-Master	.15	.15			1.00	49,068,750
1482	8¢ Boats and Ship's Hull	.15	.15			1.00	49,068,750
1483	8¢ Boat and Dock	.15	.15			1.00	49,068,750
a	Block of 4, #1480-83	.65	.45	.70	(4)	3.00	
b	As "a," blk. (engraved) omitted	1,650.00					
c	As "a," blk. (lithographed) omitted	1,250.00					

Who was invited to the Boston Tea Party?

Certainly not the British. They placed a high tax on tea brought to America — a tax Americans felt they shouldn't have to pay. So in 1773 about 100 Americans dressed up as American Indians and invaded three British tea ships, dumping all the ships' tea into the Boston Harbor. **(#1480-1483)**

1468

1469

1470

1471

1472

1473

1474

1475

1476

1477

1478

1479

1480   **1481**   **1483a**

1482   **1483**

1484

1485

1486

1487

Copernicus
1473 - 1973

8¢ US

1488

U.S. POSTAL SERVICE 8¢   U.S. POSTAL SERVICE 8¢   U.S. POSTAL SERVICE 8¢   U.S. POSTAL SERVICE 8¢   U.S. POSTAL SERVICE 8¢

Nearly 27 billion U.S. stamps are sold yearly to carry your letters to every corner of the world.	Mail is picked up from nearly a third of a million local collection boxes, as well as your mailbox.	More than 87 billion letters and packages are handled yearly—almost 300 million every delivery day.	The People in your Postal Service handle and deliver more than 500 million packages yearly.	Thousands of machines, buildings, and vehicles must be operated and maintained to keep your mail moving.
People Serving You	People Serving You	People Serving You	People Serving You	People Serving You

1489   **1490**   **1491**   **1492**   **1493**

U.S. POSTAL SERVICE 8¢   U.S. POSTAL SERVICE 8¢   U.S. POSTAL SERVICE 8¢   U.S. POSTAL SERVICE 8¢   U.S. POSTAL SERVICE 8¢

The skill of sorting mail manually is still vital to delivery of your mail.	Employees use modern, high-speed equipment to sort and process huge volumes of mail in central locations.	Thirteen billion pounds of mail are handled yearly by postal employees as they speed your letters and packages.	Our customers include 54 million urban and 12 million rural families, plus 9 million businesses.	Employees cover 4 million miles each delivery day to bring mail to your home or business.
People Serving You	People Serving You	People Serving You	People Serving You	People Serving You

1498a

1494   **1495**   **1496**   **1497**   **1498**

	Issues of 1973 (continued), Perf. 11	Un	U	PB	#	FDC	Q
	American Arts Issue						
1484	8¢ George Gershwin and Scene from "Porgy and Bess," Feb. 28	.15	.15	1.75	(12)	1.00	139,152,000
a	Vertical pair, imperf. horizontally	250.00					
1485	8¢ Robinson Jeffers, Man and Children of Carmel with Burro, Aug. 13	.15	.15	1.75	(12)	1.00	128,048,000
a	Vertical pair, imperf. horizontally	250.00					
1486	8¢ Henry Ossawa Tanner, Palette and Rainbow, Sept. 10	.15	.15	1.75	(12)	1.00	146,008,000
1487	8¢ Willa Cather, Pioneer Family and Covered Wagon, Sept. 20	.15	.15	1.75	(12)	1.00	139,608,000
a	Vertical pair, imperf. horizontally	300.00					
1488	8¢ Nicolaus Copernicus, Apr. 23	.15	.15	.65	(4)	1.00	159,475,000
a	Orange omitted	1,100.00					
b	Black omitted	1,500.00					
	Postal Service Employees Issue, Apr. 30, Perf. 10¹/₂ x 11						
1489	8¢ Stamp Counter	.15	.15			1.00	48,602,000
1490	8¢ Mail Collection	.15	.15			1.00	48,602,000
1491	8¢ Letter Facing on Conveyor	.15	.15			1.00	48,602,000
1492	8¢ Parcel Post Sorting	.15	.15			1.00	48,602,000
1493	8¢ Mail Canceling	.15	.15			1.00	48,602,000
1494	8¢ Manual Letter Routing	.15	.15			1.00	48,602,000
1495	8¢ Electronic Letter Routing	.15	.15			1.00	48,602,000
1496	8¢ Loading Mail on Truck	.15	.15			1.00	48,602,000
1497	8¢ Carrier Delivering Mail	.15	.15			1.00	48,602,000
1498	8¢ Rural Mail Delivery	.15	.15			1.00	48,602,000
a	Strip of 10, #1489-98	1.50	1.00	3.10	(20)	5.00	

#1489-98 were the first United States stamps to have printing on the back (See also #1559-62).

When was Willa Cather's first novel published?

Cather was born in 1873 in Gore, Va., and raised in Nebraska among many immigrants, who later appeared in her novels *O Pioneers!*, *My Antonia*, *Death Comes for the Archbishop* and the Pulitzer Prize-winning *One of Ours*. The author graduated from the University of Nebraska, went on to teach in Pittsburgh, Pa., and later became managing editor of *McClure's*. She left the magazine in 1912 because her first novel, *Alexander's Bridge*, was being published. **(#1487)**

	Issues of 1973 (continued), Perf. 11	Un	U	PB	#	FDC	Q
1499	8¢ Harry S. Truman, May 8	.15	.15	.55	(4)	1.00	157,052,800
	Progress in Electronics Issue, July 10 (See also #C86)						
1500	6¢ Marconi's Spark Coil and Gap	.15	.15	.55	(4)	1.00	53,005,000
1501	8¢ Transistors and Printed Circuit Board	.15	.15	.70	(4)	1.00	159,775,000
a	Black omitted	650.00					
b	Tan and lilac omitted	1,000.00					
1502	15¢ Microphone, Speaker, Vacuum Tube, TV Camera Tube	.28	.15	1.20	(4)	1.00	39,005,000
a	Black omitted	1,500.00					
1503	8¢ Lyndon B. Johnson, Aug. 27	.15	.15	1.75	(12)	1.00	152,624,000
a	Horizontal pair, imperf. vertically	300.00					
	Issues of 1973-74, Rural America Issue						
1504	8¢ Angus and Longhorn Cattle, by F.C. Murphy, Oct. 5, 1973	.15	.15	.65	(4)	1.00	145,840,000
a	Green and red brown omitted	1,150.00					
b	Vertical pair, imperf. between		—				
1505	10¢ Chautauqua Tent and Buggies, Aug. 6, 1974	.18	.15	.80	(4)	1.00	151,335,000
1506	10¢ Wheat Fields and Train, Aug. 16, 1974	.18	.15	.80	(4)	1.00	141,085,000
a	Black and blue omitted	750.00					
	Issues of 1973, Christmas Issue, Nov. 7, Perf. 10½ x 11						
1507	8¢ Small Cowper Madonna, by Raphael	.15	.15	1.85	(12)	1.00	885,160,000
	Pair with full vertical gutter between	—					
1508	8¢ Christmas Tree in Needlepoint	.15	.15	1.85	(12)	1.00	939,835,000
a	Vertical pair, imperf. between	500.00					
	Pair with full horizontal gutter between	—					
	Issues of 1973-74, Perf. 11 x 10½						
1509	10¢ 50-Star and 13-Star Flags, Dec. 8, 1973	.18	.15	3.75	(20)	1.00	
a	Horizontal pair, imperf. between	50.00					
b	Blue omitted	160.00					
c	Imperf. pair	1,150.00					
1510	10¢ Jefferson Memorial, Dec. 14, 1973	.18	.15	.80	(4)	1.00	
a	Untagged (Bureau precanceled)		.18				
b	Booklet pane of 5 + label	1.50	.30			2.25	
c	Booklet pane of 8	1.65	.30			2.50	
d	Booklet pane of 6, Aug. 5, 1974	4.50	.30			3.00	
e	Vertical pair, imperf. horizontally	300.00					
f	Vertical pair, imperf. between	—					

1499

1500

1501

1502

1503

1504

1505

1506

1507

1508

1509

1510

1511   **1518**

1525

1526

1527

1528   **1529**

1530   **1531**   **1532**   **1533**   **1537a**
1534   **1535**   **1536**   **1537**

	Issues of 1973-74 (continued), Perf. 11 x 10$^{1}/_{2}$	Un	U	PB/LP	#	FDC	Q
1511	10¢ ZIP Code, Jan. 4, 1974	.22	.15	1.50	(8)	1.00	
a	Yellow omitted	50.00					
	Pair with full horizontal gutter between	—					
1512-17	Not assigned						
	Coil Stamps, Perf. 10 Vertically						
1518	6.3¢ Liberty Bell, Oct. 1, 1974	.15	.15	.65	(2)	1.00	
a	Untagged (Bureau precanceled)		.15	.80	(2)		
b	Imperf. pair	200.00		400.00	(2)		
c	As "a," imperf. pair		110.00	200.00	(2)		
1519	10¢ red and blue Flags (1509), Dec. 8, 1973	.18	.15			1.00	
a	Imperf. pair	30.00					
1520	10¢ blue Jefferson Memorial (1510), Dec. 14, 1973	.18	.15	.55	(2)	1.00	
a	Untagged (Bureau precanceled)		.25				
b	Imperf. pair	40.00		65.00	(2)		
1521-24	Not assigned						
	Issues of 1974, Perf. 11						
1525	10¢ Veterans of Foreign Wars, Mar. 11	.16	.15	.75	(4)	1.00	149,930,000
	Perf. 10$^{1}/_{2}$ x 11						
1526	10¢ Robert Frost, Mar. 26	.16	.15	.75	(4)	1.00	145,235,000
	Perf. 11						
1527	10¢ Expo '74 World's Fair, Apr. 18	.18	.15	2.20	(12)	1.00	135,052,000
	Perf. 11 x 10$^{1}/_{2}$						
1528	10¢ Horse Racing, May 4	.18	.15	2.20	(12)	1.00	156,750,000
a	Blue omitted	900.00					
b	Red omitted	—					
	Perf. 11						
1529	10¢ Skylab, May 14	.18	.15	.80	(4)	1.50	164,670,000
a	Vertical pair, imperf. between	—					
	Universal Postal Union Issue, June 6						
1530	10¢ Michelangelo, from "School of Athens," by Raphael	.20	.15			1.00	23,769,600
1531	10¢ "Five Feminine Virtues," by Hokusai	.20	.15			1.00	23,769,600
1532	10¢ "Old Scraps," by John Fredrick Peto	.20	.15			1.00	23,769,600
1533	10¢ "The Lovely Reader," by Jean Etienne Liotard	.20	.15			1.00	23,769,600
1534	10¢ "Lady Writing Letter," by Gerard Terborch	.20	.15			1.00	23,769,600
1535	10¢ Inkwell and Quill, from "Boy with a Top," by Jean-Baptiste Simeon Chardin	.20	.15			1.00	23,769,600
1536	10¢ Mrs. John Douglas, by Thomas Gainsborough	.20	.15			1.00	23,769,600
1537	10¢ Don Antonio Noriega, by Francisco de Goya	.20	.15			1.00	23,769,600
a	Block of 8, #1530-37	1.60	1.50	3.50	(16)	4.00	
b	As "a," imperf. vertically	7,500.00					

	Issues of 1974 (continued), Perf. 11	Un	U	PB	#	FDC	Q
	Mineral Heritage Issue, June 13						
1538	10¢ Petrified Wood	.16	.15			1.00	41,803,200
a	Light blue and yellow omitted	—					
1539	10¢ Tourmaline	.16	.15			1.00	41,803,200
a	Light blue omitted	—					
b	Black and purple omitted	—					
1540	10¢ Amethyst	.16	.15			1.00	41,803,200
a	Light blue and yellow omitted	—					
1541	10¢ Rhodochrosite	.16	.15			1.00	41,803,200
a	Block of 4, #1538-41	.75	.80	.85	(4)	2.50	
b	As "a," light blue and yellow omitted	2,000.00					
c	Light blue omitted	—					
d	Black and red omitted	—					
1542	10¢ First Kentucky Settlement-Ft. Harrod, June 15	.16	.15	.75	(4)	1.00	156,265,000
a	Dull black omitted	800.00					
b	Green, black and blue omitted	3,250.00					
c	Green omitted	—					
d	Green and black omitted	—					
	American Bicentennial Issue, First Continental Congress, July 4						
1543	10¢ Carpenters' Hall	.18	.15			1.00	48,896,250
1544	10¢ "We Ask but for Peace, Liberty and Safety"	.18	.15			1.00	48,896,250
1545	10¢ "Deriving Their Just Powers from the Consent of the Governed"	.18	.15			1.00	48,896,250
1546	10¢ Independence Hall	.18	.15			1.00	48,896,250
a	Block of 4, #1543-46	.75	.75	.85	(4)	2.75	
1547	10¢ Energy Conservation, Sept. 23	.18	.15	.75	(4)	1.00	148,850,000
a	Blue and orange omitted	800.00					
b	Orange and green omitted	800.00					
c	Green omitted	900.00					
	American Folklore Issue, The Legend of Sleepy Hollow, Oct. 10						
1548	10¢ Headless Horseman and Ichabod Crane	.16	.15	.75	(4)	1.00	157,270,000
1549	10¢ Retarded Children, Oct. 12	.16	.15	.75	(4)	1.00	150,245,000
	Christmas Issue, Perf. 10½ x 11						
1550	10¢ Angel from Perussis Altarpiece, Oct. 23	.16	.15	1.75	(10)	1.00	835,180,000
	Perf. 11 x 10½						
1551	10¢ "The Road-Winter," by Currier and Ives, Oct. 23	.16	.15	2.00	(12)	1.00	882,520,000
	Precanceled Self-Adhesive, Imperf.						
1552	10¢ Dove Weather Vane atop Mount Vernon, Nov. 15	.16	.15	3.50	(20)	1.00	213,155,000
	Issues of 1975, American Arts Issue, Perf. 10½ x 11						
1553	10¢ Benjamin West, Self-Portrait, Feb. 10	.18	.15	1.85	(10)	1.00	156,995,000
	Perf. 11						
1554	10¢ Paul Laurence Dunbar and Lamp, May 1	.18	.15	1.85	(10)	1.00	146,365,000
a	Imperf. pair	1,250.00					
1555	10¢ D.W. Griffith and Motion-Picture Camera, May 27	.16	.15	.75	(4)	1.00	148,805,000
a	Brown omitted	600.00					

First Kentucky Settlement — 1542

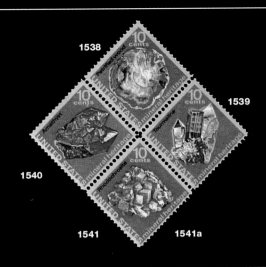

1538

1539

1540

1541

1541a

1543
1545

1544
1546

1546a

1547

1548

1549

1550

1551

1552

1553

1554

1555

1556

1557

1558

YOUTHFUL HEROINE
On the dark night of April 26, 1777, 16-year-old Sybil Ludington rode her horse "Star" alone through the Connecticut countryside rallying her father's militia to repel a raid by the British on Danbury.

1559

GALLANT SOLDIER
The conspicuously courageous actions of black foot soldier Salem Poor at the Battle of Bunker Hill on June 17, 1775, earned him citations for his bravery and leadership ability.

1560

FINANCIAL HERO
Businessman and broker Haym Salomon was responsible for raising most of the money needed to finance the American Revolution and later to save the new nation from collapse.

1561

FIGHTER EXTRAORDINARY
Peter Francisco's strength and bravery made him a legend around campfires. He fought with distinction at Brandywine, Yorktown and Guilford Court House.

1562

1563

Bunker Hill 1775 by Trumbull
US Bicentennial 10c

1564

1565   1566   1568a
1567   1568

1569   1569a
1570

204

	Issues of 1975 (continued), Perf. 11	Un	U	PB	#	FDC	Q
	Space Issues						
1556	10¢ Pioneer 10 Passing Jupiter, Feb. 28	.16	.15	.75	(4)	2.00	173,685,000
a	Red and yellow omitted	1,650.00					
b	Blue omitted	800.00					
1557	10¢ Mariner 10, Venus and Mercury, Apr. 4	.16	.15	.75	(4)	2.00	158,600,000
a	Red omitted	650.00					
b	Ultramarine and bister omitted	1,800.00					
1558	10¢ Collective Bargaining, Mar. 13	.18	.15	1.60	(8)	1.00	153,355,000
	Imperfs. of #1558 exist from printer's waste.						
	American Bicentennial Issue, Contributors to the Cause, Mar. 25, Perf. 11 x 10½						
1559	8¢ Sybil Ludington Riding Horse	.15	.15	1.50	(10)	1.00	63,205,000
a	Back inscription omitted	300.00					
1560	10¢ Salem Poor Carrying Musket	.18	.15	1.85	(10)	1.00	157,865,000
a	Back inscription omitted	350.00					
1561	10¢ Haym Salomon Figuring Accounts	.18	.15	1.85	(10)	1.00	166,810,000
a	Back inscription omitted	350.00					
b	Red omitted	300.00					
1562	18¢ Peter Francisco Shouldering Cannon	.35	.20	3.60	(10)	1.00	44,825,000
	Battle of Lexington & Concord, Apr. 19, Perf. 11						
1563	10¢ "Birth of Liberty," by Henry Sandham	.18	.15	2.20	(12)	1.00	144,028,000
a	Vertical pair, imperf. horizontally	400.00					
	Battle of Bunker Hill, June 17						
1564	10¢ "Battle of Bunker Hill," by John Trumbull	.18	.15	2.20	(12)	1.00	139,928,000
	Military Uniforms, July 4						
1565	10¢ Soldier with Flintlock Musket, Uniform Button	.18	.15			1.00	44,963,750
1566	10¢ Sailor with Grappling Hook, First Navy Jack, 1775	.18	.15			1.00	44,963,750
1567	10¢ Marine with Musket, Full-Rigged Ship	.18	.15			1.00	44,963,750
1568	10¢ Militiaman with Musket, Powder Horn	.18	.15			1.00	44,963,750
a	Block of 4, #1565-68	.75	.75	2.30	(12)	2.50	
	Apollo Soyuz Space Issue, July 15						
1569	10¢ Apollo and Soyuz after Docking, and Earth	.18	.15			2.00	80,931,600
a	Attached pair, #1569-70	.36	.25	2.20	(12)	4.00	
b	As "a," vertical pair, imperf. horizontally	2,000.00					
	Pair with full horizontal gutter between	—					
1570	10¢ Spacecraft before Docking, Earth and Project Emblem	.18	.15			2.00	80,931,600

	Issues of 1975 (continued), Perf. 11 x 10¹/₂	Un	U	PB	#	FDC	Q
1571	10¢ International Women's Year, Aug. 26	.16	.15	1.10	(6)	1.00	145,640,000
	Postal Service Bicentennial Issue, Sept. 3						
1572	10¢ Stagecoach and Trailer Truck	.18	.15			1.00	42,163,750
1573	10¢ Old and New Locomotives	.18	.15			1.00	42,163,750
1574	10¢ Early Mail Plane and Jet	.18	.15			1.00	42,163,750
1575	10¢ Satellite for Transmission of Mailgrams	.18	.15			1.00	42,163,750
a	Block of 4, #1572-75	.75	.80	2.30	(12)	1.25	
b	As "a," red "10¢" omitted	—					
	Perf. 11						
1576	10¢ World Peace Through Law, Sept. 29	.18	.15	.80	(4)	1.00	146,615,000
	Banking and Commerce Issue, Oct. 6						
1577	10¢ Engine Turning, Indian Head Penny and Morgan Silver Dollar	.18	.15			1.00	73,098,000
a	Attached pair, #1577-78	.36	.20	.80	(4)	1.25	
b	Brown and blue omitted	1,250.00					
c	As "a," brn., blue and yel. omitted	2,500.00					
1578	10¢ Seated Liberty Quarter, $20 Gold Piece and Engine Turning	.18	.15			1.00	73,098,000
	Christmas Issue, Oct. 14						
1579	(10¢) Madonna and Child, by Domenico Ghirlandaio	.18	.15	2.20	(12)	1.00	739,430,000
a	Imperf. pair	110.00					
	Plate flaw ("d" damaged)	5.00	—				
1580	(10¢) Christmas Card, by Louis Prang, 1878	.18	.15	2.20	(12)	1.00	878,690,000
a	Imperf. pair	120.00					
b	Perf. 10¹/₂ x 11	.60	.15	9.50	(12)		
	Issues of 1975-81, Americana Issue, Perf. 11 x 10¹/₂ (Designs 18¹/₂ x 22¹/₂mm; #1590-90a, 17¹/₂ x 20mm; see also #1606, 1608, 1610-19, 1622-23, 1625, 1811, 1813, 1816)						
1581	1¢ Inkwell & Quill, Dec. 8, 1977	.15	.15	.25	(4)	1.00	
a	Untagged (Bureau precanceled)		.15				
1582	2¢ Speaker's Stand, Dec. 8, 1977	.15	.15	.25	(4)	1.00	
a	Untagged (Bureau precanceled)		.15				
1583	Not assigned						
1584	3¢ Early Ballot Box, Dec. 8, 1977	.15	.15	.30	(4)	1.00	
a	Untagged (Bureau precanceled)		.15				
1585	4¢ Books, Bookmark, Eyeglasses, Dec. 8, 1977	.15	.15	.40	(4)	1.00	
a	Untagged (Bureau precanceled)		1.25				
1586-89	Not assigned						
	Booklet Stamp						
1590	9¢ Capitol Dome (1591), single from booklet (1623a), Mar. 11, 1977	.50	.20			1.00	
	Booklet Stamp, Perf. 10						
a	Single (1591) from booklet (1623c)	20.00	10.00				
	#1590 is on white paper; #1591 is on gray paper.						
	Perf. 11 x 10¹/₂						
1591	9¢ Capitol Dome, Nov. 24, 1975	.16	.15	.70	(4)	1.00	
a	Untagged (Bureau precanceled)		.18				
1592	10¢ Contemplation of Justice, Nov. 17, 1977	.18	.15	.90	(4)	1.00	
a	Untagged (Bureau precanceled)		.25				
1593	11¢ Printing Press, Nov. 13, 1975	.20	.15	.90	(4)	1.00	
1594	12¢ Torch, Apr. 8, 1981	.22	.15	1.25	(4)	1.00	

1571

1572 **1573** **1575a**
1574 **1575**

1576

1577 **1578** **1577a**

1579 **1580**

1581 **1582**
1584 **1585**

1591 **1592**
1593 **1594**

1595

1596

1597

1599

1603   **1604**

1605   **1606**

1608   **1610**

1611   **1612**

1613

1614

1615

1615C

	Issues of 1975-79, Perf. 11 x 10½	Un	U	PB/LP	#	FDC
	Americana Issue (continued) (See also #1581-82, 1584-85, 1590-99, 1603-08, 1610-19, 1622-23, 1625, 1811, 1813, 1816)					
1595	13¢ Liberty Bell, single from booklet	.25	.15			1.00
a	Booklet pane of 6, Oct. 31, 1975	1.90	.50			2.00
b	Booklet pane of 7 + label	1.75	.50			2.75
c	Booklet pane of 8	2.00	.50			2.50
d	Booklet pane of 5 + label, Apr. 2, 1976	1.40	.50			2.25
	Perf. 11					
1596	13¢ Eagle and Shield, Dec. 1, 1975	.22	.15	2.75	(12)	1.00
a	Imperf. pair	50.00				
b	Yellow omitted	200.00				
1597	15¢ Ft. McHenry Flag, June 30, 1978	.28	.15	1.75	(6)	1.00
a	Imperf. pair	17.50				
b	Gray omitted	250.00				
	Booklet Stamp, Perf. 11 x 10½					
1598	15¢ Ft. McHenry Flag (1597), single from booklet	.30	.15			1.00
a	Booklet pane of 8, June 30, 1978	3.50	.60			2.50
1599	16¢ Head of Liberty, Mar. 31, 1978	.34	.15	1.90	(4)	1.00
1600-02	Not assigned					
1603	24¢ Old North Church, Nov. 14, 1975	.45	.15	1.90	(4)	1.00
1604	28¢ Ft. Nisqually, Aug. 11, 1978	.55	.15	2.30	(4)	1.25
	Dull finish gum	1.10				
1605	29¢ Sandy Hook Lighthouse, Apr. 14, 1978	.55	.15	2.75	(4)	1.25
	Dull finish gum	2.00				
	Perf. 11 x 10½					
1606	30¢ One-Rm. Schoolhouse, Aug. 27, 1979	.55	.15	2.30	(4)	1.25
1607	Not assigned					
	Perf. 11					
1608	50¢ Whale Oil Lamp, Sept. 11, 1979	.85	.15	3.75	(4)	1.50
a	Black omitted	325.00				
b	Vertical pair, imperf. horizontally	—				
1609	Not assigned					
1610	$1 Candle and Rushlight Holder, July 2, 1979	2.00	.20	7.50	(4)	3.00
a	Brown omitted	300.00				
b	Tan, orange and yellow omitted	300.00				
c	Brown inverted	15,000.00				
1611	$2 Kerosene Table Lamp, Nov. 16, 1978	3.50	.45	14.00	(4)	5.00
1612	$5 Railroad Lantern, Aug. 23, 1979	8.00	1.50	31.00	(4)	12.50
	Coil Stamps, Perf. 10 Vertically					
1613	3.1¢ Guitar, Oct. 25, 1979	.15	.15	1.50	(2)	1.00
a	Untagged (Bureau precanceled)		.50			
b	Imperf. pair	1,350.00		3,600.00	(2)	
1614	7.7¢ Saxhorns, Nov. 20, 1976	.18	.15	1.00	(2)	1.00
a	Untagged (Bureau precanceled)		.35			
b	As "a," imperf. pair		1,400.00	4,400.00	(2)	
1615	7.9¢ Drum, Apr. 23, 1976	.15	.15	.65	(2)	1.00
a	Untagged (Bureau precanceled)		.20			
b	Imperf. pair	650.00				
1615C	8.4¢ Piano, July 13, 1978	.22	.15	3.25	(2)	1.00
d	Untagged (Bureau precanceled)		.16			
e	As "d," pair, imperf. between		50.00	—	(2)	
f	As "d," imperf. pair		15.00	30.00	(2)	

	Issues of 1975-81, Perf. 10 Vertically	Un	U	PB/LP	#	FDC
	Americana Issue (continued) (See also #1581-82, 1584-85, 1590-99, 1603-05, 1811, 1813, 1816)					
1616	9¢ slate green Capitol Dome (1591), Mar. 5, 1976	.20	.15	.90	(2)	1.00
a	Imperf. pair	125.00		250.00	(2)	
b	Untagged (Bureau precanceled)		.28			
c	As "b," imperf. pair		600.00	—		
1617	10¢ purple Contemplation of Justice (1592), Nov. 4, 1977	.20	.15	1.10	(2)	1.00
a	Untagged (Bureau precanceled)		.25			
b	Imperf. pair	60.00		125.00	(2)	
	Dull finish gum	.20				
1618	13¢ brown Liberty Bell (1595), Nov. 25, 1975	.25	.15	.60	(2)	1.00
a	Untagged (Bureau precanceled)		.45			
b	Imperf. pair	25.00		65.00	(2)	
g	Pair, imperf. between	—				
1618C	15¢ Ft. McHenry Flag (1597), June 30, 1978	.40	.15			1.00
d	Imperf. pair	20.00				
e	Pair, imperf. between	150.00				
f	Gray omitted	40.00				
1619	16¢ blue Head of Liberty (1599), Mar. 31, 1978	.32	.15	1.50	(2)	1.00
a	Huck Press printing (white background with a bluish tinge, fraction of a millimeter smaller)	.50	.15			
	Perf. 11 x 10¹/₂					
1620-21	Not assigned					
1622	13¢ Flag over Independence Hall, Nov. 15, 1975	.24	.15	5.75	(20)	1.00
a	Horizontal pair, imperf. between	50.00				
b	Imperf. pair	1,250.00				
c	Perf. 11, 1981	.65	.15	75.00	(20)	
d	As "c," vertical pair, imperf.	150.00				
e	Horizontal pair, imperf. vertically	—				
	Booklet Stamps					
1623	13¢ Flag over Capitol, single from booklet (1623a)	.22	.15			1.00
a	Booklet pane of 8, (1 #1590 and 7 #1623), Mar. 11, 1977	2.50	.60			25.00
	Booklet Stamps, Perf. 10					
b	13¢ Single from booklet	1.00	1.00			
c	Booklet pane of 8, (1 #1590a and 7 #1623b)	30.00	—			12.50
	#1623, 1623b issued only in booklets. All stamps are imperf. at one side or imperf. at one side and bottom.					
	Booklet Stamps, Perf. 11 x 10¹/₂					
d	Attached pair, #1590 and 1623	.75	—			
	Booklet Stamps, Perf. 10					
e	Attached pair, #1590a and 1623b	20.00	—			
1624	Not assigned					
	Coil Stamp, Perf. 10 Vertically					
1625	13¢ Flag over Independence Hall (1622), Nov. 15, 1975	.30	.15			1.00
a	Imperf. pair	22.50				

1622

1623a

1632

1629   1630   1631   1631a

1633

1634

1635

1636

1637

1638

1639

1640

1641

1642   1643   1644

	Issues of 1976, Perf. 11	Un	U	PB	#	FDC	Q
	American Bicentennial Issue, The Spirit of '76, Jan. 1						
1629	13¢ Drummer Boy	.20	.15			1.25	73,152,000
1630	13¢ Old Drummer	.20	.15			1.25	73,152,000
1631	13¢ Fife Player	.20	.15			1.25	73,152,000
a	Strip of 3, #1629-31	.60	.60	3.10	(12)	2.00	
b	As "a," imperf.	1,200.00					
c	Imperf. pair, #1631	900.00					
1632	13¢ Interphil 76, Jan. 17	.20	.15	1.00	(4)	1.00	157,825,000
	State Flags, Feb. 23						
1633	13¢ Delaware	.25	.20			1.25	8,720,100
1634	13¢ Pennsylvania	.25	.20			1.25	8,720,100
1635	13¢ New Jersey	.25	.20			1.25	8,720,100
1636	13¢ Georgia	.25	.20			1.25	8,720,100
1637	13¢ Connecticut	.25	.20			1.25	8,720,100
1638	13¢ Massachusetts	.25	.20			1.25	8,720,100
1639	13¢ Maryland	.25	.20			1.25	8,720,100
1640	13¢ South Carolina	.25	.20			1.25	8,720,100
1641	13¢ New Hampshire	.25	.20			1.25	8,720,100
1642	13¢ Virginia	.25	.20			1.25	8,720,100
1643	13¢ New York	.25	.20			1.25	8,720,100
1644	13¢ North Carolina	.25	.20			1.25	8,720,100

Which state is called the Goober State?

Georgia is the nation's leader in producing peanuts, which are often called goobers throughout the South. As a result, the nation's fourth state has been called the Goober State. The peanut vine grows most plentifully throughout the southwestern area of the state. Georgia is also the country's leading pecan producer and leads the country in overall nut production. **(#1636)**

	Issues of 1976 (continued), Perf. 11	Un	U	FDC	Q
	American Bicentennial Issue (continued), State Flags, Feb. 23				
1645	13¢ Rhode Island	.25	.20	1.25	8,720,100
1646	13¢ Vermont	.25	.20	1.25	8,720,100
1647	13¢ Kentucky	.25	.20	1.25	8,720,100
1648	13¢ Tennessee	.25	.20	1.25	8,720,100
1649	13¢ Ohio	.25	.20	1.25	8,720,100
1650	13¢ Louisiana	.25	.20	1.25	8,720,100
1651	13¢ Indiana	.25	.20	1.25	8,720,100
1652	13¢ Mississippi	.25	.20	1.25	8,720,100
1653	13¢ Illinois	.25	.20	1.25	8,720,100
1654	13¢ Alabama	.25	.20	1.25	8,720,100
1655	13¢ Maine	.25	.20	1.25	8,720,100
1656	13¢ Missouri	.25	.20	1.25	8,720,100
1657	13¢ Arkansas	.25	.20	1.25	8,720,100
1658	13¢ Michigan	.25	.20	1.25	8,720,100
1659	13¢ Florida	.25	.20	1.25	8,720,100
1660	13¢ Texas	.25	.20	1.25	8,720,100
1661	13¢ Iowa	.25	.20	1.25	8,720,100
1662	13¢ Wisconsin	.25	.20	1.25	8,720,100
1663	13¢ California	.25	.20	1.25	8,720,100
1664	13¢ Minnesota	.25	.20	1.25	8,720,100
1665	13¢ Oregon	.25	.20	1.25	8,720,100

What is Big Bend National Park named after?

Texas' Big Bend National Park is named for the great bend in the Rio Grande river, which is the southwestern border of the state. The park lies in southwestern Texas' basin and range region, and is home to the Chisos Mountains, which were created by volcanic action in the Age of Dinosaurs. Fossil trees found in Big Bend's Santa Elena canyons date back millions of years, and archaeologists have also found evidence of ancient cave-dweller civilizations. The Rio Grande runs from Colorado through New Mexico, borders Texas and empties into the Gulf of Mexico. **(#1660)**

1645

1646

1647

1648

1649

1650

1651

1652

1653

1654

1655

1656

1657

1658

1659

1660

1661

1662

1663

1664

1665

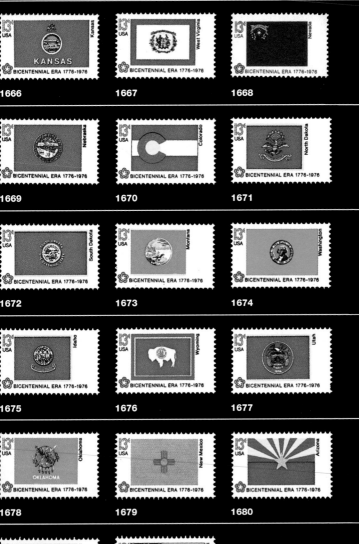

13¢ USA Kansas — KANSAS — BICENTENNIAL ERA 1776-1976 **1666**	13¢ USA West Virginia — BICENTENNIAL ERA 1776-1976 **1667**	13¢ USA Nevada — BICENTENNIAL ERA 1776-1976 **1668**
13¢ USA Nebraska — BICENTENNIAL ERA 1776-1976 **1669**	13¢ USA Colorado — BICENTENNIAL ERA 1776-1976 **1670**	13¢ USA North Dakota — BICENTENNIAL ERA 1776-1976 **1671**
13¢ USA South Dakota — BICENTENNIAL ERA 1776-1976 **1672**	13¢ USA Montana — BICENTENNIAL ERA 1776-1976 **1673**	13¢ USA Washington — BICENTENNIAL ERA 1776-1976 **1674**
13¢ USA Idaho — BICENTENNIAL ERA 1776-1976 **1675**	13¢ USA Wyoming — BICENTENNIAL ERA 1776-1976 **1676**	13¢ USA Utah — BICENTENNIAL ERA 1776-1976 **1677**
13¢ USA Oklahoma — OKLAHOMA — BICENTENNIAL ERA 1776-1976 **1678**	13¢ USA New Mexico — BICENTENNIAL ERA 1776-1976 **1679**	13¢ USA Arizona — BICENTENNIAL ERA 1776-1976 **1680**
13¢ USA Alaska — BICENTENNIAL ERA 1776-1976 **1681**	13¢ USA Hawaii — BICENTENNIAL ERA 1776-1976 **1682**	

Alexander Graham Bell 13c

Telephone Centennial USA

1683

Commercial Aviation

USA 13c 1926-1976

1684

CHEMISTRY

13c USA

1685

	Issues of 1976 (continued), Perf. 11	Un	U	PB	#	FDC	Q
	American Bicentennial Issue (continued), State Flags, Feb. 23						
1666	13¢ Kansas	.25	.20			1.25	8,720,100
1667	13¢ West Virginia	.25	.20			1.25	8,720,100
1668	13¢ Nevada	.25	.20			1.25	8,720,100
1669	13¢ Nebraska	.25	.20			1.25	8,720,100
1670	13¢ Colorado	.25	.20			1.25	8,720,100
1671	13¢ North Dakota	.25	.20			1.25	8,720,100
1672	13¢ South Dakota	.25	.20			1.25	8,720,100
1673	13¢ Montana	.25	.20			1.25	8,720,100
1674	13¢ Washington	.25	.20			1.25	8,720,100
1675	13¢ Idaho	.25	.20			1.25	8,720,100
1676	13¢ Wyoming	.25	.20			1.25	8,720,100
1677	13¢ Utah	.25	.20			1.25	8,720,100
1678	13¢ Oklahoma	.25	.20			1.25	8,720,100
1679	13¢ New Mexico	.25	.20			1.25	8,720,100
1680	13¢ Arizona	.25	.20			1.25	8,720,100
1681	13¢ Alaska	.25	.20			1.25	8,720,100
1682	13¢ Hawaii	.25	.20			1.25	8,720,100
a	Pane of 50, #1633-82	13.00	—	13.00	(50)	27.50	
1683	13¢ Telephone Centennial, Mar. 10	.22	.15	1.00	(4)	1.00	158,915,000
1684	13¢ Commercial Aviation, Mar. 19	.22	.15	2.25	(10)	1.00	156,960,000
1685	13¢ Chemistry, Apr. 6	.22	.15	2.75	(12)	1.00	158,470,000
	Pair with full vertical gutter between	—					

How did Nevada become a state?

The civil war broke out in 1861, just before Nevada's territorial government could take shape. Nevada wasn't yet part of the North or the South, although both needed Nevada's mineral resources. Most Nevadans favored the North, however, and President Lincoln needed another state to support his anti-slavery stance. Short of the 127,381 residents needed to become a state, Nevadans held a convention and drew up a state constitution. After one revision the constitution won approval, and Lincoln proclaimed Nevada a state on Oct. 31, 1864. **(#1668)**

	Issues of 1976 (continued), Perf. 11	Un	U	FDC	Q
	American Bicentennial Issue Souvenir Sheets, May 29, 5 stamps each				
1686	13¢ The Surrender of Lord Cornwallis at Yorktown, by John Trumbull	3.25	—	6.00	1,990,000
a	13¢ Two American Officers	.45	.40		1,990,000
b	13¢ Gen. Benjamin Lincoln	.45	.40		1,990,000
c	13¢ George Washington	.45	.40		1,990,000
d	13¢ John Trumbull, Col. David Cobb, General Friedrich von Steuben, Marquis de Lafayette and Thomas Nelson	.45	.40		1,990,000
e	13¢ Alexander Hamilton, John Laurens and Walter Stewart	.45	.40		1,990,000
f	"USA/13¢" omitted on "b," "c" and "d," imperf.	—	1,500.00		
g	"USA/13¢" omitted on "a" and "e"	450.00	—		
h	Imperf. (untagged)		1,750.00		
i	"USA/13¢" omitted on "b," "c" and "d"	450.00			
j	"USA/13¢" double on "b"	—			
k	"USA/13¢" omitted on "c" and "d"	—			
l	"USA/13¢" omitted on "e"	500.00			
m	"USA/13¢" omitted, imperf. (untagged)	—	—		
1687	18¢ The Declaration of Independence, 4 July 1776 at Philadelphia, by John Trumbull	4.25	—	7.50	1,983,000
a	18¢ John Adams, Roger Sherman and Robert R. Livingston	.55	.55		1,983,000
b	18¢ Thomas Jefferson and Benjamin Franklin	.55	.55		1,983,000
c	18¢ Thomas Nelson, Jr., Francis Lewis, John Witherspoon and Samuel Huntington	.55	.55		1,983,000
d	18¢ John Hancock and Charles Thomson	.55	.55		1,983,000
e	18¢ George Read, John Dickinson and Edward Rutledge	.55	.55		1,983,000
f	Design and marginal inscriptions omitted	4,750.00			
g	"USA/18¢" omitted on "a" and "c"	800.00			
h	"USA/18¢" omitted on "b," "d" and "e"	500.00			
i	"USA/18¢" omitted on "d"	500.00	500.00		
j	Black omitted in design	1,200.00			
k	"USA/18¢" omitted, imperf. (untagged)	2,250.00			
m	"USA/18¢" omitted on "b" and "e"	500.00			

The Surrender of Lord Cornwallis at Yorktown
From a Painting by John Trumbull

1686

The Declaration of Independence, 4 July 1776 at Philadelphia
From a Painting by John Trumbull

1687

Washington Crossing the Delaware
From a Painting by Emanuel Leutze / Eastman Johnson

Washington Reviewing His Ragged Army at Valley Forge
From a Painting by William T. Trego

	Issues of 1976 (continued), Perf. 11	Un	U	FDC	Q
	American Bicentennial Issue (continued) Souvenir Sheets, May 29, 5 stamps each				
1688	24¢ Washington Crossing the Delaware, by Emanuel Leutze/ Eastman Johnson	5.25	—	8.50	1,953,000
a	24¢ Boatmen	.70	.70		1,953,000
b	24¢ George Washington	.70	.70		1,953,000
c	24¢ Flagbearer	.70	.70		1,953,000
d	24¢ Men in Boat	.70	.70		1,953,000
e	24¢ Steersman and Men on Shore	.70	.70		1,953,000
f	"USA/24¢" omitted, imperf.	2,850.00			
g	"USA/24¢" omitted on "d" and "e"	—	450.00		
h	Design and marginal inscriptions omitted	2,250.00			
i	"USA/24¢" omitted on "a," "b" and "c"	500.00	—		
j	Imperf. (untagged)	2,250.00			
k	"USA/24¢" inverted on "d" and "e"	—			
1689	31¢ Washington Reviewing His Ragged Army at Valley Forge, by William T. Trego	6.25	—	9.50	1,903,000
a	31¢ Two Officers	.85	.85		1,903,000
b	31¢ George Washington	.85	.85		1,903,000
c	31¢ Officer and Brown Horse	.85	.85		1,903,000
d	31¢ White Horse and Officer	.85	.85		1,903,000
e	31¢ Three Soldiers	.85	.85		1,903,000
f	"USA/31¢" omitted, imperf.	2,100.00			
g	"USA/31¢" omitted on "a" and "c"	—			
h	"USA/31¢" omitted on "b," "d" and "e"	—	—		
i	"USA/31¢" omitted on "e"	500.00			
j	Black omitted in design	1,350.00			
k	Imperf. (untagged)		2,000.00		
l	"USA/31¢" omitted on "b" and "d"	—			
m	"USA/31¢" omitted on "a," "c" and "e"	—			
n	As "m," imperf. (untagged)	—			
p	As "h," imperf. (untagged)		2,500.00		
q	As "g," imperf. (untagged)	2,500.00			

Where does the Delaware River get its name?

In 1610, a ship from the Virginia colony sailed into the Delaware Bay. Although it wasn't the first ship in that area, it was the first one whose captain would name the bay — "De La Warr Bay," named for the governor of Virginia, Lord De La Warr. The river extends from upstate New York down into the Delaware Bay, and into the Atlantic Ocean. **(#1688)**

	Issues of 1976 (continued), Perf.11	Un	U	PB	#	FDC	Q
	American Bicentennial Issue, Benjamin Franklin, June 1						
1690	13¢ Bust of Franklin, Map of North America, 1776	.20	.15	.90	(4)	1.00	164,890,000
a	Light blue omitted	350.00					
	Declaration of Independence, by John Trumbull, July 4						
1691	13¢ Delegates	.20	.15			1.00	41,222,500
1692	13¢ Delegates and John Adams	.20	.15			1.00	41,222,500
1693	13¢ Roger Sherman, Robert R. Livingston, Thomas Jefferson and Benjamin Franklin	.20	.15			1.00	41,222,500
1694	13¢ John Hancock, Charles Thomson, George Read, John Dickinson and Edward Rutledge	.20	.15			1.00	41,222,500
a	Strip of 4, #1691-94	.85	.75	4.50	(20)	2.00	
	Olympic Games Issue, July 16						
1695	13¢ Diver and Olympic Rings	.28	.15			1.00	46,428,750
1696	13¢ Skier and Olympic Rings	.28	.15			1.00	46,428,750
1697	13¢ Runner and Olympic Rings	.28	.15			1.00	46,428,750
1698	13¢ Skater and Olympic Rings	.28	.15			1.00	46,428,750
a	Block of 4, #1695-98	1.15	.85	3.50	(12)	2.00	
b	As "a," imperf.	750.00					
1699	13¢ Clara Maass, Aug. 18	.22	.15	3.00	(12)	1.00	130,592,000
a	Horizontal pair, imperf. vertically	400.00					
1700	13¢ Adolph S. Ochs, Sept. 18	.22	.15	1.00	(4)	1.00	158,332,400
	Christmas Issue, Oct. 27						
1701	13¢ Nativity, by John Singleton Copley	.22	.15	2.75	(12)	1.00	809,955,000
a	Imperf. pair	100.00					
1702	13¢ "Winter Pastime," by Nathaniel Currier	.22	.15	2.25	(10)	1.00	481,685,000*
a	Imperf. pair	110.00					
	*Includes #1703 printing						
1703	13¢ as #1702	.22	.15	5.50	(20)	1.00	
a	Imperf. pair	125.00					
b	Vertical pair, imperf. between	—					

#1702 has overall tagging. Lettering at base is black and usually 1/2mm below design. As a rule, no "snowflaking" in sky or pond. Pane of 50 has margins on 4 sides with slogans. #1703 has block tagging the size of the printed area. Lettering at base is gray-black and usually 3/4mm below design. "Snowflaking" generally in sky and pond. Pane of 50 has margin only at right or left and no slogans.

	Issues of 1977, American Bicentennial Issue, Washington at Princeton, Jan. 3						
1704	13¢ Washington, Nassau Hall, Hessian Prisoners and 13-star Flag, by Charles Willson Peale	.22	.15	2.25	(10)	1.00	150,328,000
a	Horizontal pair, imperf. vertically	450.00					
1705	13¢ Sound Recording, Mar. 23	.22	.15	1.00	(4)	1.00	176,830,000

1690

1691   1692   1693   1694 1694a

1699

1700

1695   1696 1698a
1697   1698

1701   1702   1703

1704

1705

1977

1710

1711

1706 **1707** **1709a**
1708 **1709**

1716

1712 **1713** **1715a**
1714 **1715**

1721

1717 **1718** **1720a**
1719 **1720**

	Issues of 1977 (continued), Perf. 11	Un	U	PB	#	FDC	Q
	American Folk Art Issue, Pueblo Pottery, Apr. 13						
1706	13¢ Zia Pot	.22	.15			1.00	48,994,000
1707	13¢ San Ildefonso Pot	.22	.15			1.00	48,994,000
1708	13¢ Hopi Pot	.22	.15			1.00	48,994,000
1709	13¢ Acoma Pot	.22	.15			1.00	48,994,000
a	Block of 4, #1706-09	.90	.60	2.50	(10)	2.00	
b	As "a," imperf. vertically	2,500.00					
1710	13¢ Solo Transatlantic Flight, May 20	.22	.15	2.75	(12)	1.00	208,820,000
a	Imperf. pair	1,150.00					
1711	13¢ Colorado Statehood, May 21	.22	.15	2.75	(12)	1.00	192,250,000
a	Horizontal pair, imperf. between	500.00					
b	Horizontal pair, imperf. vertically	900.00					
c	Perf. 11.2	.35	.25				
	Butterfly Issue, June 6						
1712	13¢ Swallowtail	.22	.15			1.00	54,957,500
1713	13¢ Checkerspot	.22	.15			1.00	54,957,500
1714	13¢ Dogface	.22	.15			1.00	54,957,500
1715	13¢ Orange-Tip	.22	.15			1.00	54,957,500
a	Block of 4, #1712-15	.90	.60	2.75	(12)	2.00	
b	As "a," imperf. horizontally	—					
	American Bicentennial Issue, Lafayette's Landing in South Carolina, June 13						
1716	13¢ Marquis de Lafayette	.22	.15	1.00	(4)	1.00	159,852,000
	Skilled Hands for Independence, July 4						
1717	13¢ Seamstress	.22	.15			1.00	47,077,500
1718	13¢ Blacksmith	.22	.15			1.00	47,077,500
1719	13¢ Wheelwright	.22	.15			1.00	47,077,500
1720	13¢ Leatherworker	.22	.15			1.00	47,077,500
a	Block of 4, #1717-20	.90	.80	2.75	(12)	1.75	
	Perf. 11 x 10¹/₂						
1721	13¢ Peace Bridge, Aug. 4	.22	.15	1.00	(4)	1.00	163,625,000

Where can you cross the Peace Bridge?

The Peace Bridge, a symbol of friendship between Canada and the United States, extends over the Niagara River from Fort Potter, in Buffalo, N.Y., to Fort Erie, Ontario.

The steel bridge is owned by a company with both American and Canadian directors, and is 4,400 feet long. **(#1721)**

Join the Club for Collecting Adventure

- A Commemorative Stamp Club Album
- Custom-printed album pages featuring illustrations and mounting areas for individual stamp issues
- Stamps and mounts mailed conveniently to your home

The Commemorative Stamp Club provides a convenient, comprehensive and attractive method for collecting and saving U.S. stamps. Your membership means the start of an exciting adventure, one that will introduce you to America's best—the places, people, events and ideals honored through commemorative stamps.

And if you're looking for further excitement, you can expand your horizons by choosing to receive definitive stamps, other special issues (such as the Music series and the World War II sheets) and album pages. These are offered at the end of each year.

Other Membership Benefits

You'll receive clear acetate mounts to hold and protect your stamps and a free one-year subscription to *Stamps etc.*, a publication mailed four times a year with full-color illustrations of all stamps, postal cards, aerogrammes, stamped envelopes and other collectibles available through mail order.

A no-risk, money-back guarantee assures your satisfaction. If you discontinue your membership within 30 days, simply return the album pages and stamps with a label from one of your shipments, and we'll send you a complete refund; the album is yours to keep.

To Join

For more detailed information, use the postage-paid request card in this book or write to:

**U.S. POSTAL SERVICE GUIDE
COMMEMORATIVE STAMP CLUB
PHILATELIC FULFILLMENT SERVICE CENTER
PO BOX 449980
KANSAS CITY MO 64144-9980**

Issue Date
April 27, 1994

First Day City
San Francisco,
California

Designer
Al Hirschfeld

Stars of the Silent Screen

The first two decades of the 20th century left movie stars speechless. The only way dialogue could be conveyed on screen was through printed text intercut with the action. But by the 1920s, several performers had overcome film's technical limitations to create cinematic personalities that the world has never forgotten.

Some, like Charlie Chaplin and Lon Chaney, created vivid characters; some, like Rudolph Valentino and Theda Bara, were exotic flames; and others, like Buster Keaton and Harold Lloyd, raised visual humor to heights it has rarely attained since.

Issue Date
April 28, 1994

First Day City
Cincinnati, Ohio

Designer
Ned Seidler

Garden Flowers

In the world's temperate regions—including most of the United States—nature's artistic medium changes during the cold months into a sullen pencil drawing. As the days lengthen and warm, the earth breaks out its box of crayons to color stalk and branch. By summer, a well-tended garden is nearly as flamboyant as the tropics.

Flowers, bright as flags, sunbathe in the golden day as their perfumes ride the breeze. These blooms have a purely practical purpose: to propagate the plant by way of the birds and insects that sail the air among them. But to our senses, they appear as arias of hue, pure celebrations of life itself.

UNITED STATES
POSTAL SERVICE™

(9404)

	Issues of 1977 (continued), Perf. 11	Un	U	PB	#	FDC	Q
	American Bicentennial Issue, Battle of Oriskany, Aug. 6						
1722	13¢ Herkimer at Oriskany, by Frederick Yohn	.22	.15	2.50	(10)	1.25	156,296,000
	Energy Issue, Oct. 20						
1723	13¢ Energy Conservation	.22	.15			1.00	79,338,000
a	Attached pair, #1723-24	.45	.40	2.75	(12)	1.25	
1724	13¢ Energy Development	.22	.15			1.00	79,338,000
1725	13¢ First Civil Settlement— Alta, California, Sept. 9	.22	.15	1.00	(4)	1.00	154,495,000
	American Bicentennial Issue, Articles of Confederation, Sept. 30						
1726	13¢ Members of Continental Congress in Conference	.22	.15	1.00	(4)	1.00	168,050,000
1727	13¢ Talking Pictures, Oct. 6	.22	.15	1.00	(4)	1.00	156,810,000
	American Bicentennial Issue, Surrender at Saratoga, Oct. 7						
1728	13¢ Surrender of Burgoyne, by John Trumbull	.22	.15	2.50	(10)	1.00	153,736,000
	Christmas Issue, Oct. 21						
1729	13¢ Washington at Valley Forge, by J.C. Leyendecker	.22	.15	5.75	(20)	1.00	882,260,000
a	Imperf. pair	75.00					
1730	13¢ Rural Mailbox	.22	.15	2.50	(10)	1.00	921,530,000
a	Imperf. pair	275.00					
	Issues of 1978						
1731	13¢ Carl Sandburg, Jan. 6	.22	.15	1.00	(4)	1.00	156,560,000
	Captain Cook Issue, Jan. 20						
1732	13¢ Capt. James Cook– Alaska, by Nathaniel Dance	.22	.15			1.00	101,077,500
a	Attached pair, #1732-33	.50	.30			1.50	
b	As "a," imperf. between	4,500.00					
1733	13¢ *Resolution* and *Discovery* – Hawaii, by John Webber	.22	.15			1.00	101,077,500
a	Vertical pair, imperf. horizontally	—					
1734	13¢ Indian Head Penny, Jan. 11	.24	.15	1.50	(4)	1.00	
	Pair with full horizontal gutter between	—					
a	Horizontal pair, imperf. vertically	300.00					
1735	15¢ A Stamp, May 22	.24	.15	1.25	(4)	1.00	
a	Imperf. pair	80.00					
b	Vertical pair, imperf. horizontally	300.00					
	Booklet Stamp, Perf. 11 x 10½						
1736	15¢ orange Eagle (1735), single from booklet	.25	.15			1.00	
a	Booklet pane of 8, May 22	2.25	.60			2.50	
	Roses Booklet Issue, July 11, Perf. 10						
1737	15¢ Roses, single from booklet	.25	.15			1.00	
a	Booklet pane of 8	2.25	.60			2.50	
b	As "a," imperf.	—					

#1736-37 issued only in booklets. All stamps are imperf. on one side or on one side and bottom.

Minimum value listed for a stamp is 15 cents; for a First Day Cover (FDC), $1.00. This minimum represents a fair-market price for having a dealer locate and provide a single stamp or cover from his or her stock. Dealers may charge less per stamp or cover for a group of such stamps or covers, or less for a single stamp or cover.

Herkimer at Oriskany 1777 by Yohn
US Bicentennial 13 cents

1722

1723 **1723a**
1724

First Civil Settlement·Alta California·1777

1725

Drafting the Articles of Confederation
York Town, Pennsylvania 1777 13 USA

1726

1727

Surrender at Saratoga 1777 by Trumbull
US Bicentennial 13 cents

1728

VALLEY FORGE
USA 13c

1729

Christmas 13c

1730

Carl Sandburg
USA 13c

1731

Alaska 1778 Capt. James Cook 13c USA
Capt. James Cook Hawaii 1778 13c USA

1732 **1732a**
1733

USA 13c

1734

A US Postage

1735

15c USA

1737

1738 1739 1740 1741 1742 1742a

1744

1745 1746 1748a
1747 1748

1750

1752

1749

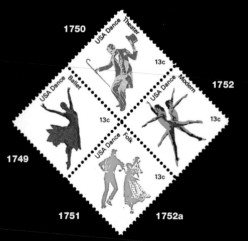

1751 1752a

1753

1754 1755 1756

	Issues of 1980, Perf. 11	Un	U	PB/LP	#	FDC	Q
	Windmills Booklet Issue, Feb. 7						
1738	15¢ Virginia, 1720	.30	.15			1.00	
1739	15¢ Rhode Island, 1790	.30	.15			1.00	
1740	15¢ Massachusetts, 1793	.30	.15			1.00	
1741	15¢ Illinois, 1860	.30	.15			1.00	
1742	15¢ Texas, 1890	.30	.15			1.00	
a	Booklet pane of 10, #1738-42	3.60	.60			3.50	
	#1737-42 issued only in booklets. All stamps are imperf. top or bottom, or top or bottom and right side.						
	Issues of 1978 (continued), Coil Stamp, Perf. 10 Vertically						
1743	15¢ orange Eagle (1735), May 22	.25	.15	.65	(2)	1.00	
a	Imperf. pair	90.00		—	(2)		
	Black Heritage Issue, Harriet Tubman, Feb. 1, Perf. 10¹/₂ x 11						
1744	13¢ Harriet Tubman and Cart Carrying Slaves	.22	.15	3.00	(12)	1.00	156,525,000
	American Folk Art Issue, Quilts, Mar. 8, Perf. 11						
1745	13¢ Basket design, red and orange	.22	.15			1.00	41,295,600
1746	13¢ Basket design, red	.22	.15			1.00	41,295,600
1747	13¢ Basket design, orange	.22	.15			1.00	41,295,600
1748	13¢ Basket design, brown	.22	.15			1.00	41,295,600
a	Block of 4, #1745-48	.90	.60	3.00	(12)	2.00	
	American Dance Issue, Apr. 26						
1749	13¢ Ballet	.22	.15			1.00	39,399,600
1750	13¢ Theater	.22	.15			1.00	39,399,600
1751	13¢ Folk	.22	.15			1.00	39,399,600
1752	13¢ Modern	.22	.15			1.00	39,399,600
a	Block of 4, #1749-52	.90	.60	3.00	(12)	1.75	
	American Bicentennial Issue, French Alliance, May 4						
1753	13¢ King Louis XVI and Benjamin Franklin, by Charles Gabriel Sauvage	.22	.15	1.05	(4)	1.00	102,920,000
	Perf. 10¹/₂ x 11						
1754	13¢ Early Cancer Detection, May 18	.24	.15	1.05	(4)	1.00	152,355,000
	Performing Arts Issue, Jimmie Rodgers, May 24, Perf. 11						
1755	13¢ Jimmie Rodgers with Locomotive, Guitar and Brakeman's Cap	.24	.15	3.00	(12)	1.00	94,625,000
	George M. Cohan, July 3						
1756	15¢ George M. Cohan, "Yankee Doodle Dandy" and Stars	.26	.15	3.50	(12)	1.00	151,570,000

When was George M. Cohan introduced to music?

George M. Cohan, who wrote, directed, produced and starred in more than 40 plays and musicals, was introduced to theater when he was a child, performing vaudeville acts with his parents and sister. The group was known as "The Four Cohans," and Cohan began writing songs when he was a teenager. His most famous tunes included *Yankee Doodle Dandy* and *Give my Regards to Broadway*. (**#1756**)

	Issues of 1978 (continued), Perf. 11	Un	U	PB	#	FDC	Q
	CAPEX '78 Souvenir Sheet, June 10						
1757	13¢ Souvenir sheet of 8	1.65	1.65	1.90	(8)	2.75	15,170,400
a	13¢ Cardinal	.20	.15				15,170,400
b	13¢ Mallard	.20	.15				15,170,400
c	13¢ Canada Goose	.20	.15				15,170,400
d	13¢ Blue Jay	.20	.15				15,170,400
e	13¢ Moose	.20	.15				15,170,400
f	13¢ Chipmunk	.20	.15				15,170,400
g	13¢ Red Fox	.20	.15				15,170,400
h	13¢ Raccoon	.20	.15				15,170,400
i	Yellow, green, red, brown and black (litho.) omitted	5,000.00					
1758	15¢ Photography, June 26	.26	.15	3.25	(12)	1.00	163,200,000
1759	15¢ Viking Missions to Mars, July 20	.26	.15	1.20	(4)	2.00	158,880,000
	Wildlife Conservation Issue, American Owls, Aug. 26						
1760	15¢ Great Gray Owl	.26	.15			1.00	46,637,500
1761	15¢ Saw-Whet Owl	.26	.15			1.00	46,637,500
1762	15¢ Barred Owl	.26	.15			1.00	46,637,500
1763	15¢ Great Horned Owl	.26	.15			1.00	46,637,500
a	Block of 4, #1760-63	1.05	.85	1.25	(4)	2.00	
	American Trees Issue, Oct. 9						
1764	15¢ Giant Sequoia	.26	.15			1.00	42,034,000
1765	15¢ White Pine	.26	.15			1.00	42,034,000
1766	15¢ White Oak	.26	.15			1.00	42,034,000
1767	15¢ Gray Birch	.26	.15			1.00	42,034,000
a	Block of 4, #1764-67	1.05	.85	3.50	(12)	2.00	
b	As "a," imperf. horizontally	12,500.00					
	Christmas Issue, Oct. 18						
1768	15¢ Madonna and Child with Cherubim, by Andrea della Robbia	.26	.15	3.50	(12)	1.00	963,370,000
a	Imperf. pair	90.00					
1769	15¢ Child on Hobby Horse and Christmas Trees	.26	.15	3.50	(12)	1.00	916,800,000
a	Imperf. pair	100.00					
b	Vertical pair, imperf. horizontally	1,750.00					
	Pair with full horizontal gutter between	—					

What are gray birch trees used for?

Gray birches, which rarely grow higher than 40 feet, are commonly used for firewood and in the making of spools, shoe pegs and wood pulp, because their grayish-white bark is harder than that of most other birch trees. You can find gray birch trees in the area stretching from Newfoundland to Delaware and Lake Ontario. They usually grow in pairs or groups. **(#1767)**

1757a, b, c, d

1757e, f, g, h

1757

1758

1759

1760   1761   1763a

1762   1763

1764   1765   1767a

1766   1767

1768   1769

1770

1771

1772

1773

1774

1775   **1776**   **1778a**

1777   **1778**

1779   **1780**   **1782a**

1781   **1782**

1783   **1784**   **1786a**

1785   **1786**

	Issues of 1979, Perf. 11	Un	U	PB	#	FDC	Q
1770	15¢ Robert F. Kennedy, Jan. 12	.26	.15	1.20	(4)	2.00	159,297,600
	Black Heritage Issue, Martin Luther King, Jr., Jan. 13						
1771	15¢ Martin Luther King, Jr., and Civil Rights Marchers	.26	.15	3.50	(12)	1.00	166,435,000
a	Imperf. pair	—					
1772	15¢ International Year of the Child, Feb. 15	.26	.15	1.20	(4)	1.00	162,535,000
	Literary Arts Issue, John Steinbeck, Feb. 27, Perf. 10¹/₂ x 11						
1773	15¢ John Steinbeck, by Philippe Halsman	.26	.15	1.20	(4)	1.00	155,000,000
1774	15¢ Albert Einstein, Mar. 4	.28	.15	1.20	(4)	1.50	157,310,000
	Pair with full horizontal gutter between	—					
	American Folk Art Issue, Pennsylvania Toleware, Apr. 19, Perf. 11						
1775	15¢ Straight-Spout Coffeepot	.28	.15			1.00	43,524,000
1776	15¢ Tea Caddy	.28	.15			1.00	43,524,000
1777	15¢ Sugar Bowl	.28	.15			1.00	43,524,000
1778	15¢ Curved-Spout Coffeepot	.28	.15			1.00	43,524,000
a	Block of 4, #1775-78	1.15	.85	2.90	(10)	2.00	
b	As "a," imperf. horizontally	3,750.00					
	American Architecture Issue, June 4						
1779	15¢ Virginia Rotunda, by Thomas Jefferson	.28	.15			1.00	41,198,400
1780	15¢ Baltimore Cathedral, by Benjamin Latrobe	.28	.15			1.00	41,198,400
1781	15¢ Boston State House, by Charles Bulfinch	.28	.15			1.00	41,198,400
1782	15¢ Philadelphia Exchange, by William Strickland	.28	.15			1.00	41,198,400
a	Block of 4, #1779-82	1.15	.85	1.35	(4)	2.00	
	Endangered Flora Issue, June 7						
1783	15¢ Persistent Trillium	.28	.15			1.00	40,763,750
1784	15¢ Hawaiian Wild Broadbean	.28	.15			1.00	40,763,750
1785	15¢ Contra Costa Wallflower	.28	.15			1.00	40,763,750
1786	15¢ Antioch Dunes Evening Primrose	.28	.15			1.00	40,763,750
a	Block of 4, #1783-86	1.15	.85	3.50	(12)	2.00	
b	As "a," imperf.	600.00					
	As "a," full vertical gutter between	—					

Who was the Joad family?

The Joads were John Steinbeck's fictional Oklahoma family featured in his book *The Grapes of Wrath*. Although the family wasn't real, many people lived the lives of the Joads in their search for work during the Great Depression. *Grapes* won the 1940 Pulitzer Prize, and Steinbeck went on to write over a dozen more books. He won the Nobel Prize for literature in 1962. **(#1773)**

235

	Issues of 1979 (continued), Perf. 11	Un	U	PB	#	FDC	Q
1787	15¢ Seeing Eye Dogs, June 15	.28	.15	5.75	(20)	1.00	161,860,000
a	Imperf. pair	400.00					
1788	15¢ Special Olympics, Aug. 9	.28	.15	2.90	(10)	1.00	165,775,000
	American Bicentennial Issue, John Paul Jones, Sept. 23, Perf. 11 x 12						
1789	15¢ John Paul Jones, by Charles Willson Peale	.28	.15	2.90	(10)	1.00	160,000,000
a	Perf. 11	.30	.15	3.10	(10)		
b	Perf. 12	2,000.00	1,000.00				
c	Vertical pair, imperf. horizontally	200.00					
d	As "a," vertical pair, imperf. horizontally	150.00					
	Numerous varieties of printer's waste of #1789 exist.						
	Olympic Summer Games Issue, Sept. 5, Perf. 11 (See also #C97)						
1790	10¢ Javelin Thrower	.20	.20	3.00	(12)	1.00	67,195,000
	Sept. 28						
1791	15¢ Runner	.28	.15			1.00	46,726,250
1792	15¢ Swimmer	.28	.15			1.00	46,726,250
1793	15¢ Rowers	.28	.15			1.00	46,726,250
1794	15¢ Equestrian Contestant	.28	.15			1.00	46,726,250
a	Block of 4, #1791-94	1.15	.85	3.50	(12)	2.00	
b	As "a," imperf.	1,400.00					
	Issues of 1980, Olympic Winter Games Issue, Feb. 1, Perf. 11 x 10½						
1795	15¢ Speed Skater	.32	.15			1.00	52,073,750
1796	15¢ Downhill Skier	.32	.15			1.00	52,073,750
1797	15¢ Ski Jumper	.32	.15			1.00	52,073,750
1798	15¢ Hockey Goaltender	.32	.15			1.00	52,073,750
a	Perf. 11	1.05	—	13.00	(12)		
b	Block of 4, #1795-98	1.30	1.00			2.00	
c	Block of 4, #1795a-98a	4.25	—				
	Issues of 1979 (continued), Christmas Issue, Oct. 18, Perf. 11						
1799	15¢ Virgin and Child with Cherubim, by Gerard David	.28	.15	3.40	(12)	1.00	873,710,000
a	Imperf. pair	100.00					
b	Vertical pair, imperf. horizontally	700.00					
c	Vertical pair, imperf. between	2,750.00					
1800	15¢ Santa Claus, Christmas Tree Ornament	.28	.15	3.40	(12)	1.00	931,880,000
a	Green and yellow omitted	600.00					
b	Green, yellow and tan omitted	650.00					
	Performing Arts Issue, Will Rogers, Nov. 4						
1801	15¢ Will Rogers Portrait and Rogers as a Cowboy Humorist	.28	.15	3.40	(12)	1.00	161,290,000
a	Imperf. pair	250.00					
1802	15¢ Vietnam Veterans, Nov. 11	.28	.15	2.90	(10)	2.50	172,740,000
	Issues of 1980 (continued), Performing Arts Issue, W.C. Fields, Jan. 29						
1803	15¢ W.C. Fields Portrait and Fields as a Juggler	.28	.15	3.40	(12)	1.25	168,995,000
	Black Heritage Issue, Benjamin Banneker, Feb. 15						
1804	15¢ Benjamin Banneker Portrait and Banneker as Surveyor	.28	.15	3.40	(12)	1.00	160,000,000
a	Horizontal pair, imperf. vertically	800.00					

1787   **1788**   **1789**

1790

1791   **1792**   **1794a**
1793   **1794**

1795   **1796**   **1798b**
1797   **1798**

1799   **1800**

1802

1801   **1803**   **1804**

237

1813   **1816**

1805   **1807**   **1809**
1806   **1808**   **1810**

1822

1818

1821   **1823**

1824   **1825**   **1826**

1827   **1828**   **1830a**
1829   **1830**

	Issues of 1980 (continued), Perf. 11	Un	U	PB/LP	#	FDC	Q
	Letter Writing Issue, Feb. 25						
1805	15¢ Letters Preserve Memories	.28	.15			1.00	38,933,000
1806	15¢ purple P.S. Write Soon	.28	.15			1.00	38,933,000
1807	15¢ Letters Lift Spirits	.28	.15			1.00	38,933,000
1808	15¢ green P.S. Write Soon	.28	.15			1.00	38,933,000
1809	15¢ Letters Shape Opinions	.28	.15			1.00	38,933,000
1810	15¢ red and blue P.S. Write Soon	.28	.15			1.00	38,933,000
a	Vertical Strip of 6, #1805-10	1.75	1.50	10.00	(36)	2.50	
	Issues of 1980-81, Americana Issue, Coil Stamps, Perf. 10 Vertically						
	(See also #1581-82, 1584-85, 1590-99, 1603-06, 1608, 1610-19, 1622-23, 1625)						
1811	1¢ dark blue, greenish Inkwell and Quill (1581), Mar. 6, 1980	.15	.15	.30	(2)	1.00	
a	Imperf. pair	*175.00*		*325.00*	(2)		
1812	Not assigned						
1813	3.5¢ Weaer Violins, June 23, 1980	.15	.15	.90	(2)	1.00	
a	Untagged (Bureau precanceled)		.15				
b	Imperf. pair	*225.00*		—	(2)		
1814-15	Not assigned						
1816	12¢ red brown, *beige* Torch from Statue of Liberty (1594), Apr. 8, 1981	.24	.15	1.25	(2)	1.00	
a	Untagged (Bureau precanceled)		.25				
b	Imperf. pair	*175.00*		*300.00*	(2)		
1817	Not assigned						
	Issues of 1981, Perf. 11 x 10¹/₂						
1818	18¢ B Stamp, Mar. 15	.32	.15	1.50	(4)	1.00	
	Booklet Stamp, Perf. 10						
1819	18¢ B Stamp (1818), single from booklet	.40	.15			1.00	
a	Booklet pane of 8, Mar. 15	3.50	*1.50*			3.00	
	Coil Stamp, Perf. 10 Vertically						
1820	18¢ B Stamp (1818), Mar. 15	.40	.15	1.60	(2)	1.00	
a	Imperf. pair	*100.00*		—	(2)		
	Issues of 1980 (continued), Perf. 10¹/₂ x 11						
1821	15¢ Frances Perkins, April 10	.28	.15	1.20	(4)	1.00	163,510,000
	Perf. 11						
1822	15¢ Dolley Madison, May 20	.28	.15	1.40	(4)	1.00	256,620,000
1823	15¢ Emily Bissell, May 31	.28	.15	1.20	(4)	1.00	95,695,000
a	Vertical pair, imperf. horizontally	300.00					
1824	15¢ Helen Keller/Anne Sullivan, June 27	.28	.15	1.20	(4)	1.00	153,975,000
1825	15¢ Veterans Administration, July 21	.28	.15	1.20	(4)	1.00	160,000,000
a	Horizontal pair, imperf. vertically	450.00					
	American Bicentennial Issue, General Bernardo de Galvez, July 23						
1826	15¢ General Bernardo de Galvez and Revolutionary Flag at Battle of Mobile	.28	.15	1.20	(4)	1.00	103,855,000
a	Red, brown and blue omitted	*800.00*					
b	Bl., brn., red and yel. omitted	*1,400.00*					
	Coral Reefs Issue, Aug. 26						
1827	15¢ Brain Coral, Beaugregory Fish	.26	.15			1.00	51,291,250
1828	15¢ Elkhorn Coral, Porkfish	.26	.15			1.00	51,291,250
1829	15¢ Chalice Coral, Moorish Idol	.26	.15			1.00	51,291,250
1830	15¢ Finger Coral, Sabertooth Blenny	.26	.15			1.00	51,291,250
a	Block of 4, #1827-30	1.05	.85	3.50	(12)	2.00	
b	As "a," imperf.	*1,250.00*					
c	As "a," imperf. between, vertically	—					
d	As "a," imperf. vertically	*3,000.00*					

	Issues of 1980 (continued), Perf. 11	Un	U	PB	#	FDC	Q
1831	15¢ Organized Labor, Sept. 1	.28	.15	3.50	(12)	1.00	166,590,000
a	Imperf. pair	400.00					
	Literary Arts Issue, Edith Wharton, Sept. 5, Perf. 10½ x 11						
1832	15¢ Edith Wharton Reading Letter	.28	.15	1.20	(4)	1.00	163,275,000
	Perf. 11						
1833	15¢ Education, Sept. 12	.28	.15	1.70	(6)	1.00	160,000,000
a	Horizontal pair, imperf. vertically	250.00					
	American Folk Art Issue, Pacific Northwest Indian Masks, Sept. 25						
1834	15¢ Heiltsuk, Bella Bella Tribe	.30	.15			1.00	38,101,000
1835	15¢ Chilkat Tlingit Tribe	.30	.15			1.00	38,101,000
1836	15¢ Tlingit Tribe	.30	.15			1.00	38,101,000
1837	15¢ Bella Coola Tribe	.30	.15			1.00	38,101,000
a	Block of 4, #1834-37	1.25	.85	3.25	(10)	2.00	
	American Architecture Issue, Oct. 9						
1838	15¢ Smithsonian Institution, by James Renwick	.30	.15			1.00	38,756,000
1839	15¢ Trinity Church, by Henry Hobson Richardson	.30	.15			1.00	38,756,000
1840	15¢ Pennsylvania Academy of Fine Arts, by Frank Furness	.30	.15			1.00	38,756,000
1841	15¢ Lyndhurst, by Alexander Jefferson Davis	.30	.15			1.00	38,756,000
a	Block of 4, #1838-41	1.25	.85	1.50	(4)	2.00	
	Christmas Issue, Oct. 31						
1842	15¢ Madonna and Child from Epiphany Window, Washington Cathedral	.28	.15	3.40	(12)	1.00	693,250,000
a	Imperf. pair	80.00					
	Pair with full vertical gutter between	—					
1843	15¢ Wreath and Toys	.28	.15	5.75	(20)	1.00	718,715,000
a	Imperf. pair	80.00					
b	Buff omitted	—					

What was the first American nationwide labor group?

Philadelphia ironworker William H. Sylvis founded the National Union of Iron Molders in 1859. A small group of other national labor unions formed soon after, and Sylvis united them into the National Labor Union in 1866, which dissolved six years later. Meanwhile, the Noble Order of the Knights of Labor was established in 1869, and is known today as the American Federation of Labor. The Knights included farmers and merchants in addition to wage earners, and fought for equal pay, the abolition of child labor and an eight-hour workday. **(#1831)**

Organized Labor
Proud and Free
USA 15c

1831

Edith Wharton

USA 15c

1832

Glas by Josef Albers USA 15c
Learning
never ends

1833

Heiltsuk, Bella Bella
Indian Art USA 15c

Chilkat Tlingit
Indian Art USA 15c

Tlingit
Indian Art USA 15c

Bella Coola
Indian Art USA 15c

1834   **1835**   **1837a**

1836   **1837**

Renwick 1818-1895 Smithsonian Washington
Architecture USA 15c

Richardson 1838-1886 Trinity Church Boston
Architecture USA 15c

Furness 1839-1912 Penn Academy Philadelphia
Architecture USA 15c

AJ Davis 1803-1892 Lyndhurst Terrytown NY
Architecture USA 15c

1838   **1839**   **1841a**

Christmas USA 15c

1842

USA 15c
Season's Greetings

1843

1844

1845

1846

1847

1848

1849

1850

1851

1852

1853

1854

1855

1856

1857

1858

1859

1860

1861

1862

1863

1864

1865

1866

1867

1868

1869

	Issues of 1980-85, Perf. 11	Un	U	PB	#	FDC
	Great Americans Issue (See also #2168-73, 2176-80, 2182-86, 2188, 2190-92, 2194-97)					
1844	1¢ Dorothea Dix, Sept. 23, 1983	.15	.15	.35	(6)	1.00
a	Imperf. pair	350.00				
b	Vertical pair, imperf. between	—				
	Perf. 10½ x 11					
1845	2¢ Igor Stravinsky, Nov. 18, 1982	.15	.15	.25	(4)	1.00
a	Vertical pair, full gutter between	—				
1846	3¢ Henry Clay, July 13, 1983	.15	.15	.35	(4)	1.00
1847	4¢ Carl Schurz, June 3, 1983	.15	.15	.40	(4)	1.00
1848	5¢ Pearl Buck, June 25, 1983	.15	.15	.50	(4)	1.00
	Perf. 11					
1849	6¢ Walter Lippman, Sept. 19, 1985	.15	.15	.75	(6)	1.00
a	Vertical pair, imperf. between	2,300				
1850	7¢ Abraham Baldwin, Jan. 25, 1985	.15	.15	.75	(6)	1.00
1851	8¢ Henry Knox, July 25, 1985	.15	.15	.80	(4)	1.00
1852	9¢ Sylvanus Thayer, June 7, 1985	.16	.15	1.00	(6)	1.00
1853	10¢ Richard Russell, May 31, 1984	.18	.15	1.10	(6)	1.00
a	Vertical pair, imperf. between	1,100.00				
b	Horizontal pair, imperf. between	2,250.00				
1854	11¢ Alden Partridge, Feb. 12, 1985	.20	.15	1.10	(4)	1.00
	Perf. 10½ x 11					
1855	13¢ Crazy Horse, Jan. 15, 1982	.24	.15	1.40	(4)	1.00
	Perf. 11					
1856	14¢ Sinclair Lewis, Mar. 21, 1985	.25	.15	1.55	(6)	1.00
a	Vertical pair, imperf. horizontally	150.00				
b	Horizontal pair, imperf. between	8.50				
c	Vertical pair, imperf. between	2,000.00				
	Perf. 10½ x 11					
1857	17¢ Rachel Carson, May 28, 1981	.32	.15	1.50	(4)	1.00
1858	18¢ George Mason, May 7, 1981	.32	.15	2.25	(4)	1.00
1859	19¢ Sequoyah, Dec. 27, 1980	.35	.15	2.00	(4)	1.00
1860	20¢ Ralph Bunche, Jan. 12, 1982	.40	.15	3.00	(4)	1.00
1861	20¢ Thomas H. Gallaudet, June 10, 1983	.38	.15	3.00	(4)	1.00
	Perf. 11					
1862	20¢ Harry S. Truman, Jan. 26, 1984	.38	.15	2.40	(6)	1.00
b	Overall tagging, 1990	—	—			
1863	22¢ John J. Audubon, Apr. 23, 1985	.40	.15	2.50	(6)	1.00
a	Vertical pair, imperf. horizontally	2,500.00				
b	Vertical pair, imperf. between	—				
c	Horizontal pair, imperf. between	1,750.00				
1864	30¢ Frank C. Laubach, Sept. 2, 1984	.55	.15	3.50	(6)	1.00
	Perf. 10½ x 11					
1865	35¢ Charles R. Drew, MD, June 3, 1981	.65	.15	2.75	(4)	1.25
1866	37¢ Robert Millikan, Jan. 26, 1982	.70	.15	3.25	(4)	1.25
	Perf. 11					
1867	39¢ Grenville Clark, May 20, 1985	.70	.15	4.25	(6)	1.25
a	Vertical pair, imperf. horizontally	600.00				
b	Vertical pair, imperf. between	1,250.00				
1868	40¢ Lillian M. Gilbreth, Feb. 24, 1984	.70	.15	4.60	(6)	1.25
1869	50¢ Chester W. Nimitz, Feb. 22, 1985	.90	.15	4.50	(4)	1.25

1870-73 Not assigned

	Issues of 1981, Perf. 11	Un	U	PB/PNC	#	FDC	Q
1874	15¢ Everett Dirksen, Jan. 4	.28	.15	1.25	(4)	1.00	160,155,000
	Black Heritage Issue, Whitney Moore Young, Jan. 30						
1875	15¢ Whitney Moore Young at Desk	.28	.15	1.40	(4)	1.00	159,505,000
	Flower Issue, April 23						
1876	18¢ Rose	.35	.15			1.00	52,654,000
1877	18¢ Camellia	.35	.15			1.00	52,654,000
1878	18¢ Dahlia	.35	.15			1.00	52,654,000
1879	18¢ Lily	.35	.15			1.00	52,654,000
a	Block of 4, #1876-79	1.40	.85	1.65	(4)	2.50	
	Wildlife Booklet Issue, May 14						
1880	18¢ Bighorn Sheep	.35	.15			1.00	
1881	18¢ Puma	.35	.15			1.00	
1882	18¢ Harbor Seal	.35	.15			1.00	
1883	18¢ Bison	.35	.15			1.00	
1884	18¢ Brown Bear	.35	.15			1.00	
1885	18¢ Polar Bear	.35	.15			1.00	
1886	18¢ Elk (Wapiti)	.35	.15			1.00	
1887	18¢ Moose	.35	.15			1.00	
1888	18¢ White-Tailed Deer	.35	.15			1.00	
1889	18¢ Pronghorn Antelope	.35	.15			1.00	
a	Booklet pane of 10, #1880-89	9.00	—			5.00	
	#1880-89 issued only in booklets. All stamps are imperf. at one side or imperf. at one side and bottom.						
	Flag and Anthem Issue, April 24						
1890	18¢ "...for amber waves of grain"	.32	.15	2.00	(6)	1.00	
a	Imperf. pair	100.00					
b	Vertical pair, imperf. horizontally	—					
	Coil Stamp, Perf. 10 Vertically						
1891	18¢ "...from sea to shining sea"	.36	.15	4.75	(3)	1.00	
a	Imperf. pair	20.00					
	Beginning with #1891, all coil stamps except #1947 feature a small plate number at the bottom of the design at varying intervals in a roll, depending on the press used. The basic "plate number coil" (PNC) collecting unit is a strip of three stamps, with the plate number appearing on the middle stamp. PNC values are for the most common plate number.						
	Booklet Stamps, Perf. 11						
1892	6¢ USA Circle of Stars, single from booklet (1893a)	.55	.15			1.00	
1893	18¢ "...for purple mountain majesties," single from booklet (1893a)	.32	.15			1.00	
a	Booklet pane of 8 (2 #1892 & 6 #1893)	3.25	—			2.50	
b	As "a," imperf. vertically between	*80.00*	—				
	#1892-93 issued only in booklets. All stamps are imperf. at one side or imperf. at one side and bottom.						
	Flag Over Supreme Court Issue, Dec. 17 (Except #1896b, issued June 1, 1982)						
1894	20¢ Flag Over Supreme Court	.35	.15	2.25	(6)	1.00	
a	Imperf. pair	40.00					
b	Vertical pair, imperf. horizontally	*650.00*					
c	Dark blue omitted	*90.00*					
d	Black omitted	*300.00*					
	Coil Stamp, Perf. 10 Vertically						
1895	20¢ Flag Over Supreme Court (1894)	.35	.15	4.00	(3)	1.00	
a	Imperf. pair	10.00					
b	Black omitted	40.00					
c	Blue omitted	—					
e	Untagged (Bureau precanceled)	.50	.50	45.00	(3)		

Rose USA 18c   Camellia USA 18c

Dahlia USA 18c   Lily USA 18c

1874   **1875**

1876	**1877**	**1879a**
1878	**1879**	

...for purple mountains majesties

1880	**1881**	**1889a**
1882	**1883**	
1884	**1885**	
1886	**1887**	
1888	**1889**	

1892   **1893a**

1893

...for amber waves of grain   ...from sea to shining sea

Omnibus 1880s
USA 1c

897

Locomotive 1870s
USA 2c

1897A

Handcar 1880s
USA 3c

1898

Stagecoach 1890s
USA 4c

1898A

Motorcycle
1913
USA 5c

899

Sleigh 1880s
USA 5.2c Nonprofit Org.

1900

Bicycle 1870s
USA 5.9c

1901

Baby Buggy 1880s
USA 7.4c

1902

Mail Wagon 1880s
USA 9.3c Bulk Rate

903

Hansom Cab 1890s
USA 10.9c Bulk Rate

1904

RR Caboose 1890s
USA 11c Bulk Rate

1905

Electric Auto 1917
USA 17c

906

Surrey 1890s
USA 18c

1907

Fire Pumper
1860s
USA 20c

1908

USA $9.35

The Gift of Self
USA 18c
American Red Cross
1881-1981

SAVINGS AND LOANS
SAVE
USA 18c

	Issues of 1981 (continued), Perf. 11 x 10½	Un	U	PB/PNC/LP	#	FDC	Q
	Booklet Stamp						
1896	20¢ Flag over Supreme Court (1894), single from booklet	.35	.15			1.00	
a	Booklet pane of 6	2.50	—			6.00	
b	Booklet pane of 10, June 1, 1982	4.25	—			10.00	
	Issues of 1981-84, Perf. 10 Vertically						
	Coil Stamps, Transportation Issue (See also #2123-36, 2225-26, 2228, 2231, 2252-66, 2452-53A, 2457, 2464, 2468)						
1897	1¢ Omnibus 1880s, Aug. 19, 1983	.15	.15	.55	(3)	1.00	
b	Imperf. pair	700.00		—	(3)		
1897A	2¢ Locomotive 1870s, May 20, 1982	.15	.15	.50	(3)	1.00	
e	Imperf. pair	50.00		—	(3)		
1898	3¢ Handcar 1880s, Mar. 25, 1983	.15	.15	.95	(3)	1.00	
1898A	4¢ Stagecoach 1890s, Aug. 19, 1982	.15	.15	1.65	(3)	1.00	
b	Untagged (Bureau precanceled)	.15	.15	4.75	(3)	1.00	
c	As "b," imperf. pair	700.00					
d	Imperf. pair	900.00	—				
1899	5¢ Motorcycle 1913, Oct. 10, 1983	.15	.15	.25	(3)	1.00	
a	Imperf. pair	—					
1900	5.2¢ Sleigh 1880s, Mar. 21, 1983	.15	.15	8.00	(3)	1.00	
a	Untagged (Bureau precanceled)	.15	.15	10.00	(3)	1.00	
1901	5.9¢ Bicycle 1870s, Feb. 17, 1982	.18	.15	9.00	(3)	1.00	
a	Untagged (Bureau precanceled)	.18	.18	20.00	(3)	1.00	
b	As "a," imperf. pair	200.00		—	(2)		
1902	7.4¢ Baby Buggy 1880s, April 7, 1984	.18	.15	8.50	(3)	1.00	
a	Untagged (Bureau precanceled)	.20	.20	3.75	(3)	1.00	
1903	9.3¢ Mail Wagon 1880s, Dec. 15, 1981	.25	.15	8.00	(3)	1.00	
a	Untagged (Bureau precanceled)	.22	.22	4.00	(3)	1.00	
b	As "a," imperf. pair	140.00		—	(2)		
1904	10.9¢ Hansom Cab 1890s, Mar. 26, 1982	.24	.15	16.00	(3)	1.00	
a	Untagged (Bureau precanceled)	.24	.24	27.50	(3)	1.00	
b	As "a," imperf. pair	175.00		—	(2)		
1905	11¢ RR Caboose 1890s, Feb. 3, 1984	.24	.15	4.00	(3)	1.00	
a	Untagged (Bureau precanceled)	.24	.15	3.25	(3)	1.00	
1906	17¢ Electric Auto 1917, June 25, 1981	.32	.15	3.00	(3)	1.00	
a	Untagged (Bureau precanceled)	.35	.35	4.75	(3)	1.00	
b	Imperf. pair	165.00		—	(2)		
c	As "a," imperf. pair	650.00		—	(2)		
1907	18¢ Surrey 1890s, May 18, 1981	.34	.15	4.00	(3)	1.00	
a	Imperf. pair	120.00		—	(2)		
1908	20¢ Fire Pumper 1860s, Dec. 10, 1981	.32	.15	3.00	(3)	1.00	
a	Imperf. pair	110.00		300.00	(2)		

Values for plate # coil strips of 3 stamps for #1897-1908 are for the most common plate numbers. Other plate #s and strips of 5 stamps may have higher values.

	Issue of 1983, Express Mail Booklet Issue, Aug. 12, Perf. 10 Vertically						
1909	$9.35 Eagle and Moon, single from booklet	22.50	14.00			45.00	
a	Booklet pane of 3	62.50	—			125.00	

#1909 issued only in booklets. All stamps are imperf. at top and bottom or imperf. at top, bottom and right side.

	Issues of 1981 (continued), Perf. 10½ x 11						
1910	18¢ American Red Cross, May 1	.32	.15	1.35	(4)	1.00	165,175,000
	Perf. 11						
1911	18¢ Savings and Loans, May 8	.32	.15	1.50	(4)	1.00	107,240,000

	Issues of 1981 (continued), Perf. 11	Un	U	PB	#	FDC	Q
	Space Achievement Issue, May 21						
1912	18¢ Exploring the Moon—Moon Walk	.32	.15			1.00	42,227,375
1913	18¢ Benefiting Mankind (upper left)—Columbia Space Shuttle	.32	.15			1.00	42,227,375
1914	18¢ Benefiting Mankind (upper right)	.32	.15			1.00	42,227,375
1915	18¢ Understanding the Sun—Skylab	.32	.15			1.00	42,227,375
1916	18¢ Probing the Planets—Pioneer II	.32	.15			1.00	42,227,375
1917	18¢ Benefiting Mankind (lower left)—Columbia Space Shuttle	.32	.15			1.00	42,227,375
1918	18¢ Benefiting Mankind (lower right)	.32	.15			1.00	42,227,375
1919	18¢ Comprehending the Universe—Telescope	.32	.15			1.00	42,227,375
a	Block of 8, #1912-19	3.00	2.75	3.00	(8)	3.00	
b	As "a," imperf.	8,000.00					
1920	18¢ Professional Management, June 18	.32	.15	1.40	(4)	1.00	99,420,000
	Preservation of Wildlife Habitats Issue, June 26						
1921	18¢ Save Wetland Habitats— Great Blue Heron	.35	.15			1.00	44,732,500
1922	18¢ Save Grassland Habitats— Badger	.35	.15			1.00	44,732,500
1923	18¢ Save Mountain Habitats— Grizzly Bear	.35	.15			1.00	44,732,500
1924	18¢ Save Woodland Habitats— Ruffled Grouse	.35	.15			1.00	44,732,500
a	Block of 4, #1921-24	1.40	1.00	1.90	(4)	2.50	
1925	18¢ International Year of the Disabled, June 29	.32	.15	1.40	(4)	1.00	100,265,000
a	Vertical pair, imperf. horizontally	2,750.00					
1926	18¢ Edna St. Vincent Millay, July 10	.32	.15	1.40	(4)	1.00	99,615,000
a	Black omitted	400.00	—				
1927	18¢ Alcoholism, Aug. 19	.42	.15	15.00	(6)	1.00	97,535,000
a	Imperf. pair	350.00					

What's a timber line?

The line on a mountain beyond which trees cannot grow is called the timber line. Trees can't grow past this line because of the cold temperatures, and hardly any plants or animals live beyond this point. Below the timber line, however, loggers and hunters find much moss- and shrub-fed plant and animal life. **(#1923)**

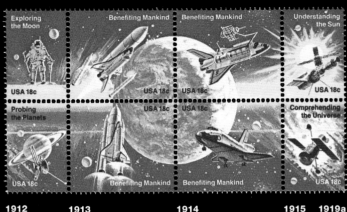

1912   1913   1914   1915   1919a

1916   1917   1918   1919

1920

1921   1922   1924a

1923   1924

1925

1926

1927

1928   **1929**   **1931a**

1930   **1931**

1932   **1933**

1934   **1935**   **1936**

1937   **1938**   **1938a**

1939   **1940**

1941

	Issues of 1981 (continued), Perf. 11	Un	U	PB	#	FDC	Q
	American Architecture Issue, Aug. 28						
1928	18¢ NYU Library, by Sanford White	.42	.15			1.00	41,827,000
1929	18¢ Biltmore House, by Richard Morris Hunt	.42	.15			1.00	41,827,000
1930	18¢ Palace of the Arts, by Bernard Maybeck	.42	.15			1.00	41,827,000
1931	18¢ National Farmer's Bank, by Louis Sullivan	.42	.15			1.00	41,827,000
a	Block of 4, #1928-31	1.75	1.00	2.00	(4)	2.50	
	American Sports Issue, Babe Zaharias and Bobby Jones, Sept. 22, Perf. 10½ x 11						
1932	18¢ Babe Zaharias Holding Trophy	.32	.15	1.75	(4)	1.00	101,625,000
1933	18¢ Bobby Jones Teeing off	.32	.15	1.50	(4)	1.00	99,170,000
	Perf. 11						
1934	18¢ Frederic Remington, Oct. 9	.32	.15	1.50	(4)	1.00	101,155,000
a	Vertical pair, imperf. between	250.00					
b	Brown omitted	600.00					
1935	18¢ James Hoban, Oct. 13	.32	.16	1.60	(4)	1.00	101,200,000
1936	20¢ James Hoban, Oct. 13	.35	.15	1.65	(4)	1.00	167,360,000
	American Bicentennial Issue, Yorktown-Virginia Capes, Oct. 16						
1937	18¢ Battle of Yorktown 1781	.35	.15			1.00	81,210,000
1938	18¢ Battle of the Virginia Capes 1781	.35	.15			1.00	81,210,000
a	Attached pair, #1937-38	.90	.15	1.90	(4)	1.50	
b	As "a," black omitted	450.00					
	Christmas Issue, Oct. 28						
1939	20¢ Madonna and Child, by Botticelli	.38	.15	1.60	(4)	1.00	597,720,000
a	Imperf. pair	110.00					
b	Vertical pair, imperf. horizontally	1,650.00					
1940	20¢ Felt Bear on Sleigh	.38	.15	1.60	(4)	1.00	792,600,000
a	Imperf. pair	250.00					
b	Vertical pair, imperf. horizontally	—					
1941	20¢ John Hanson, Nov. 5	.38	.15	1.60	(4)	1.00	167,130,000

How did a song signify British surrender?

Britain's General Cornwallis surrendered his troops to American and French forces in Yorktown, Virginia on October 19, 1781. Cornwallis' troops, blockaded from both land and sea, had hoped to ferry his forces across the York River Oct. 16, but a storm had made the attempt useless.

Once the British troops had surrendered, a British band at Yorktown played a tune called "The World Turned Upside Down." The Treaty of Paris — which recognized the independence of the United States — was signed soon after.

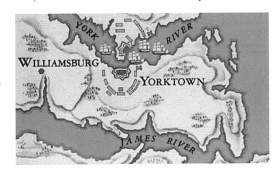

(#1937)

	Issues of 1981 (continued), Perf. 11	Un	U	PB/LP	#	FDC	Q
	Desert Plants Issue, Dec. 11						
1942	20¢ Barrel Cactus	.35	.15			1.00	47,890,000
1943	20¢ Agave	.35	.15			1.00	47,890,000
1944	20¢ Beavertail Cactus	.35	.15			1.00	47,890,000
1945	20¢ Saguaro	.35	.15			1.00	47,890,000
a	Block of 4, #1942-45	1.50	.15	1.60	(4)	2.50	
b	As "a," deep brown omitted	7,500.00					
c	#1945 vertical pair, imperf.	5,250.00					
	Perf. 11 x 10¹/₂						
1946	20¢ C Stamp, Oct. 11	.38	.15	1.85	(4)	1.00	
	Coil Stamp, Perf. 10 Vertically						
1947	20¢ brown Eagle (1946), Oct. 11	.60	.15	1.50	(2)	1.00	
a	Imperf. pair	1,750.00		—	(2)		
	Booklet Stamp, Perf. 11 x 10¹/₂						
1948	20¢ brown Eagle (1946), single from booklet	.38	.15			1.00	
a	Booklet pane of 10, Oct. 11	4.50	—			3.50	
	Issues of 1982, Bighorn Sheep Booklet Issue, Jan. 8, Perf. 11						
1949	20¢ Bighorn Sheep, single from booklet	.50	.15			1.00	
a	Booklet pane of 10	5.00	—			6.00	
b	As "a," imperf. between	100.00					
	#1949 issued only in booklets. All stamps are imperf. at one side or imperf. at one side and bottom.						
1950	20¢ Franklin D. Roosevelt, Jan. 30	.38	.15	1.60	(4)	1.00	163,939,200
	Perf. 11 x 10¹/₂						
1951	20¢ Love, Feb. 1	.38	.15	1.60	(4)	1.00	446,745,000
a	Perf. 11	.48	.15	2.00	(4)		
b	Imperf. pair	275.00					
c	Blue omitted	200.00					
	Perf. 11						
1952	20¢ George Washington, Feb. 22	.38	.15	1.60	(4)	1.00	180,700,000

What was the Warm Springs Foundation?

Polio crippled Franklin Delano Roosevelt — President of the U.S. from 1933 to 1945 — in 1921. Roosevelt fought his illness by swimming in warm mineral water pools at Warm Springs, Ga. While there he met many polio patients who said they couldn't afford to pay for treatment, so Roosevelt bought the springs and later established the Warm Springs Foundation, which offered low-cost treatment for polio patients. **(#1950)**

1942   **1943**   **1945** **1945a**

1944

1946   **1949**

1950   **1951**

1952

	Issues of 1982 (continued), Perf. 10½ x 11	Un	U	FDC	Q
	State Birds & Flowers Issue, Apr. 14				
1953	20¢ Alabama	.45	.25	1.25	13,339,000
1954	20¢ Alaska	.45	.25	1.25	13,339,000
1955	20¢ Arizona	.45	.25	1.25	13,339,000
1956	20¢ Arkansas	.45	.25	1.25	13,339,000
1957	20¢ California	.45	.25	1.25	13,339,000
1958	20¢ Colorado	.45	.25	1.25	13,339,000
1959	20¢ Connecticut	.45	.25	1.25	13,339,000
1960	20¢ Delaware	.45	.25	1.25	13,339,000
1961	20¢ Florida	.45	.25	1.25	13,339,000
1962	20¢ Georgia	.45	.25	1.25	13,339,000
1963	20¢ Hawaii	.45	.25	1.25	13,339,000
1964	20¢ Idaho	.45	.25	1.25	13,339,000
1965	20¢ Illinois	.45	.25	1.25	13,339,000
1966	20¢ Indiana	.45	.25	1.25	13,339,000
1967	20¢ Iowa	.45	.25	1.25	13,339,000
1968	20¢ Kansas	.45	.25	1.25	13,339,000
1969	20¢ Kentucky	.45	.25	1.25	13,339,000
1970	20¢ Louisiana	.45	.25	1.25	13,339,000
1971	20¢ Maine	.45	.25	1.25	13,339,000
1972	20¢ Maryland	.45	.25	1.25	13,339,000
1973	20¢ Massachusetts	.45	.25	1.25	13,339,000
1974	20¢ Michigan	.45	.25	1.25	13,339,000
1975	20¢ Minnesota	.45	.25	1.25	13,339,000
1976	20¢ Mississippi	.45	.25	1.25	13,339,000
1977	20¢ Missouri	.45	.25	1.25	13,339,000

Where do larks usually live?

Larks enjoy living in wide open spaces, such as deserts, fields, grasslands and tundras. So you can bet you won't find too many of them in the city. You *will* find them in North America, more often in the spacious areas of the West, and Colorado is no exception. That's why Colorado chose the Lark Bunting as its state bird. **(#1958)**

255

	Issues of 1982 (continued), Perf. 10½ x 11						
		Un	U	PB	#	FDC	Q
	State Birds & Flowers Issue (continued), Apr. 14						
1978	20¢ Montana	.45	.25			1.25	13,339,000
1979	20¢ Nebraska	.45	.25			1.25	13,339,000
1980	20¢ Nevada	.45	.25			1.25	13,339,000
1981	20¢ New Hampshire	.45	.25			1.25	13,339,000
1982	20¢ New Jersey	.45	.25			1.25	13,339,000
1983	20¢ New Mexico	.45	.25			1.25	13,339,000
1984	20¢ New York	.45	.25			1.25	13,339,000
1985	20¢ North Carolina	.45	.25			1.25	13,339,000
1986	20¢ North Dakota	.45	.25			1.25	13,339,000
1987	20¢ Ohio	.45	.25			1.25	13,339,000
1988	20¢ Oklahoma	.45	.25			1.25	13,339,000
1989	20¢ Oregon	.45	.25			1.25	13,339,000
1990	20¢ Pennsylvania	.45	.25			1.25	13,339,000
1991	20¢ Rhode Island	.45	.25			1.25	13,339,000
1992	20¢ South Carolina	.45	.25			1.25	13,339,000
1993	20¢ South Dakota	.45	.25			1.25	13,339,000
1994	20¢ Tennessee	.45	.25			1.25	13,339,000
1995	20¢ Texas	.45	.25			1.25	13,339,000
1996	20¢ Utah	.45	.25			1.25	13,339,000
1997	20¢ Vermont	.45	.25			1.25	13,339,000
1998	20¢ Virginia	.45	.25			1.25	13,339,000
1999	20¢ Washington	.45	.25			1.25	13,339,000
2000	20¢ West Virginia	.45	.25			1.25	13,339,000
2001	20¢ Wisconsin	.45	.25			1.25	13,339,000
2002	20¢ Wyoming	.45	.25			1.25	13,339,000
a	Any single, perf. 11	.50	.30				
b	Pane of 50	22.50	—			30.00	
c	Pane of 50, perf. 11	25.00	—				
d	Pane of 50, imperf.	—					

How fast can the roadrunner run?

The roadrunner — also known as the chaparral cock or snake killer — is a member of the cuckoo family, and can run up to 15 miles an hour. While roadrunners have the capabilities to fly, they rarely do, preferring to stay on the ground. The roadrunner — New Mexico's state bird — lives in the Southwestern U.S. and Mexico. **(#1983)**

Montana USA 20c  *Western Meadowlark & Bitterroot*	Nebraska USA 20c  *Western Meadowlark & Goldenrod*	Nevada USA 20c  *Mountain Bluebird & Sagebrush*	New Hampshire USA 20c  *Purple Finch & Lilac*	New Jersey USA 20c  *American Goldfinch &*
1978	**1979**	**1980**	**1981**	**1982**
New Mexico USA 20c  *Roadrunner & Yucca Flower*	New York USA 20c *Eastern Bluebird & Rose*	North Carolina USA 20c  *Cardinal & Flowering Dogwood*	North Dakota USA 20c  *Western Meadowlark & Wild Prairie Rose*	Ohio USA 20c  *Cardinal & Red Carnation*
1983	**1984**	**1985**	**1986**	**1987**
Oklahoma USA 20c *Scissor-tailed Flycatcher & Mistletoe*	Oregon USA 20c  *Western Meadowlark & Oregon Grape*	Pennsylvania USA 20c  *Ruffed Grouse & Mountain Laurel*	Rhode Island USA 20c  *Rhode Island Red & Violet*	South Carolina USA 20c  *Carolina Wren & Carolina Jessamine*
1988	**1989**	**1990**	**1991**	**1992**
South Dakota USA 20c  *Ring-Necked Pheasant & Pasqueflower*	Tennessee USA 20c  *Mockingbird & Iris*	Texas USA 20c  *Mockingbird & Bluebonnet*	Utah USA 20c  *California Gull & Sego Lily*	Vermont USA 20c  *Hermit Thrush & Red Clover*
1993	**1994**	**1995**	**1996**	**1997**
Virginia USA 20c  *Cardinal & Flowering Dogwood*	Washington USA 20c  *American Goldfinch & Rhododendron*	West Virginia USA 20c  *Cardinal & Rhododendron Maximum*	Wisconsin USA 20c  *Robin & Wood Violet*	Wyoming USA 20c *Western Meadowlark & Indian Paintbrush*

Library of Congress
USA 20c

Wise shoppers stretch dollars
Consumer Education
USA 20c

2003 **2004** **2005**

USA 20c
Solar energy Knoxville World's Fair

USA 20c
Synthetic fuels Knoxville World's Fair

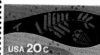
USA 20c
Breeder reactor Knoxville World's Fair

USA 20c
Fossil fuels Knoxville World's Fair

Horatio Alger
USA 20c

THE BARRYMORES
Performing Arts USA 20c

2006 **2007** **2009a** **2010** **2012**

2008 **2009**

Aging together
USA 20c

2011

Dr. Mary Walker
Army Surgeon
Medal of Honor
USA 20c

International Peace Garden
1932 1982 USA 20c

America's
ABC
Libraries
XYZ
USA 20c
Legacies To Mankind

Jackie Robinson
Black Heritage USA 20c

2013 **2014** **2015** **2016**

Touro Synagogue
Newport RI 1763
To bigotry, no sanction.
To persecution, no assistance.
George Washington
USA 20c

Frank Lloyd Wright 1867-1959 Fallingwater Mill Run PA
Architecture USA 20c

Mies van der Rohe 1886-1969 Illinois Inst Tech Chicago
Architecture USA 20c

2017

USA 20c
Wolf Trap Farm Park
for the performing arts

Walter Gropius 1883-1969 Gropius House Lincoln MA
Architecture USA 20c

Eero Saarinen 1910-1961 Dulles Airport Washington DC
Architecture USA 20c

	Issues of 1982 (continued), Perf. 11	Un	U	PB/PNC/LP	#	FDC	Q
2003	20¢ USA/The Netherlands, Apr. 20	.38	.15	3.50	(6)	1.00	109,245,000
a	Imperf. pair	400.00					
2004	20¢ Library of Congress, Apr. 21	.38	.15	1.60	(4)	1.00	112,535,000
	Coil Stamp, Perf. 10 Vertically						
2005	20¢ Consumer Education, Apr. 27	.75	.15	35.00	(3)	1.00	
a	Imperf. pair	100.00		400.00	(2)		

Value for plate no. coil strip of 3 stamps is for most common plate nos. Other plate nos. and strips of 5 stamps may have higher values.

	Knoxville World's Fair Issue, Apr. 29, Perf. 11	Un	U	PB/PNC/LP	#	FDC	Q
2006	20¢ Solar Energy	.40	.15			1.00	31,160,000
2007	20¢ Synthetic Fuels	.40	.15			1.00	31,160,000
2008	20¢ Breeder Reactor	.40	.15			1.00	31,160,000
2009	20¢ Fossil Fuels	.40	.15			1.00	31,160,000
a	Block of 4, #2006-09	1.75	1.00	1.75	(4)	2.50	
2010	20¢ Horatio Alger, Apr. 30	.38	.15	1.60	(4)	1.00	107,605,000
2011	20¢ Aging Together, May 21	.38	.15	1.60	(4)	1.00	173,160,000
	Performing Arts Issue, The Barrymores, June 8						
2012	20¢ Portraits of John, Ethel and Lionel Barrymore	.38	.15	1.60	(4)	1.00	107,285,000
2013	20¢ Dr. Mary Walker, June 10	.38	.15	1.60	(4)	1.00	109,040,000
2014	20¢ International Peace Garden, June 30	.38	.15	1.60	(4)	1.00	183,270,000
a	Black and green omitted	250.00					
2015	20¢ America's Libraries, July 13	.38	.15	1.60	(4)	1.00	169,495,000
a	Vertical pair, imperf. horizontally	300.00					
	Black Heritage Issue, Jackie Robinson, Aug. 2, Perf. 10½ x 11						
2016	20¢ Jackie Robinson Portrait and Robinson Stealing Home Plate	1.00	.15	5.25	(4)	2.00	164,235,000
	Perf. 11						
2017	20¢ Touro Synagogue, Aug. 22	.38	.15	11.50	(20)	1.00	110,130,000
a	Imperf. pair	1,250.00					
2018	20¢ Wolf Trap Farm Park, Sept. 1	.38	.15	1.60	(4)	1.00	110,995,000
	American Architecture Issue, Sept. 30						
2019	20¢ Fallingwater, by Frank Lloyd Wright	.38	.15			1.00	41,335,000
2020	20¢ Illinois Institute of Technology, by Mies van der Rohe	.38	.15			1.00	41,335,000
2021	20¢ Gropius House, by Walter Gropius	.38	.15			1.00	41,335,000
2022	20¢ Dulles Airport by Eeno Saarinen	.38	.15			1.00	41,335,000
a	Block of 4, #2019-22	1.60	1.00	2.25	(4)	2.50	

The stamp listings contain a number of "a," "b," "c," etc. additions which include recognized varieties and errors. These listings are as complete as space permits.

	Issues of 1982 (continued), Perf. 11	Un	U	PB	#	FDC	Q
2023	20¢ St. Francis of Assisi, Oct. 7	.38	.15	1.60	(4)	1.00	174,180,000
2024	20¢ Ponce de Leon, Oct. 12	.38	.15	3.25	(6)	1.00	110,261,000
a	Imperf. pair	600.00					
	Christmas Issue						
2025	13¢ Puppy and Kitten, Nov. 3	.26	.15	1.25	(4)	1.00	234,010,000
a	Imperf. pair	600.00					
2026	20¢ Madonna and Child, by Tiepolo, Oct. 28	.38	.15	11.00	(20)	1.00	703,295,000
a	Imperf. pair	150.00					
b	Horizontal pair, imperf. vertically	—					
c	Vertical pair, imperf. horizontally	—					
	Seasons Greetings Issue, Oct. 28						
2027	20¢ Children Sledding	.50	.15			1.00	197,220,000
2028	20¢ Children Building a Snowman	.50	.15			1.00	197,220,000
2029	20¢ Children Skating	.50	.15			1.00	197,220,000
2030	20¢ Children Trimming a Tree	.50	.15			1.00	197,220,000
a	Block of 4, #2027-30	2.00	1.00	2.50	(4)	2.50	
b	As "a," imperf.	3,000.00					
c	As "a," imperf. horizontally	—					
	Issues of 1983						
2031	20¢ Science & Industry, Jan. 19	.38	.15	1.60	(4)	1.00	118,555,000
a	Black omitted	1,400.00					
	Balloons Issue, March 31						
2032	20¢ Intrepid, 1861	.38	.15			1.00	56,557,000
2033	20¢ Hot Air Ballooning (wording lower right)	.38	.15			1.00	56,557,000
2034	20¢ Hot Air Ballooning (wording upper left)	.38	.15			1.00	56,557,000
2035	20¢ Explorer II, 1935	.38	.15			1.00	56,557,000
a	Block of 4, #2032-35	1.65	1.00	1.75	(4)	2.50	
b	As "a," imperf.	—					
2036	20¢ U.S./Sweden Treaty, Mar. 24	.38	.15	1.60	(4)	1.00	118,225,000
2037	20¢ Civilian Conservation Corps, Apr. 5	.38	.15	1.60	(4)	1.00	114,290,000
a	Imperf. pair	2,500.00					
2038	20¢ Joseph Priestley, Apr. 13	.38	.15	1.60	(4)	1.00	165,000,000
2039	20¢ Voluntarism, Apr. 20	.40	.15	3.00	(6)	1.00	120,430,000
a	Imperf. pair	850.00					
2040	20¢ Concord—German Immigration, Apr. 29	.38	.15	1.60	(4)	1.00	117,025,000

Who created two million jobs during the Depression?

Over two million men served in the Civilian Conservation Corps, which was part of President Franklin Delano Roosevelt's New Deal, enacted in 1933. The Corps provided jobs and training to unemployed young men, and developed natural resources nationwide by planting trees, building dams and fighting forest fires. Congress abolished the Corps in 1942 once WWII had begun and the country's attention was diverted from the Depression. **(#2037)**

2023

2024

2025

2026

2027

2029

2028

2030

2030a

2031

2032

2034

2033

2035

2035a

2036

2037

2039

2040

2038

2041

2042

2043

2044

2045

2046

2047

2048
2050

2049
2051

2051a

2052

2053

2055
2057

2056
2058

2058a

2054

First American streetcar, New York City, 1832 — USA 20c
Early electric streetcar, Montgomery, Ala., 1886 — USA 20c
"Bobtail" horsecar, Sulphur Rock, Ark., 1926 — USA 20c
St. Charles streetcar, New Orleans, La., 1923 — USA 20c

2059   **2060**   **2062a**
2061   **2062**

2063

2064

2065

2066

2071

2067   **2068**   **2070a**
2069   **2070**

265

2072   **2073**   **2074**   **2075**

2080

2081

2076   **2077**   **2079a**
2078   **2079**

2086

2087

2082   **2083**   **2085a**
2084   **2085**

	Issues of 1984 (continued), Perf. 11 x 10½	Un	U	PB	#	FDC	Q
2072	20¢ Love, Jan. 31	.40	.15	11.50	(20)	1.00	554,675,000
a	Horizontal pair, imperf. vertically	200.00					
	Black Heritage Issue, Carter G. Woodson, Feb. 1, Perf. 11						
2073	20¢ Carter G. Woodson Holding History Book	.40	.15	1.75	(4)	1.00	120,000,000
a	Horizontal pair, imperf. vertically	—					
2074	20¢ Soil and Water Conservation, Feb. 6	.38	.15	1.60	(4)	1.00	106,975,000
2075	20¢ 50th Anniversary of Credit Union Act, Feb. 10	.38	.15	1.60	(4)	1.00	107,325,000
	Orchids Issue, Mar. 5						
2076	20¢ Wild Pink	.42	.15			1.00	76,728,000
2077	20¢ Yellow Lady's-Slipper	.42	.15			1.00	76,728,000
2078	20¢ Spreading Pogonia	.42	.15			1.00	76,728,000
2079	20¢ Pacific Calypso	.42	.15			1.00	76,728,000
a	Block of 4, #2076-79	1.80	1.00	2.00	(4)	2.50	
2080	20¢ 25th Anniversary of Hawaii Statehood, Mar. 12	.40	.15	1.70	(4)	1.00	120,000,000
2081	20¢ National Archives, Apr. 16	.40	.15	1.70	(4)	1.00	108,000,000
	Olympic Summer Games Issue, May 4 (See also #2048-52, C101-12)						
2082	20¢ Diving	.60	.15			1.00	78,337,500
2083	20¢ Long Jump	.60	.15			1.00	78,337,500
2084	20¢ Wrestling	.60	.15			1.00	78,337,500
2085	20¢ Kayak	.60	.15			1.00	78,337,500
a	Block of 4, #2082-85	2.40	1.00	3.25	(4)	2.50	
2086	20¢ Louisiana World Exposition, May 11	.38	.15	1.60	(4)	1.00	130,320,000
2087	20¢ Health Research, May 17	.40	.15	1.70	(4)	1.00	120,000,000

What's a Calypso?

Depending on who you ask, you could get a few different answers. In Homer's *Odyssey*, Calypso was a sea nymph who kept Odyssus on her island for seven years.
Calypso is also known as a type of music from Trinidad, often sung as a satirical ballad. But the Pacific Calypso, also known as *Calypso bulbosa*, is an orchid that grows in swampy regions of the Northern Hemisphere. **(#2079)**

	Issues of 1984 (continued), Perf. 11	Un	U	PB	#	FDC	Q
	Performing Arts Issue, Douglas Fairbanks, May 23						
2088	20¢ Douglas Fairbanks Portrait and Fairbanks in Swashbuckling Pirate Role	.38	.15	12.00	(20)	1.00	117,050,000
	American Sports Issue, Jim Thorpe, May 24						
2089	20¢ Jim Thorpe on Football Field	.40	.15	1.85	(4)	1.50	115,725,000
	Performing Arts Issue, John McCormack, June 6						
2090	20¢ John McCormack Portrait and McCormack in Tenor Role	.40	.15	1.70	(4)	1.00	116,600,000
2091	20¢ 25th Anniversary of St. Lawrence Seaway, June 26	.40	.15	1.70	(4)	1.00	120,000,000
2092	20¢ Migratory Bird Hunting and Preservation Act, July 2	.50	.15	2.50	(4)	1.00	123,575,000
a	Horizontal pair, imperf. vertically	400.00					
2093	20¢ Roanoke Voyages, July 13	.38	.15	1.60	(4)	1.00	120,000,000
	Pair with full horizontal gutter between	—					
	Literary Arts Issue, Herman Melville, Aug. 1						
2094	20¢ Herman Melville	.38	.15	1.60	(4)	1.00	117,125,000
2095	20¢ Horace Moses, Aug. 6	.45	.15	3.50	(6)	1.00	117,225,000
2096	20¢ Smokey the Bear, Aug. 13	.38	.15	1.75	(4)	1.00	95,525,000
a	Horizontal pair, imperf. between	300.00					
b	Vertical pair, imperf. between	250.00					
c	Block of 4, imperf. between vertically and horizontally	4,500.00					
	American Sports Issue, Roberto Clemente, Aug. 17						
2097	20¢ Roberto Clemente Wearing Pittsburgh Pirates Cap, Puerto Rican Flag in Background	1.00	.15	6.75	(4)	2.00	119,125,000
a	Horizontal pair, imperf. vertically	1,600.00					
	American Dogs Issue, Sept. 7						
2098	20¢ Beagle and Boston Terrier	.40	.15			1.00	54,065,000
2099	20¢ Chesapeake Bay Retriever and Cocker Spaniel	.40	.15			1.00	54,065,000
2100	20¢ Alaskan Malamute and Collie	.40	.15			1.00	54,065,000
2101	20¢ Black and Tan Coonhound and American Foxhound	.40	.15			1.00	54,065,000
a	Block of 4, #2098-2101	1.75	1.00	2.00	(4)	2.50	

Where's the Okefenokee Swamp?

The Okefenokee Swamp, one of America's wetlands, lies in southeastern Georgia and northeastern Florida. It covers over 700 square miles, about 450 of which have been bought by the U.S. government and set aside as the Okefenokee National Wildlife Refuge. Animals that live in the swamp include many types of birds, bears, bobcats, otters, opossums and alligators, and over 50 kinds of fish live in its waters. **(#2092)**

2088 **2089** **2090**

2091 **2092**

2093

2094 **2095** **2096** **2097**

2098 **2099** **2101a**

2100 **2101**

2102

2103

2104

2105

2106

2107

2108

2109

2110

2111

2114

2115b

2116

	Issues of 1984 (continued), Perf. 11	Un	U	PB/PNC	#	FDC	Q
2102	20¢ Crime Prevention, Sept. 26	.38	.15	1.70	(4)	1.00	120,000,000
2103	20¢ Hispanic Americans, Oct. 31	.38	.15	1.60	(4)	1.00	108,140,000
a	Vertical pair, imperf. horizontally	1,500.00					
2104	20¢ Family Unity, Oct. 1	.40	.15	12.00	(20)	1.00	117,625,000
a	Horizontal pair, imperf. vertically	600.00					
2105	20¢ Eleanor Roosevelt, Oct. 11	.38	.15	1.60	(4)	1.00	112,896,000
2106	20¢ A Nation of Readers, Oct. 16	.38	.15	1.60	(4)	1.00	116,500,000
	Christmas Issue, Oct. 30						
2107	20¢ Madonna and Child, by Fra Filippo Lippi	.40	.15	1.70	(4)	1.00	751,300,000
2108	20¢ Santa Claus	.40	.15	1.70	(4)	1.00	786,225,000
a	Horizontal pair, imperf. vertically	950.00					
	Perf. 10½						
2109	20¢ Vietnam Veterans' Memorial, Nov. 10	.40	.15	1.75	(4)	1.00	105,300,000
	Issues of 1985, Perf. 11						
	Performing Arts Issue, Jerome Kern, Jan. 23						
2110	22¢ Jerome Kern Portrait and Kern Studying Sheet Music	.40	.15	1.75	(4)	1.00	124,500,000
2111	22¢ D Stamp, Feb. 1	.60	.15	4.50	(6)	1.00	
a	Imperf. pair	55.00					
b	Vertical pair, imperf. horizontally	1,350.00					
	Coil Stamp, Perf. 10 Vertically						
2112	22¢ green Eagle (2111), Feb. 1	.60	.15	6.00	(3)	1.00	
a	Imperf. pair	50.00					
	Booklet Stamp, Perf. 11						
2113	22¢ green Eagle (2111), single from booklet	.80	.15			1.00	
a	Booklet pane of 10, Feb. 1	8.00				7.50	
b	As "a," imperf. between horizontally	—					
	Issues of 1985-87, Flag Over Capitol Issue						
2114	22¢ Flag Over Capitol, Mar. 29, 1985	.40	.15	1.80	(4)	1.00	
	Pair with full horizontal gutter between	—					
	Coil Stamp, Perf. 10 Vertically						
2115	22¢ Flag Over Capitol (2114), Mar. 29, 1985	.40	.15	4.00	(3)	1.00	
a	Imperf. pair	10.00					
b	Inscribed "T" at bottom, May 23, 1987	.48	.15	4.00	(3)	1.00	
c	Black field of stars	—	—				
	#2115b issued for test on prephosphored paper. Paper is whiter and colors are brighter than on #2115.						
	Booklet Stamp, Perf. 10 Horizontally						
2116	22¢ Flag over Capitol, single from booklet	.48	.15			1.00	
a	Booklet pane of 5, Mar. 29, 1985	2.50	—			3.50	
	#2116 issued only in booklets. All stamps are imperf. at both sides or imperf. at both sides and bottom.						

	Issues of 1985 (continued), Perf. 10 vertically					
		Un	U	PNC	#	FDC
	Seashells Booklet Issue, Apr. 4					
2117	22¢ Frilled Dogwinkle	.40	.15			1.00
2118	22¢ Reticulated Helmet	.40	.15			1.00
2119	22¢ New England Neptune	.40	.15			1.00
2120	22¢ Calico Scallop	.40	.15			1.00
2121	22¢ Lightning Whelk	.40	.15			1.00
a	Booklet pane of 10	4.00	—			7.50
b	As "a," violet omitted	850.00				
c	As "a," imperf. between vertically	600.00				
e	Strip of 5, #2117-21	2.00	—			
	Express Mail Booklet Issue, Apr. 29					
2122	$10.75 Eagle and Moon, booklet single	17.00	6.75			40.00
a	Booklet pane of 3	52.50	—			95.00
	#2122 issued only in booklets. All stamps are imperf. at top and bottom or at top, bottom and one side.					
	Issues of 1985-89, Coil Stamps, Transportation Issue (See also #1897-1908, 2225-31, 2252-66, 2451-68)					
2123	3.4¢ School Bus 1920s, June 8, 1985	.15	.15	1.00	(3)	1.00
a	Untagged (Bureau precanceled)	.15	.15	5.50	(3)	1.00
2124	4.9¢ Buckboard 1880s, June 21, 1985	.15	.15	1.10	(3)	1.00
a	Untagged (Bureau precanceled)	.16	.16	1.65	(3)	
2125	5.5¢ Star Route Truck 1910s, Nov. 1, 1986	.15	.15	1.75	(3)	1.00
a	Untagged (Bureau precanceled)	.15	.15	1.90	(3)	1.00
2126	6¢ Tricycle 1880s, May 6, 1985	.15	.15	1.40	(3)	1.00
a	Untagged (Bureau precanceled)	.15	.15	2.00	(3)	
b	As "a," imperf. pair	190.00				
2127	7.1¢ Tractor 1920s, Feb. 6, 1987	.15	.15	2.50	(3)	1.00
a	Untagged (Bureau precanceled "Nonprofit org.")	.15	.15	2.75	(3)	5.00
a	Untagged (Bureau precanceled "Nonprofit 5-Digit ZIP + 4"), May 26, 1989	.15	.15	2.50	(3)	1.00
2128	8.3¢ Ambulance 1860s, June 21, 1985	.18	.15	1.50	(3)	1.00
a	Untagged (Bureau precanceled)	.18	.18	1.75	(3)	
2129	8.5¢ Tow Truck 1920s, Jan. 24, 1987	.16	.15	2.75	(3)	1.00
a	Untagged (Bureau precanceled)	.16	.16	2.75	(3)	
2130	10.1¢ Oil Wagon 1890s, Apr. 18, 1985	.22	.15	2.50	(3)	1.00
a	Untagged (Bureau precanceled, black)	.22	.22	2.75	(3)	1.00
a	Untagged (Bureau precanceled, red)	.22	.22	2.50	(3)	1.00
b	As "a," black precancel, imperf. pair	100.00				
b	As "a," red precancel, imperf. pair	15.00				
2131	11¢ Stutz Bearcat 1933, June 11, 1985	.22	.15	1.65	(3)	1.00
2132	12¢ Stanley Steamer 1909, Apr. 2, 1985	.24	.15	2.25	(3)	1.00
a	Untagged (Bureau precanceled)	.24	.24	2.50	(3)	
b	As "a," type II	.24	.24	17.00	(3)	
	Type II has "Stanley Steamer 1909" 1/2mm shorter (171/2mm) than #2132 (18mm).					
2133	12.5¢ Pushcart 1880s, Apr. 18, 1985	.25	.15	2.75	(3)	1.25
a	Untagged (Bureau precanceled)	.25	.25	3.50	(3)	
b	As "a," imperf. pair	50.00				
2134	14¢ Iceboat 1880s, Mar. 23, 1985	.28	.15	2.25	(3)	1.25
a	Imperf. pair	90.00				
2135	17¢ Dog Sled 1920s, Aug. 20, 1986	.30	.15	3.00	(3)	1.25
a	Imperf. pair	500.00				
2136	25¢ Bread Wagon 1880s, Nov. 22, 1986	.45	.15	4.00	(3)	1.25
a	Imperf. pair	10.00				

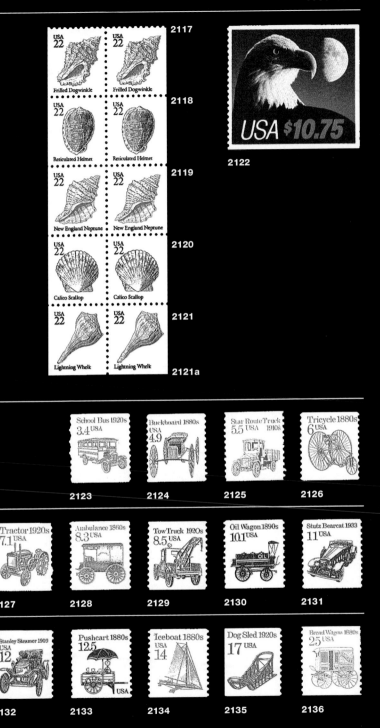

2117

2118

2119

2120

2121

2121a

2122

2123 — School Bus 1920s 3.4 USA

2124 — Buckboard 1880s USA 4.9

2125 — Star Route Truck 5.5 USA 1910s

2126 — Tricycle 1880s 6 USA

2127 — Tractor 1920s 7.1 USA

2128 — Ambulance 1860s 8.3 USA

2129 — Tow Truck 1920s 8.5 USA

2130 — Oil Wagon 1890s 10.1 USA

2131 — Stutz Bearcat 1933 11 USA

2132 — Stanley Steamer 1909 USA 12

2133 — Pushcart 1880s 12.5 USA

2134 — Iceboat 1880s USA 14

2135 — Dog Sled 1920s 17 USA

2136 — Bread Wagon 1880s 25 USA

Frilled Dogwinkle — USA 22
Reticulated Helmet — USA 22
New England Neptune — USA 22
Calico Scallop — USA 22
Lightning Whelk — USA 22

2137

2138   **2139**   **2141a**
2140   **2141**

2142

2143

2144

2145

2146

2147

2149   **2150**

2152   **2153**

	Issues of 1985 (continued), Perf. 11	Un	U	PB/PNC	#	FDC	Q
	Black Heritage Issue, Mary McLeod Bethune, Mar. 5						
2137	22¢ Mary McLeod Bethune Portrait	.40	.15	1.75	(4)	1.00	120,000,000
	American Folk Art Issue, Duck Decoys, Mar. 22						
2138	22¢ Broadbill Decoy	.60	.15			1.00	75,000,000
2139	22¢ Mallard Decoy	.60	.15			1.00	75,000,000
2140	22¢ Canvasback Decoy	.60	.15			1.00	75,000,000
2141	22¢ Redhead Decoy	.60	.15			1.00	75,000,000
a	Block of 4, #2138-41	3.00	1.00	3.50	(4)	2.75	
2142	22¢ Winter Special Olympics, Mar. 25	.40	.15	1.70	(4)	1.00	120,580,000
a	Vertical pair, imperf. horizontally	650.00					
2143	22¢ Love, Apr. 17	.40	.15	1.70	(4)	1.00	729,700,000
a	Imperf. pair	1,750.00					
2144	22¢ Rural Electrification Administration, May 11	.45	.15	22.50	(20)	1.00	124,750,000
2145	22¢ AMERIPEX '86, May 25	.40	.15	1.70	(4)	1.00	203,496,000
a	Red, black and blue omitted	225.00					
b	Red and black omitted	1,250.00					
2146	22¢ Abigail Adams, June 14	.40	.15	1.80	(4)	1.00	126,325,000
a	Imperf. pair	350.00					
2147	22¢ Frederic A. Bartholdi, July 18	.40	.15	1.80	(4)	1.00	130,000,000
2148	Not assigned						
	Coil Stamps, Perf. 10 Vertically						
2149	18¢ George Washington, Washington Monument, Nov. 6	.32	.15	3.00	(3)	1.25	
a	Untagged (Bureau precanceled)	.35	.35	3.25	(3)		
b	Imperf. pair	950.00					
c	As "a," imperf. pair	700.00		4.50	(3)		
2150	21.1¢ Sealed Envelopes, Oct. 22	.40	.15	3.25	(3)	1.25	
a	Untagged (Bureau precanceled)	.38	.38	3.75	(3)		
2151	Not assigned						
	Perf. 11						
2152	22¢ Korean War Veterans, July 26	.40	.15	1.90	(4)	1.00	119,975,000
2153	22¢ Social Security Act, 50th Anniversary Aug. 14	.40	.15	1.90	(4)	1.00	120,000,000

Who wed one president and mothered another?

Abigail Smith Adams wed John Adams, second President of the United States, and was mother to John Quincy Adams, the sixth President.

Adams was not a passive First Lady. A well-educated woman, she promoted women's rights and urged her husband to do the same. She opposed slavery and ensured that her daughter Abigail would receive a good education, rare for young women at that time. Adams was also known for her witty correspondence with her husband while he was away. **(#2146)**

	Issues of 1985 (continued), Perf. 11	Un	U	PB	#	FDC	Q
2154	22¢ World War I Veterans, Aug. 26	.40	.15	2.00	(4)	1.00	119,975,000
	American Horses Issue, Sept. 25						
2155	22¢ Quarter Horse	.75	.15			1.00	36,985,000
2156	22¢ Morgan	.75	.15			1.00	36,985,000
2157	22¢ Saddlebred	.75	.15			1.00	36,985,000
2158	22¢ Appaloosa	.75	.15			1.00	36,985,000
a	Block of 4, #2155-58	4.00	1.00	4.75	(4)	2.50	
2159	22¢ Public Education, Oct. 1	.42	.15	2.00	(4)	1.00	120,000,000
	International Youth Year Issue, Oct. 7						
2160	22¢ YMCA Youth Camping	.48	.15			1.00	32,500,000
2161	22¢ Boy Scouts	.48	.15			1.00	32,500,000
2162	22¢ Big Brothers/Big Sisters	.48	.15			1.00	32,500,000
2163	22¢ Camp Fire	.48	.15			1.00	32,500,000
a	Block of 4, #2160-63	2.00	1.00	2.75	(4)	1.25	
2164	22¢ Help End Hunger, Oct. 15	.42	.15	1.90	(4)	1.00	120,000,000
	Christmas Issue, Oct. 30						
2165	22¢ Genoa Madonna, by Luca Della Robbia	.40	.15	1.70	(4)	1.00	759,200,000
a	Imperf. pair	100.00					
2166	22¢ Poinsettia Plants	.40	.15	1.70	(4)	1.00	757,600,000
a	Imperf. pair	130.00					

Where does the quarter horse get its name?

Quarter horses were originally bred in the early 1700s, when breeders mixed English thorough-breds with Spanish horses of North America. The horses ran short spurts exceptionally well. They were often used in sprint races, usually 1/4 mile long, which explains why these horses are known today as quarter horses.

(#2155)

2154

2155
2157

2156
2158

2158a

2159

2160
2162

2161
2163

2163a

2164

2165

2166

277

2167

2168

2169

2170

2171

2172

2173

2176

2177

2178

2179

2180

2182

2183

2184

2184A

2184B

2185

2186

2188

2190

2191

2192

2193

2194

2194A

2195

2196

	Issues of 1986, Perf. 11	Un	U	PB	#	FDC	Q
2167	22¢ Arkansas Statehood, Jan. 3	.40	.15	1.90	(4)	1.00	130,000,000
a	Vertical pair, imperf. horizontally	—					
	Issues of 1986-91, Great Americans Issue (See also #1844-69)						
2168	1¢ Margaret Mitchell, June 30, 1986	.15	.15	.25	(4)	1.00	
2169	2¢ Mary Lyon, Feb. 28, 1987	.15	.15	.25	(4)	1.00	
2170	3¢ Paul Dudley White, MD, Sept. 15, 1986	.15	.15	.30	(4)	1.00	
2171	4¢ Father Flanagan, July 14, 1986	.15	.15	.35	(4)	1.00	
2172	5¢ Hugo L. Black, Feb. 27, 1986	.15	.15	.40	(4)	1.00	
2173	5¢ Luis Munoz Marin, Feb. 18, 1990	.15	.15	.50	(4)	1.25	
2174-75	Not assigned						
2176	10¢ Red Cloud, Aug. 15, 1987	.18	.15	.85	(4)	1.00	
a	Overall tagging, 1990	.30	.15				
2177	14¢ Julia Ward Howe, Feb. 12, 1987	.25	.15	1.10	(4)	1.00	
2178	15¢ Buffalo Bill Cody, June 6, 1988	.28	.15	1.20	(4)	1.25	
a	Overall tagging, 1990	—	—				
2179	17¢ Belva Ann Lockwood, June 18, 1986	.30	.15	1.45	(4)	1.00	
2180	21¢ Chester Carlson, Oct. 21, 1988	.38	.15	1.75	(4)	1.25	
2181	Not assigned						
2182	23¢ Mary Cassatt, Nov. 4, 1988	.42	.15	1.90	(4)	1.25	
2183	25¢ Jack London, Jan. 11, 1986	.45	.15	2.00	(4)	1.25	
a	Booklet pane of 10, May 3, 1988	4.50	—			6.00	
b	Overall tagging, 1990	—	—				
2184	28¢ Sitting Bull, Sept. 28, 1989	.50	.15	2.50	(4)	1.00	
2184A	29¢ Earl Warren, Mar. 9	.50	.15	2.90	(4)		
2184B	29¢ Thomas Jefferson	.50	.15	2.50	(4)	1.25	
2185	35¢ Dennis Chavez, Apr. 3, 1991	.65	.15	3.25	(4)		
2186	40¢ Claire Lee Chennault, Sept. 6, 1990	.70	.15	3.25	(4)	1.00	
2187	Not assigned						
2188	45¢ Harvey Cushing, MD, June 17, 1988	.80	.15	3.50	(4)	1.00	
a	Overall tagging, 1990	—	—				
2189	Not assigned						
2190	52¢ Hubert H. Humphrey, June 3, 1991	.90	.15	4.00	(4)	1.25	
2191	56¢ John Harvard, Sept. 3, 1986	.90	.15	4.00	(4)	1.25	
2192	65¢ H.H. 'Hap' Arnold, Nov. 5, 1988	1.20	.18	5.00	(4)	1.50	
2193	75¢ Wendell Willkie	1.30	.20	5.50	(4)		
2194	$1 Bernard Revel, Sept. 23, 1986	2.50	.50	9.50	(4)	2.00	
2194A	$1 Johns Hopkins, June 7, 1989	1.75	.50	7.25	(4)	3.00	
b	Overall tagging, 1990	—	—				
2195	$2 William Jennings Bryan, Mar. 19, 1986	3.00	.50	13.00	(4)	5.00	
2196	$5 Bret Harte, Aug. 25, 1987	7.00	1.00	28.00	(4)	15.00	
	Booklet Stamp, Perf. 10						
2197	25¢ Jack London (2183), single from booklet	.45	.15			1.25	
a	Booklet pane of 6, May 3, 1988	2.65				4.00	

Minimum value listed for a stamp is 15 cents; for a First Day Cover (FDC), $1.00. This minimum represents a fair-market price for having a dealer locate and provide a single stamp or cover from his or her stock. Dealers may charge less per stamp or cover for a group of such stamps or covers, or less for a single stamp or cover.

Issues of 1986, Perf. 10 Vertically	Un	U	PB	#	FDC	Q
United States—Sweden Stamp Collecting Booklet Issue, Jan. 23						
2198 22¢ Handstamped Cover	.45	.15			1.00	16,999,200
2199 22¢ Boy Examining Stamp Collection	.45	.15			1.00	16,999,200
2200 22¢ #836 Under Magnifying Glass	.45	.15			1.00	16,999,200
2201 22¢ 1986 Presidents Miniature Sheet	.45	.15			1.00	16,999,200
a Booklet pane of 4, #2198-2201	2.00	—			4.00	16,999,200
b As "a," black omitted on #2198, 2201	45.00					
c As "a," blue omitted on #2198-2200	2,250.00					
d As "a," buff omitted	—					
#2198-2201 issued only in booklets. All stamps are imperf. at top and bottom or imperf. at top, bottom and right side.						
Perf. 11						
2202 22¢ Love, Jan. 30	.40	.15	1.70	(4)	1.00	948,860,000
Black Heritage Issue, Sojourner Truth, Feb. 4						
2203 22¢ Sojourner Truth Portrait and Truth Lecturing	.40	.15	1.75	(4)	1.00	130,000,000
2204 22¢ Republic of Texas, 150th Anniversary, Mar. 2	.42	.15	1.75	(4)	1.00	136,500,000
a Horizontal pair, imperf. vertically	1,000.00					
b Dark red omitted	2,750.00					
Fish Booklet Issue, Mar. 21, Perf. 10 Horizontally						
2205 22¢ Muskellunge	.50	.15			1.00	43,998,000
2206 22¢ Atlantic Cod	.50	.15			1.00	43,998,000
2207 22¢ Largemouth Bass	.50	.15			1.00	43,998,000
2208 22¢ Bluefin Tuna	.50	.15			1.00	43,998,000
2209 22¢ Catfish	.50	.15			1.00	43,998,000
a Booklet pane of 5, #2205-09	3.25	—			2.50	43,998,000
#2205-09 issued only in booklets. All stamps are imperf. at sides or imperf. at sides and bottom.						
Perf. 11						
2210 22¢ Public Hospitals, Apr. 11	.40	.15	1.75	(4)	1.00	130,000,000
a Vertical pair, imperf. horizontally	400.00					
b Horizontal pair, imperf. vertically	1,350.00					
Performing Arts Issue, Duke Ellington, Apr. 29						
2211 22¢ Duke Ellington Portrait and Piano Keys	.40	.15	1.90	(4)	1.00	130,000,000
a Vertical pair, imperf. horizontally	1,000.00					
2212-15 Not assigned						

How big can a muskellunge grow?

A muskellunge, the largest fish of the North American pike family, can grow to about six feet and weigh up to 100 pounds. Most muskellunges are smaller, ranging in size from two and a half to four feet long and weighing between 10 and 35 pounds. Muskies are found in lakes and rivers in southern Canada, as well as the Great Lakes, the upper Mississippi Valley, and the St. Lawrence and Ohio rivers. Larger muskies feed on other fish, ducks, muskrats and other vertebrates. **(#2205)**

2198   2199   2200   2201   2201a

2202   2203   2204

2205

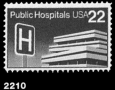

2210

2211

2206

2207

2208

2209

2209a

2216a

2216b

2216c

2216d

2216e

2216f

2216g

2216h

2216i

2217a

2217b

2217c

2217d

2217e

2217f

2217g

2217h

2217i

Issues of 1986 (continued), Perf. 11	Un	U	FDC	Q
AMERIPEX '86 Issue, Presidents Miniature Sheets, May 22				
2216 Sheet of 9	3.50		4.00	5,825,050
a 22¢ George Washington	.38	.20	1.00	
b 22¢ John Adams	.38	.20	1.00	
c 22¢ Thomas Jefferson	.38	.20	1.00	
d 22¢ James Madison	.38	.20	1.00	
e 22¢ James Monroe	.38	.20	1.00	
f 22¢ John Quincy Adams	.38	.20	1.00	
g 22¢ Andrew Jackson	.38	.20	1.00	
h 22¢ Martin Van Buren	.38	.20	1.00	
i 22¢ William H. Harrison	.38	.20	1.00	
j Blue omitted	3,500.00			
k Black inscription omitted	1,500.00			
l Imperf.	10,500.00			
2217 Sheet of 9	3.50		4.00	5,825,050
a 22¢ John Tyler	.38	.20	1.00	
b 22¢ James Polk	.38	.20	1.00	
c 22¢ Zachary Taylor	.38	.20	1.00	
d 22¢ Millard Fillmore	.38	.20	1.00	
e 22¢ Franklin Pierce	.38	.20	1.00	
f 22¢ James Buchanan	.38	.20	1.00	
g 22¢ Abraham Lincoln	.38	.20	1.00	
h 22¢ Andrew Johnson	.38	.20	1.00	
i 22¢ Ulysses S. Grant	.38	.20	1.00	

What did the Monroe Doctrine establish?

The Monroe Doctrine, set forth by President James Monroe in an address to Congress in 1823, recognized the independent nations of the Western Hemisphere and guaranteed them against any threats of "future colonization by any European powers." His statement pushed for the U.S. to disallow the creation of any new colonies in the Americas. The doctrine was seldom invoked until President Grover Cleveland used it to threaten Britain in 1895 when the British would not settle their dispute with Venezuela. **(#2216e)**

	Issues of 1986 (continued), Perf. 11	Un	U		FDC	Q
	AMERIPEX '86 Issue (continued), Presidents Miniature Sheets, May 22					
2218	Sheet of 9	3.50			4.00	5,825,050
a	22¢ Rutherford B. Hayes	.38	.20		1.00	
b	22¢ James A. Garfield	.38	.20		1.00	
c	22¢ Chester A. Arthur	.38	.20		1.00	
d	22¢ Grover Cleveland	.38	.20		1.00	
e	22¢ Benjamin Harrison	.38	.20		1.00	
f	22¢ William McKinley	.38	.20		1.00	
g	22¢ Theodore Roosevelt	.38	.20		1.00	
h	22¢ William H. Taft	.38	.20		1.00	
i	22¢ Woodrow Wilson	.38	.20		1.00	
j	Brown omitted	—				
k	Black inscription omitted	2,600.00				
2219	Sheet of 9	3.50			4.00	5,825,050
a	22¢ Warren G. Harding	.38	.20		1.00	
b	22¢ Calvin Coolidge	.38	.20		1.00	
c	22¢ Herbert Hoover	.38	.20		1.00	
d	22¢ Franklin D. Roosevelt	.38	.20		1.00	
e	22¢ White House	.38	.20		1.00	
f	22¢ Harry S. Truman	.38	.20		1.00	
g	22¢ Dwight D. Eisenhower	.38	.20		1.00	
h	22¢ John F. Kennedy	.38	.20		1.00	
i	22¢ Lyndon B. Johnson	.38	.20		1.00	

Who was the youngest man ever elected President?

Theodore Roosevelt became President at the age of 42 — upon the death of William McKinley — but wasn't elected a President until he was 46. John F. Kennedy, on the other hand, was 43 when he was elected President. Not only was Kennedy the youngest elected President in U.S. history, but in 1963 he was unfortunately the youngest to die in office, at the age of 46. **(#2219h)**

Rutherford B. Hayes 1877-1881

James A. Garfield 1881-1881

Chester A. Arthur 1881-1885

Grover Cleveland 1885-89, 1893-97

Benjamin Harrison 1889-1893

2218a   **2218b**   **2218c**   **2218d**   **2218e**

William McKinley 1897-1901

Theodore Roosevelt 1901-1909

William H. Taft 1909-1913

Woodrow Wilson 1913-1921

2218f   **2218g**   **2218h**   **2218i**

Warren G. Harding 1921-1923

Calvin Coolidge 1923-1929

Herbert C. Hoover 1929-1933

Franklin D. Roosevelt 1933-1945

USA 22

2219a   **2219b**   **2219c**   **2219d**   **2219e**

Harry S. Truman 1945-1953

Dwight D. Eisenhower 1953-1961

John F. Kennedy 1961-1963

Lyndon B. Johnson 1963-1969

2219f   **2219g**   **2219h**   **2219i**

285

USA 22 Elisha Kent Kane
USA 22 Adolphus W. Greely
USA 22 Vilhjalmur Stefansson
USA 22 Robert E. Peary, Matthew Henson

Liberty 1886-1986 USA 22

Omnibus 1880s 1 USA

Locomotive 1870s 2 USA

2220   **2221**   **2223a**

2222   **2223**

2224

2225

2226

Navajo Art USA 22
Navajo Art USA 22
Navajo Art USA 22
Navajo Art USA 22

T.S. Eliot 22 USA

Wood Carving: Highlander Figure — Folk Art USA 22
Wood Carving: Ship Figurehead — Folk Art USA 22
Wood Carving: Nautical Figure — Folk Art USA 22
Wood Carving: Cigar Store Figure — Folk Art USA 22

2239

2235   **2236**   **2238a**

2237   **2238**

2240   **2241**   **2243a**

2242   **2243**

CHRISTMAS 22 USA — Perugino, National Gallery

USA 22 GREETINGS

USA 22 1837-1987 Michigan Statehood

22 USA Pan American Games Indianapolis 1987

2244   **2245**

2246

2247

LOVE USA 22

Jean Baptiste Pointe Du Sable 22 — Black Heritage USA

Enrico Caruso 22 USA

GIRL SCOUTS USA 22

2248

2249

2250

2251

	Issues of 1986 (continued), Perf. 11	Un	U	PB/PNC	#	FDC	Q
	Arctic Explorers Issue, May 28						
2220	22¢ Elisha Kent Kane	.45	.15			1.00	32,500,000
2221	22¢ Adolphus W. Greely	.45	.15			1.00	32,500,000
2222	22¢ Vilhjalmur Stefansson	.45	.15			1.00	32,500,000
2223	22¢ Robert E. Peary, Matthew Henson	.45	.15			1.00	32,500,000
a	Block of 4, #2220-23	2.00	1.00	3.00	(4)	2.50	
b	As "a," black omitted	9,000.00					
2224	22¢ Statue of Liberty, July 4	.40	.15	2.00	(4)	1.00	220,725,000
	Issues of 1986-87, Reengraved Transportation Issue, Coil Stamps, Perf. 10 Vertically						
	(See also #1897-1908, 2123-36, 2252-66, 2452-53A, 2457, 2464, 2468)						
2225	1¢ Omnibus, Nov. 26, 1986	.15	.15	.65	(3)	1.00	
2226	2¢ Locomotive, Mar. 6, 1987	.15	.15	.75	(3)	1.00	
2227, 2229-30, 2232-34 Not assigned							
2228	4¢ Stagecoach (1898A), Aug. 1986	.15	.15	1.40	(3)		
2231	8.3¢ Ambulance (Bureau precanceled), Aug. 29, 1986	.16	.16	3.75	(3)		
	On #2228, "Stagecoach 1890s" is 17mm long; on #1898A, it is 19^1/₂mm long. On #2231, "Ambulance 1860s" is 18mm long; on #2128, it is 18^1/₂mm long.						
	American Folk Art Issue, Navajo Blankets, Sept. 4, Perf. 11						
2235	22¢ Navajo Blanket, black and white lines dominate	.40	.15			1.00	60,131,250
2236	22¢ Navajo Blanket, black and white diamonds dominate	.40	.15			1.00	60,131,250
2237	22¢ Navajo Blanket, white diamonds dominate	.40	.15			1.00	60,131,250
2238	22¢ Navajo Blanket, black-and-white bordered patterns dominate	.40	.15			1.00	60,131,250
a	Block of 4, #2235-38	1.65	1.00	2.25	(4)	2.50	
b	As "a," black omitted	350.00					
	Literary Arts Issue, T.S. Eliot, Sept. 26						
2239	22¢ T.S. Eliot Portrait	.40	.15	1.90	(4)	1.00	131,700,000
	American Folk Art Issue, Wood-Carved Figurines, Oct. 1						
2240	22¢ Highlander Figure	.42	.15			1.00	60,000,000
2241	22¢ Ship Figurehead	.42	.15			1.00	60,000,000
2242	22¢ Nautical Figure	.42	.15			1.00	60,000,000
2243	22¢ Cigar Store Figure	.42	.15			1.00	60,000,000
a	Block of 4, #2240-43	1.75	1.00	2.25	(4)	2.50	
b	As "a," imperf. vertically	1,500.00					
	Christmas Issue, Oct. 24						
2244	22¢ Madonna and Child, by Perugino	.40	.15	1.90	(4)	1.00	690,100,000
2245	22¢ Village Scene	.40	.15	1.90	(4)	1.00	882,150,000
	Issues of 1987						
2246	22¢ Michigan Statehood, Jan. 26	.40	.15	1.90	(4)	1.00	167,430,000
	Pair with full vertical gutter between	—					
2247	22¢ Pan American Games, Jan. 29	.40	.15	1.90	(4)	1.00	166,555,000
a	Silver omitted	1,500.00					
	Perf. 11^1/₂ x 11						
2248	22¢ Love, Jan. 30	.40	.15	1.90	(4)	1.00	842,360,000
	Black Heritage Issue, Jean Baptiste Point Du Sable, Feb. 20, Perf. 11						
2249	22¢ Portrait of Du Sable and Chicago Settlement	.40	.15	1.90	(4)	1.00	142,905,000
	Performing Arts Issue, Enrico Caruso, Feb. 27						
2250	22¢ Caruso as the Duke of Mantua in *Rigoletti*	.40	.15	1.90	(4)	1.00	130,000,000
2251	22¢ Girl Scouts, Mar. 12	.40	.15	1.90	(4)	1.00	149,980,000

	Issues of 1987-88, Perf. 10 Vertically	Un	U	PNC	#	FDC	Q
	Coil Stamps, Transportation Issue (See also #1897-1908, 2123-36, 2225-31, 2451-68)						
2252	3¢ Conestoga Wagon 1800s, Feb. 29, 1988	.15	.15	.85	(3)	1.25	
2253	5¢ Milk Wagon 1900s, Sept. 25, 1987	.15	.15	1.10	(3)	1.25	
2254	5.3¢ Elevator 1900s, Bureau precanceled, Sept. 16, 1988	.15	.15	1.25	(3)	1.25	
2255	7.6¢ Carreta 1770s, Bureau precanceled, Aug. 30, 1988	.15	.15	2.50	(3)	1.25	
2256	8.4¢ Wheel Chair 1920s, Bureau precanceled, Aug. 12, 1988	.15	.15	2.50	(3)	1.25	
a	Imperf. pair	750.00					
2257	10¢ Canal Boat 1880s, Apr. 11, 1987	.18	.15	1.50	(3)	1.00	
2258	13¢ Patrol Wagon 1880s, Bureau precanceled, Oct. 29, 1988	.22	.22	2.75	(3)	1.25	
2259	13.2¢ Coal Car 1870s, Bureau precanceled, July 19, 1988	.22	.22	3.00	(3)	1.25	
a	Imperf. pair	120.00					
2260	15¢ Tugboat 1900s, July 12, 1988	.24	.15	3.00	(3)	1.25	
2261	16.7¢ Popcorn Wagon 1902, Bureau precanceled, July 7, 1988	.28	.28	3.75	(3)	1.25	
a	Imperf. pair	180.00					
2262	17.5¢ Racing Car 1911, Sept. 25, 1987	.30	.15	3.75	(3)	1.00	
a	Untagged (Bureau precanceled)	.30	.30	3.75	(3)	1.00	
b	Imperf. pair	1,750.00					
2263	20¢ Cable Car 1880s, Oct. 28, 1988	.35	.15	3.75	(3)	1.25	
a	Imperf. pair	75.00					
2264	20.5¢ Fire Engine 1920s, Bureau precanceled, Sept. 28, 1988	.38	.38	3.75	(3)	1.25	
2265	21¢ Railroad Mail Car 1920s, Bureau precanceled, Aug. 16, 1988	.38	.38	3.75	(3)	1.25	
a	Imperf. pair	65.00					
2266	24.1¢ Tandem Bicycle 1890s, Bureau precanceled, Oct. 26, 1988	.42	.42	4.50	(3)	1.25	
	Issues of 1987 (continued), Special Occasions Booklet Issue, Apr. 20, Perf. 10						
2267	22¢ Congratulations!	.55	.15			1.00	1,222,140,000
2268	22¢ Get Well!	.55	.15			1.00	611,070,000
2269	22¢ Thank you!	.55	.15			1.00	611,070,000
2270	22¢ Love You, Dad!	.55	.15			1.00	611,070,000
2271	22¢ Best Wishes!	.55	.15			1.00	611,070,000
2272	22¢ Happy Birthday!	.55	.15			1.00	1,222,140,000
2273	22¢ Love You, Mother!	.55	.15			1.00	611,070,000
2274	22¢ Keep In Touch!	.55	.15			1.00	611,070,000
a	Booklet pane of 10, #2268-71, 2273-74 and 2 each of #2267, 2272	6.75	—			4.00	611,070,000

#2267-74 issued only in booklets. All stamps are imperf. at one or two sides or imperf. at sides and bottom.

Conestoga Wagon 1800s
3 USA

2252

Milk Wagon 1900s
5 USA

2253

Elevator 1900s
5.3 USA
Nonprofit Carrier Route Sort

2254

Carreta 1770s
7.6 USA
Nonprofit

2255

Wheel Chair 1920s
8.4 USA
Nonprofit

2256

Canal Boat 1880s
10 USA

2257

Patrol Wagon 1880s
USA 13
Presorted First-Class

2258

Coal Car 1870s
13.2 USA
Bulk Rate

2259

Tugboat 1900s
USA 15

2260

Popcorn Wagon 1902
16.7 USA
Bulk Rate

2261

Racing Car 1911
USA 17.5

2262

USA 20
Cable Car 1880s

2263

Fire Engine 1900s
20.5 USA
ZIP+4 Presort

2264

Railroad Mail Car 1920s
Presorted First-Class
21 USA

2265

Tandem Bicycle 1890s
24.1 USA
ZIP+4

2266

Congratulations! 22 USA

Get Well! USA 22
Thank You!
USA 22

Love You, Dad! USA 22
Best Wishes! USA 22
Happy Birthday! USA 22

USA 22
Love You, Mother!
Keep In Touch! USA 22
Happy Birthday! USA 22

Congratulations! 22 USA

2274a

2267
2268   2269
2270
2271   2272
2273
2274

2275 **2276** **2277**

2278

2280 **2281**

2283

2283a

2285b

2284 **2285**

	Issues of 1987 (continued), Perf. 11	Un	U	PB/PNC	#	FDC	Q
2275	United Way, Apr. 28	.40	.15	1.90	(4)	1.00	156,995,000
2276	Flag with Fireworks, May 9	.40	.15	1.90	(4)	1.00	
a	Booklet pane of 20, Nov. 30	8.50	—			18.00	
	Issues of 1988-89 (All issued in 1988 except #2280 on prephosphored paper)						
2277	25¢ E Stamp, Mar. 22	.45	.15	2.00	(4)	1.00	
2278	25¢ Flag with Clouds, May 6	.40	.15	1.90	(4)	1.00	
	Pair with full vertical gutter between	—					
	Coil Stamps, Perf. 10 Vertically						
2279	25¢ E Stamp (2277), Mar. 22	.45	.15	3.00	(3)	1.00	
a	Imperf. pair	100.00					
2280	25¢ Flag over Yosemite, May 20	.45	.15	4.25	(3)	1.00	
	Prephosphored paper, Feb. 14, 1989	.45	.15	4.25	(3)		
a	Imperf. pair	15.00					
b	Black trees	100.00	—				
2281	25¢ Honeybee, Sept. 2	.45	.15	3.25	(3)	1.00	
a	Imperf. pair	45.00					
b	Black omitted	60.00					
d	Pair, imperf. between	900.00					
	Booklet Stamp, Perf. 10						
2282	25¢ E Stamp (2277), single from booklet	.50	.15			1.00	
a	Booklet pane of 10, Mar. 22	6.50	—			6.00	
	Pheasant Booklet Issue, Perf. 11						
2283	25¢ Pheasant, single from booklet	.50	.15			1.25	
a	Booklet pane of 10, Apr. 29	6.00	—			6.00	
c	As "a," red removed from sky	65.00	—				
d	As "a," imperf. horizontally between	—					
	#2283 issued only in booklets. All stamps have one or two imperf. edges. Imperf. and part perf. pairs and panes exist from printer's waste.						
	Owl and Grosbeak Booklet Issue, Perf. 10						
2284	25¢ Owl, single from booklet	.45	.15			1.25	
2285	25¢ Grosbeak, single from booklet	.45	.15			1.25	
b	Booklet pane of 10, 5 each of #2284, 2285, May 28	4.50	—			6.00	
	#2284 and 2285 issued only in booklets. All stamps are imperf. at one side or imperf. at one side and bottom.						
2285A	25¢ Flag with Clouds (2278), single from booklet	.45	.15			1.25	
c	Booklet pane of 6, July 5	2.75	—			4.00	

Why do honeybees fight one another?

Hives are highly prized among bees, and it's not unusual for one colony of bees to attack another. Each colony has its own odor, and several guard bees protect the entrance to their colony's hive with their sense of smell. They attack anything — bees, animals or people — that doesn't carry their odor. When danger is great, the guards release a chemical substance to notify other bees that the guards need help. **(#2281)**

	Issues of 1987 (continued), Perf. 11	Un	U	FDC	Q
	American Wildlife Issue, June 13				
2286	22¢ Barn Swallow	.85	.15	1.00	12,952,500
2287	22¢ Monarch Butterfly	.85	.15	1.00	12,952,500
2288	22¢ Bighorn Sheep	.85	.15	1.00	12,952,500
2289	22¢ Broad-tailed Hummingbird	.85	.15	1.00	12,952,500
2290	22¢ Cottontail	.85	.15	1.00	12,952,500
2291	22¢ Osprey	.85	.15	1.00	12,952,500
2292	22¢ Mountain Lion	.85	.15	1.00	12,952,500
2293	22¢ Luna Moth	.85	.15	1.00	12,952,500
2294	22¢ Mule Deer	.85	.15	1.00	12,952,500
2295	22¢ Gray Squirrel	.85	.15	1.00	12,952,500
2296	22¢ Armadillo	.85	.15	1.00	12,952,500
2297	22¢ Eastern Chipmunk	.85	.15	1.00	12,952,500
2298	22¢ Moose	.85	.15	1.00	12,952,500
2299	22¢ Black Bear	.85	.15	1.00	12,952,500
2300	22¢ Tiger Swallowtail	.85	.15	1.00	12,952,500
2301	22¢ Bobwhite	.85	.15	1.00	12,952,500
2302	22¢ Ringtail	.85	.15	1.00	12,952,500
2303	22¢ Red-winged Blackbird	.85	.15	1.00	12,952,500
2304	22¢ American Lobster	.85	.15	1.00	12,952,500
2305	22¢ Black-tailed Jack Rabbit	.85	.15	1.00	12,952,500
2306	22¢ Scarlet Tanager	.85	.15	1.00	12,952,500
2307	22¢ Woodchuck	.85	.15	1.00	12,952,500
2308	22¢ Roseate Spoonbill	.85	.15	1.00	12,952,500
2309	22¢ Bald Eagle	.85	.15	1.00	12,952,500
2310	22¢ Alaskan Brown Bear	.85	.15	1.00	12,952,500

How many black bears aren't really black?

The American black bear — smallest of the North American bears at five feet tall — may confuse you with its not-necessarily-black coat. Many of these speedy tree climbers have black coats and brown noses. Some have white patches on their chests. Other black bears, called "cinnamon bears," have a lighter brown coat. Alaska's "glacier bears" have gray coats, and the "island white bear" has white fur to match its white claws. **(#2299)**

22 USA *Barn Swallow*
22 USA *Monarch*
22 USA *Bighorn Sheep*
22 USA *Broad-tailed Hummingbird*
22 USA *Cottontail*

2286   2287   2288   2289   2290

22 USA *Osprey*
22 USA *Mountain Lion*
22 USA *Luna Moth*
22 USA *Mule Deer*
22 USA *Gray Squirrel*

2291   2292   2293   2294   2295

22 USA *Armadillo*
22 USA *Eastern Chipmunk*
22 USA *Moose*
22 USA *Black Bear*
22 USA *Tiger Swallowtail*

2296   2297   2298   2299   2300

22 USA *Bobwhite*
22 USA *Ringtail*
22 USA *Red-winged Blackbird*
22 USA *American Lobster*
22 USA *Black-tailed Jack Rabbit*

2301   2302   2303   2304   2305

22 USA *Scarlet Tanager*
22 USA *Woodchuck*
22 USA *Roseate Spoonbill*
22 USA *Bald Eagle*
22 USA *Alaskan Brown Bear*

	Issues of 1987 (continued), Perf. 11	Un	U	PB	#	FDC	Q
	American Wildlife Issue (continued), June 13						
2311	22¢ Iiwi	.85	.15			1.00	12,952,500
2312	22¢ Badger	.85	.15			1.00	12,952,500
2313	22¢ Pronghorn	.85	.15			1.00	12,952,500
2314	22¢ River Otter	.85	.15			1.00	12,952,500
2315	22¢ Ladybug	.85	.15			1.00	12,952,500
2316	22¢ Beaver	.85	.15			1.00	12,952,500
2317	22¢ White-tailed Deer	.85	.15			1.00	12,952,500
2318	22¢ Blue Jay	.85	.15			1.00	12,952,500
2319	22¢ Pika	.85	.15			1.00	12,952,500
2320	22¢ Bison	.85	.15			1.00	12,952,500
2321	22¢ Snowy Egret	.85	.15			1.00	12,952,500
2322	22¢ Gray Wolf	.85	.15			1.00	12,952,500
2323	22¢ Mountain Goat	.85	.15			1.00	12,952,500
2324	22¢ Deer Mouse	.85	.15			1.00	12,952,500
2325	22¢ Black-tailed Prairie Dog	.85	.15			1.00	12,952,500
2326	22¢ Box Turtle	.85	.15			1.00	12,952,500
2327	22¢ Wolverine	.85	.15			1.00	12,952,500
2328	22¢ American Elk	.85	.15			1.00	12,952,500
2329	22¢ California Sea Lion	.85	.15			1.00	12,952,500
2330	22¢ Mockingbird	.85	.15			1.00	12,952,500
2331	22¢ Raccoon	.85	.15			1.00	12,952,500
2332	22¢ Bobcat	.85	.15			1.00	12,952,500
2333	22¢ Black-footed Ferret	.85	.15			1.00	12,952,500
2334	22¢ Canada Goose	.85	.15			1.00	12,952,500
2335	22¢ Red Fox	.85	.15			1.00	12,952,500
a	Pane of 50, #2286-2335	47.50				30.00	
	Any single, red omitted	—					

Why are ladybugs heroes?

In the late 19th century the "cottony cushion scale" aphid — a small insect that sucks the juices from plants — almost destroyed California's fruit crops. The critters were halted when fruit farmers sprinkled their crops with ladybugs — who feed chiefly on aphids and other insects — and the crops were salvaged. Fruit farmers worldwide now consider ladybugs to be heroes for their beneficial eating habits. **(#2315)**

	Issues of 1987-90, Perf. 11	Un	U	PB	#	FDC	Q
	Constitution Bicentennial Issue, Ratification of the Constitution						
2336	22¢ Delaware, July 4, 1987	.40	.15	1.90	(4)	1.00	168,000,000
2337	22¢ Pennsylvania, Aug. 26, 1987	.42	.15	1.90	(4)	1.00	186,575,000
2338	22¢ New Jersey, Sept. 11, 1987	.42	.15	1.90	(4)	1.00	184,325,000
a	Black omitted	5,250.00					
2339	22¢ Georgia, Jan. 6, 1988	.40	.15	1.90	(4)	1.00	168,845,000
2340	22¢ Connecticut, Jan. 9, 1988	.40	.15	1.90	(4)	1.00	155,170,000
2341	22¢ Massachusetts, Feb. 6, 1988	.40	.15	1.90	(4)	1.00	102,100,000
2342	22¢ Maryland, Feb. 15, 1988	.40	.15	1.90	(4)	1.00	103,325,000
2343	25¢ South Carolina, May 23, 1988	.45	.15	2.00	(4)	1.25	162,045,000
2344	25¢ New Hampshire, June 21, 1988	.45	.15	2.00	(4)	1.25	153,295,000
2345	25¢ Virginia, June 25, 1988	.45	.15	2.00	(4)	1.25	160,245,000
2346	25¢ New York, July 26, 1988	.45	.15	2.00	(4)	1.25	183,290,000
2347	25¢ North Carolina, Aug. 22, 1989	.45	.15	2.00	(4)	1.25	
2348	25¢ Rhode Island, May 29, 1990	.45	.15	2.00	(4)	1.25	164,130,000
2349	22¢ Friendship with Morocco, July 17	.40	.15	1.70	(4)	1.00	157,475,000
a	Black omitted	300.00					
	Issues of 1987, Literary Arts Issue, William Faulkner, Aug. 3						
2350	22¢ Portrait of Faulkner	.40	.15	1.70	(4)	1.00	156,225,000
	American Folk Art Issue, Lacemaking, Aug. 14						
2351	22¢ Squash Blossoms	.42	.15			1.00	40,995,000
2352	22¢ Floral Piece	.42	.15			1.00	40,995,000
2353	22¢ Floral Piece	.42	.15			1.00	40,995,000
2354	22¢ Dogwood Blossoms	.42	.15			1.00	40,995,000
a	Block of 4, #2351-54	1.75	1.00	2.25	(4)	2.75	
b	As "a," white omitted	1,000.00					

How did the U.S. become "friends" with Morocco?

Morocco befriended the U.S. by publicly acknowledging America's independence in 1777 — an unpopular move at the time. As the Republic battled the British for independence, Sultan Sidi Muhammed chose to allow American ships the right-of-entry into Morocco without a treaty. The gesture spawned further talks, which resulted in the Treaty of Peace and Friendship, ratified by  the U.S. in 1787. Such a treaty marked a new beginning in international relations; it was the first one signed between any Arab, Muslim or African state and the U.S. **(#2349)**

Dec 7, 1787 USA
Delaware 22
2336

Dec 12, 1787 22 USA
Pennsylvania
2337

Dec 18, 1787 USA
New Jersey 22
2338

22 USA January 2, 1788
Georgia
2339

22 USA January 9, 1788
Connecticut
2340

22 USA Feb 6, 1788
Massachusetts
2341

April 28, 1788 USA
Maryland 22
2342

25 USA May 23, 1788
South Carolina
2343

25 USA June 21, 1788
New Hampshire
2344

June 25, 1788 USA
Virginia 25
2345

July 26, 1788 USA
New York 25
2346

25 USA November 21, 1789
North Carolina
2347

25 USA May 29, 1790
Rhode Island
2348

Friendship
with Morocco
1787-1987
USA 22
2349

William Faulkner
22
2350

Lacemaking USA 22

Lacemaking USA 22

Lacemaking USA 22

Lacemaking USA 22

2351   **2352**   **2354a**

2353   **2354**

297

The Bicentennial
of the Constitution of
the United States
of America
1787-1987 USA 22
2355

We the people
of the United States,
in order to form
a more perfect Union...
Preamble, U.S. Constitution USA 22
2356

Establish justice,
insure domestic tranquility,
provide for the common defense,
promote the general welfare...
Preamble, U.S. Constitution USA 22
2357

And secure
the blessings of liberty
to ourselves
and our posterity...
Preamble, U.S. Constitution USA 22
2358

Do ordain
and establish this
Constitution for the
United States of America.
Preamble, U.S. Constitution USA 22
2359

2359a

2360   **2361**

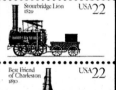

Stourbridge Lion
1829 USA 22
2362

Best Friend
of Charleston
1830 USA 22
2363

John Bull
1831 USA 22
2364

Brother Jonathan
1832 USA 22
2365

Gowan & Marx
1839 USA 22
2366

2366a

CHRISTMAS 22 USA
Moroni, National Gallery
2367

USA 22 GREETINGS
2368

	Issues of 1987 (continued), Perf. 10 Horizontally	Un	U	PB	#	FDC	Q
	Constitution Bicentennial Issue, Drafting of the Constitution Booklet Issue, Aug. 28						
2355	22¢ "The Bicentennial..."	.50	.15			1.00	121,944,000
2356	22¢ "We the people..."	.50	.15			1.00	121,944,000
2357	22¢ "Establish justice..."	.50	.15			1.00	121,944,000
2358	22¢ "And secure..."	.50	.15			1.00	121,944,000
2359	22¢ "Do ordain..."	.50	.15			1.00	121,944,000
a	Booklet pane of 5, #2355-59	2.75	—			3.00	121,944,000
	#2355-59 issued only in booklets. All stamps are imperf. at sides or imperf. at sides and bottom.						
	Signing of the Constitution, Sept. 17, Perf. 11						
2360	22¢ Constitution and Signer's Hand Holding Quill Pen, Sept. 17	*1.90*	.15	1.70	(4)	1.00	168,995,000
2361	22¢ Certified Public Accountants, Sept. 21	1.90	.15	8.75	(4)	2.00	163,145,000
a	Black omitted	*850.00*					
	Locomotives Booklet Issue, Oct. 1, Perf. 10 Horizontally						
2362	22¢ Stourbridge Lion, 1829	.60	.15			1.00	142,501,200
2363	22¢ Best Friend of Charleston, 1830	.60	.15			1.00	142,501,200
2364	22¢ John Bull, 1831	.60	.15			1.00	142,501,200
2365	22¢ Brother Jonathan, 1832	.60	.15			1.00	142,501,200
2366	22¢ Gowan & Marx, 1839	.60	.15			1.00	142,501,200
a	Booklet pane of 5, #2362-66	3.25	—			3.00	142,501,200
b	As "a," black omitted on #2366	—					
	#2362-66 issued only in booklets. All stamps are imperf. at sides or imperf. at sides and bottom.						
	Christmas Issue, Oct. 23, Perf. 11						
2367	22¢ Madonna and Child, by Moroni	.40	.15	1.70	(4)	1.00	528,790,000
2368	22¢ Christmas Ornaments	.40	.15	1.70	(4)	1.00	978,340,000
	Pair with full vertical gutter between	—					

What were the first Christmas tree ornaments like?

The first Christmas tree ornaments were probably edible — red apples adorned a tree used in a famous German play about Adam and Eve. By 1605 many Germans used the trees as Christmas decorations and brightened them with lit candles and paper roses. Soon after came fruits and nuts, and by the mid-1800s people all over the world were decorating their Christmas trees. **(#2368)**

	Issues of 1988, Perf. 11	Un	U	PB	#	FDC	Q
	Winter Olympic Games Issue, Jan. 10						
2369	22¢ Skier and Olympic Rings	.40	.15	1.70	(4)	1.00	158,870,000
2370	22¢ Australia Bicentennial, Jan. 26	.40	.15	1.70	(4)	1.00	145,560,000
	Black Heritage Issue, James Weldon Johnson, Feb. 2						
2371	22¢ Portrait of Johnson and Music from "Lift Ev'ry Voice and Sing"	.40	.15	1.70	(4)	1.00	97,300,000
	American Cats Issue, Feb. 5						
2372	22¢ Siamese and Exotic Shorthair	.42	.15			1.00	39,639,000
2373	22¢ Abyssinian and Himalayan	.42	.15			1.00	39,639,000
2374	22¢ Maine Coon and Burmese	.42	.15			1.00	39,639,000
2375	22¢ American Shorthair and Persian	.42	.15			1.00	39,639,000
a	Block of 4, #2372-75	1.90	1.00	2.25	(4)	3.50	
	American Sports Issue, Knute Rockne, Mar. 9						
2376	22¢ Rockne Holding Football on Field	.40	.15	2.00	(4)	1.50	97,300,000
	Francis Ouimet, June 13						
2377	25¢ Portrait of Ouimet and Ouimet Hitting Fairway Shot	.45	.15	2.00	(4)	1.50	153,045,000
2378	25¢ Love, July 4	.45	.15	1.90	(4)	1.25	841,240,000
2379	45¢ Love, Aug. 8	.65	.20	3.00	(4)	1.25	179,553,550
	Summer Olympic Games Issue, Aug. 19						
2380	25¢ Gymnast on Rings	.45	.15	1.90	(4)	1.25	157,215,000

How is the koala bear like other types of bears?

It isn't, really. As a matter of fact, koala bears aren't bears at all. They're *marsupials*, which means the mothers have a pouch for their young. A baby koala lives in its mother's pouch for six months, until the newborn is better developed and more capable of living outside the pouch. After that the young koala spends six more months riding on its mother's back. **(#2370)**

300

2370

2369

2371

2372
2374

2373
2375

2375a

2378

2376

2377

2379

2380

301

1928 Locomobile

1929 Pierce-Arrow

1931 Cord

1932 Packard

1935 Duesenberg

2381
2382
2383
2384
2385

2385a

Nathaniel Palmer

Lt. Charles Wilkes

Richard E. Byrd

Lincoln Ellsworth

2386   **2387**   **2389a**
2388   **2389**

2390   **2391**   **2393a**
2392   **2393**

	Issues of 1988 (continued), Perf. 10 Horizontally	Un	U	PB	#	FDC	Q
	Classic Cars Booklet Issue, Aug. 25						
2381	25¢ 1928 Locomobile	.50	.15			1.25	127,047,600
2382	25¢ 1929 Pierce-Arrow	.50	.15			1.25	127,047,600
2383	25¢ 1931 Cord	.50	.15			1.25	127,047,600
2384	25¢ 1932 Packard	.50	.15			1.25	127,047,600
2385	25¢ 1935 Duesenberg	.50	.15			1.25	127,047,600
a	Booklet pane of 5, #2381-85	2.75	—			3.00	127,047,600
	#2381-85 issued only in booklets. All stamps are imperf. at sides or imperf. at sides and bottom.						
	Antarctic Explorers Issue, Sept. 14, Perf. 11						
2386	25¢ Nathaniel Palmer	.55	.15			1.25	40,535,625
2387	25¢ Lt. Charles Wilkes	.55	.15			1.25	40,535,625
2388	25¢ Richard E. Byrd	.55	.15			1.25	40,535,625
2389	25¢ Lincoln Ellsworth	.55	.15			1.25	40,535,625
a	Block of 4, #2386-89	2.40	1.00	2.50	(4)	3.00	
b	As "a," black omitted	1,500.00					
c	As "a," imperf. horizontally	3,000.00					
	American Folk Art Issue, Carousel Animals, Oct. 1						
2390	25¢ Deer	.60	.15			1.50	76,253,750
2391	25¢ Horse	.60	.15			1.50	76,253,750
2392	25¢ Camel	.60	.15			1.50	76,253,750
2393	25¢ Goat	.60	.15			1.50	76,253,750
a	Block of 4, #2390-93	2.50	1.00	2.75	(4)	3.50	

What kind of cars did New York & Ohio Auto make?

Brothers J.W. and W.D. Packard started their own auto manufacturing
company — the New York & Ohio Automobile Company — in 1899.
In 1902 they changed the name to one that stuck for another 50 years:
Packard. The Packard boys' cars were loved all over the U.S. — in 1903,
their $3,000 model spanned the states in 61 days (without highways).
The cars lost popularity after a corporate merger with Studebaker, but
Packards went on to become
one of America's most loved
"classic" cars. **(#2384)**

	Issues of 1988 (continued), Perf. 11	Un	U	PB	#	FDC	Q
2394	$8.75 Express Mail, Oct. 4	14.50	8.00	55.00	(4)	25.00	
	Special Occasions Booklet Issue, Oct. 22						
2395	25¢ Happy Birthday	.45	.15			1.25	120,000,000
2396	25¢ Best Wishes	.45	.15			1.25	120,000,000
a	Booklet pane of 6, 3 #2395 and 3 #2396 with gutter between	3.00	—				
2397	25¢ Thinking of You	.45	.15			1.25	120,000,000
2398	25¢ Love You	.45	.15			1.25	120,000,000
a	Booklet pane of 6, 3 #2397 and 3 #2398 with gutter between	3.00	—				
b	As "a," imperf. horizontally	—					
	#2395-98a issued only in booklets. All stamps are imperf. on one side or on one side and top or bottom.						
	Christmas Issue, Oct. 20, Perf. 11						
2399	25¢ Madonna and Child, by Botticelli	.45	.15	1.90	(4)	1.25	843,835,000
a	Gold omitted	40.00					
2400	25¢ One-Horse Open Sleigh and Village Scene	.45	.15	1.90	(4)	1.25	1,037,610,000
	Pair with full vertical gutter between	—					

What are birthday candles made of?

Not all birthday candles are made of wax. They've been made from many things including animal fats, paraffin (a petroleum-based waxy substance), berry wax and beeswax. Birthday candles are usually mass-produced, but can be homemade by repeatedly dipping a wick into a melted pot of wax. **(#2395)**

2394

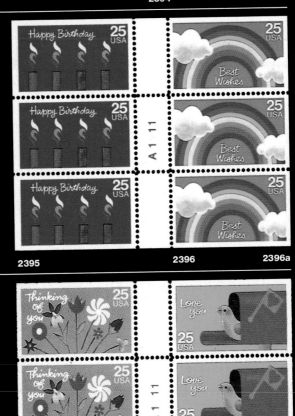

2395   2396   2396a

2397   2398   2398a

2400

2401

2402

2403

2404

2410

2411

2412

2413

2405
2406
2407
2408
2409

2409a

2414

2415

2416

2417

2418

	Issues of 1989, Perf. 11	Un	U	PB	#	FDC	Q
2401	25¢ Montana Statehood, Jan. 15	.45	.15	1.90	(4)	1.25	165,495,000
	Black Heritage Issue, A. Philip Randolph, Feb. 3						
2402	25¢ Portrait of Randolph, Pullman Porters and Railroad Cars	.45	.15	1.90	(4)	1.25	151,675,000
2403	25¢ North Dakota Statehood, Feb. 21	.45	.15	1.90	(4)	1.25	163,000,000
2404	25¢ Washington Statehood, Feb. 22	.45	.15	1.90	(4)	1.25	264,625,000
	Steamboats Booklet Issue, Mar. 3, Perf. 10 Horizontally						
2405	25¢ Experiment 1788-90	.45	.15			1.25	159,154,200
2406	25¢ Phoenix 1809	.45	.15			1.25	159,154,200
2407	25¢ New Orleans 1812	.45	.15			1.25	159,154,200
2408	25¢ Washington 1816	.45	.15			1.25	159,154,200
2409	25¢ Walk in the Water 1818	.45	.15			1.25	159,154,200
a	Booklet pane of 5, #2405-09	2.50	—			4.00	159,154,200
	#2405-09 issued only in booklets. All stamps are imperf. at sides or imperf. at sides and bottom.						
	Perf. 11						
2410	25¢ World Stamp Expo '89, Mar. 16	.45	.15	1.90	(4)	1.25	163,984,000
	Performing Arts Issue, Arturo Toscanini, Mar. 25						
2411	25¢ Portrait of Toscanini Conducting with Baton	.45	.15	1.90	(4)	1.25	152,250,000
	Issues of 1989-90, Constitution Bicentennial Issue						
2412	25¢ U.S. House of Representatives, Apr. 4, 1989	.45	.15	1.90	(4)	1.25	138,760,000
2413	25¢ U.S. Senate, Apr. 6, 1989	.45	.15	1.90	(4)	1.25	137,985,000
2414	25¢ Executive Branch, Apr. 16, 1989	.45	.15	1.90	(4)	1.25	138,580,000
2415	25¢ Supreme Court, Feb. 2, 1990	.45	.15	1.90	(4)	1.25	150,545,000
	Issues of 1989 (continued)						
2416	25¢ South Dakota Statehood, May 3	.45	.15	1.90	(4)	1.25	164,680,000
	American Sports Issue, Lou Gehrig, June 10						
2417	25¢ Portrait of Gehrig, Gehrig Swinging Bat	.48	.15	2.50	(4)	2.50	262,755,000
	Literary Arts Issue, Ernest Hemingway, July 17						
2418	25¢ Portrait of Hemingway, African Landscape in Background	.45	.15	1.90	(4)	1.25	191,755,000

Who played in 2,130 consecutive baseball games?

Lou Gehrig played in a record 2,130 consecutive games with the New York Yankees from 1925 to 1939. Gehrig batted for a career .340 average and hit 493 home runs in his 17-year career. The first baseman also broke an American League record by driving in 184 runs, but his spotlight was often stolen by his teammate — Babe Ruth.
(#2417)

307

	Issues of 1989 (continued), Perf. 11 x 11½	Un	U	PB	#	FDC	Q
	Priority Mail Issue, July 20						
2419	$2.40 Moon Landing	4.00	2.00	17.00	(4)	7.00	
a	Black omitted	3,500.00					
b	Imperf. pair	1,150.00					
	Perf. 11						
2420	25¢ Letter Carriers, Aug. 30	.45	.15	1.90	(4)	1.25	188,400,000
	Constitution Bicentennial Issue, Drafting of the Bill of Rights, Sept. 25						
2421	25¢ Stylized U.S. Flag, Eagle With Quill Pen in Mouth	.45	.15	1.90	(4)	1.25	191,860,000
a	Black omitted	300.00					
	Prehistoric Animals Issue, Oct. 1						
2422	25¢ Tyrannosaurus	.45	.15			1.25	101,747,000
2423	25¢ Pteranodon	.45	.15			1.25	101,747,000
2424	25¢ Stegosaurus	.45	.15			1.25	101,747,000
2425	25¢ Brontosaurus	.45	.15			1.25	101,747,000
a	Block of 4, #2422-25	2.00	1.00	2.25	(4)	3.00	
b	As "a," black omitted	1,100.00					
	America/PUAS Issue, Oct. 12 (See also #C121)						
2426	25¢ Southwest Carved Figure (A.D. 1150-1350), Emblem of the Postal Union of the Americas	.45	.15	2.00	(4)	1.25	137,410,000
	Christmas Issue, Oct. 19, Perf. 11½						
2427	25¢ Madonna and Child, by Caracci	.45	.15	1.90	(4)	1.25	913,335,000
a	Booklet pane of 10	4.50	—			6.00	
	Perf. 11						
2428	25¢ Sleigh Full of Presents	.45	.15	1.90	(4)	1.25	900,000,000
a	Vertical pair, imperf. horizontally	2,000.00					
	Booklet Stamp Issue, Perf. 11½						
2429	25¢ Single from booklet pane (#2428)	.45	.15				399,243,000
a	Booklet pane of 10	4.50	—			6.00	39,924,300
b	As "a," imperf. horiz. between	—					
c	As "a," red omitted	—					
	In #2429, runners on sleigh are twice as thick as in #2428; bow on package at rear of sleigh is same color as package; board running underneath sleigh is pink.						
2430	Not assigned						
	Self-Adhesive, Die-Cut						
2431	25¢ Eagle and Shield, Nov. 10	.50	.20			1.00	75,441,000
a	Booklet pane of 18	9.00					
b	Vertical pair, no die-cutting between	850.00					
2432	Not assigned						
	World Stamp Expo '89 Issue Souvenir Sheet, Nov. 17, Imperf.						
2433	Reproduction of #122, 90¢ Lincoln, and three essays of #122	11.00	9.00			7.00	2,227,600
a-d	Single stamp from sheet	1.90	1.75				

2420

2421

2419

2422   **2423**   **2425a**

2424   **2425**

2426

2428   **2431**

2427

WORLD STAMP EXPO '89℠

The classic 1869 U.S. Abraham Lincoln stamp is reborn in these four larger versions commemorating World Stamp Expo '89, held in Washington, D.C. during the 20th Universal Postal Congress of the UPU. These stamps show the issued colors and three of the trial proof color combinations.

2434

2436

2435

2437

2437a

20th Universal Postal Congress

A review of historical methods of delivering the mail in the United States is the theme of these four stamps issued in commemoration of the convening of the 20th Universal Postal Congress in Washington, D.C. from November 13 through December 15, 1989. The United States, as host nation to the Congress for the first time in ninety-two years, welcomed more than 1,000 delegates from most of the member nations of the Universal Postal Union to the major international event.

2438

2439

2440

2442

2443

	Issues of1989 (continued), Perf. 11	Un	U	PB	#	FDC	Q
	20th UPU Congress Issues, Classic Mail Transportation, Nov. 19 (See also #C122-26)						
2434	25¢ Stagecoach	.45	.15			1.25	40,956,000
2435	25¢ Paddlewheel Steamer	.45	.15			1.25	40,956,000
2436	25¢ Biplane	.45	.15			1.25	40,956,000
2437	25¢ Depot-Hack Type Automobile	.45	.15			1.25	40,956,000
a	Block of 4, #2434-37	2.00	2.00	2.75	(4)	3.00	
b	As "a," dark blue omitted	1,000.00					
	Souvenir Sheet, Nov. 27, Imperf. (See also #C122-26)						
2438	Designs of #2434-37	4.00	1.75			2.00	2,047,200
a-d	Single stamp from sheet	.60	.25				
	Issues of 1990, Perf. 11						
2439	25¢ Idaho Statehood, Jan. 6	.45	.15	2.00	(4)	1.25	173,000,000
	Perf. 12¹/₂ x 13						
2440	25¢ Love, January 18	.45	.15	2.00	(4)	1.25	886,220,000
a	Imperf. pair	850.00					
	Booklet Stamp, Perf. 11¹/₂						
2441	25¢ Love, single from booklet	.45	.15			1.25	995,178,000
a	Booklet pane of 10, Jan. 18	4.50	—			6.00	
b	As "a," bright pink omitted	2,250.00					
	Black Heritage Issue, Ida B. Wells, Feb. 1, Perf. 11						
2442	25¢ Portrait of Ida B. Wells, Marchers in Background	.45	.15	2.00	(4)	1.25	153,125,000
	Beach Umbrella Booklet Issue, Perf. 11¹/₂ x 11						
2443	15¢ Beach Umbrella, single from booklet	.28	.15			1.25	
a	Booklet pane of 10, Feb. 3	2.80	—			4.25	
b	As "a," blue omitted	1,800.00					

#2443 issued only in booklets. All stamps are imperf. at one side or imperf. at one side and bottom.

Who made the first steamboats?

John Fitch made the first workable steamboat in the U.S. in 1787, but it wasn't until 1807 that Robert Fulton's *Clermont* became the first financially successful steamboat. It slowly made its way from New York City to Albany, N.Y. in about 30 hours. Many people rode steamboats for transportation purposes until the invention of the railroads, and steamboat races from New Orleans to St. Louis thrilled thousands who lined the banks of the Mississippi in the early 1800s.
(#2435)

	Issues of 1990 (continued), Perf. 11	Un	U	PB	#	FDC	Q
2444	25¢ Wyoming Statehood, Feb. 23	.45	.15	2.00	(4)	1.25	169,495,000
	Classic Films Issue, Mar. 23						
2445	25¢ The Wizard of Oz	.70	.15			1.25	44,202,000
2446	25¢ Gone With the Wind	.70	.15			1.25	44,202,000
2447	25¢ Beau Geste	.70	.15			1.25	44,202,000
2448	25¢ Stagecoach	.70	.15			1.25	44,202,000
a	Block of 4, #2445-48	3.25	1.00	3.50	(4)	3.00	
	Literary Arts Issue, Marianne Moore, Apr. 18						
2449	25¢ Portrait of Marianne Moore	.45	.15	2.00	(4)	1.25	150,000,000
2450	Not assigned						
	Issues of 1990-92, Transportation Issue, Coil Stamps, Perf. 10 Vertically						
2451	4¢ Steam Carriage 1866, Jan. 25, 1991	.15	.15	1.25	(3)	1.25	
a	Imperf. pair	675.00					
2452	5¢ Circus Wagon 1900s, Aug. 31	.15	.15	1.10	(3)	1.25	
2453	5¢ Canoe 1800s, Bureau precanceled, intaglio printing, May 25, 1991	.15	.15	1.50	(3)	1.25	
2454	5¢ Canoe 1800s, precanceled, gravure printing, Oct. 22, 1991	.15	.15	1.50	(3)	1.25	
2455-56	Not assigned						
2457	10¢ Tractor Trailer, Bureau precanceled, May 25, 1991	.18	.18	2.00	(3)	1.25	
2458-63	Not assigned						
2464	23¢ Lunch Wagon 1890s, Apr. 12, 1991	.42	.15	3.75	(3)	1.25	
a	Imperf. pair	175.00					
2465-67	Not assigned						
2468	$1 Seaplane 1914, Apr. 20	1.75	.50	6.50	(3)	2.00	
	1990 continued, Lighthouses Booklet Issue, Apr. 26, Perf. 10 Vertically						
2470	25¢ Admiralty Head, WA	.45	.15			1.25	146,721,600
2471	25¢ Cape Hatteras, NC	.45	.15			1.25	146,721,600
2472	25¢ West Quoddy Head, ME	.45	.15			1.25	146,721,600
2473	25¢ American Shoals, FL	.45	.15			1.25	146,721,600
2474	25¢ Sandy Hook, NJ	.45	.15			1.25	146,721,600
a	Booklet pane of 5, #2470-74	2.50	—			4.00	146,721,600
b	As "a," white (USA 25) omitted	75.00					
	Self-Adhesive Issue, Die-Cut						
2475	25¢ Flag, single from pane	.50	.25			1.25	36,168,000
a	Pane of 12, May 18	6.00					3,140,000

Who wrote the original "Wizard of Oz"?

L. Frank Baum wrote 14 children's books based on a land called "Oz." His first, *The Wonderful Wizard of Oz*, was published in 1900. Other authors continued his *Oz* series after his death in 1919. *The Wizard of Oz*, made in 1939, became one of the most popular films in motion picture history. Baum based many of his stories on his experiences living in Aberdeen, South Dakota. **(#2445)**

2444

2449

| 2445 | 2446 | 2448a |
| 2447 | 2448 | |

| 2451 | 2452 | 2453 | 2454 |

| 2457 | 2464 | 2468 |

2474a

| 2470 | 2471 | 2472 | 2473 | 2474 |

2475

2476

2478

2479

2480

2481

2482

2487

2489

2491

2493

2494

2495

2496

2497

2498

2499

2500   **2500a**

2501

2502

2503

2504

2505   **2505a**

2506

2507   **2507a**

314

	Issues of 1990-1993 (continued)	Un	U	PB	#	FDC	Q
	Wildlife Issue, Perf. 11						
2476	$2 Bobcat, June 1	3.50	1.25	13.50	(4)	5.00	
2477	Not assigned						
	Issues of 1993 (Self-Adhesive)						
2478	29¢ Red Squirrel	.50	.15				
2479	29¢ Rose	.50	.15				
2480	29¢ Pine cone	.50	.15				
	Issues of 1991-92						
2481	1¢ American Kestrel, June 22	.15	.15	.15	(4)	1.25	
2482	3¢ Eastern Bluebird, June 22	.15	.15	.30	(4)	1.25	
2483-86	Not assigned						
	Perf. 11½ x 11						
2487	19¢ Fawn, Mar. 11	.35	.15	1.90	(4)	1.25	
2488	Not assigned						
2489	30¢ Cardinal, June 22	.50	.15	2.25	(4)	1.25	
2490	Not assigned						
2491	45¢ Pumpkinseed Sunfish, Dec. 2, 1992	.78	.15	3.90	(4)		
a	Black omitted	—	—				
2492	Not assigned						
	Wood Duck Booklet Issue, April 12, Perf. 10						
2493	29¢ Black and multicolored	.50	.15			1.25	
a	Booklet pane of 10	5.00				7.25	
	Perf. 11						
2494	29¢ Red and multicolored	.50	.15			1.25	
a	Booklet pane of 10	5.00				7.25	
2495	29¢ African Violet	.50	.15				
a	Booklet pane of 10	5.00					
	#2493-95a issued only in bklts. All stamps are imperf. top or bottom, or top or bottom and right edge.						
	Issues of 1990 (continued), Olympians Issue, July 6, Perf. 11						
2496	25¢ Jesse Owens	.45	.15			1.25	35,717,500
2497	25¢ Ray Ewry	.45	.15			1.25	35,717,500
2498	25¢ Hazel Wightman	.45	.15			1.25	35,717,500
2499	25¢ Eddie Eagan	.45	.15			1.25	35,717,500
2500	25¢ Helene Madison	.45	.15			1.25	35,717,500
a	Strip of 5, #2496-2500	2.50	—	5.00	(10)	3.00	7,143,500
	Indian Headdresses Booklet Issue, Aug. 17						
2501	25¢ Assiniboine Headdress	.45	.15			1.25	123,825,600
2502	25¢ Cheyenne Headdress	.45	.15			1.25	123,825,600
2503	25¢ Comanche Headdress	.45	.15			1.25	123,825,600
2504	25¢ Flathead Headdress	.45	.15			1.25	123,825,600
2505	25¢ Shoshone Headdress	.45	.15			1.25	123,825,600
a	Booklet pane of 10, 2 each of #2501-05	4.75	—			6.00	61,912,800
b	As "a," black omitted	—					
	#2501-05 issued only in booklets. All stamps imperf. top or bottom, or top or bottom and right edge.						
	Micronesia/Marshall Islands Issue, Sept. 28						
2506	25¢ Canoe and Flag of the Federated States of Micronesia	.45	.15			1.25	76,250,000
a	Black omitted	—					
2507	25¢ Stick Chart, Canoe and Flag of the Marshall Islands	.45	.15			1.25	76,250,000
a	Pair, #2506-07	1.00	.16	2.25	(4)	2.00	61,000,000

	Issues of 1990 (continued), Perf. 11	Un	U	PB	#	FDC	Q
	Creatures of the Sea Issue, Oct. 1						
2508	25¢ Killer Whales	.45	.15			1.25	69,566,000
2509	25¢ Northern Sea Lions	.45	.15			1.25	69,566,000
2510	25¢ Sea Otter	.45	.15			1.25	69,566,000
2511	25¢ Common Dolphin	.45	.15			1.25	69,566,000
a	Block of 4, #2508-11	2.00	—	2.25	(4)	3.00	69,566,000
b	As "a," black omitted	1,000.00					
	America/PUAS Issue, Oct. 12 (See also #C127)						
2512	25¢ Grand Canyon	.45	.15	2.00	(4)	1.25	150,760,000
2513	25¢ Dwight D. Eisenhower	.45	.15	2.00	(4)	1.25	142,692,000
a	Imperf. pair	2,000.00					
	Christmas Issue, Oct. 18, Perf. 11½						
2514	25¢ Madonna and Child, by Antonello	.45	.15	2.00	(4)	1.25	499,995,000
a	Booklet pane of 10	4.50				6.00	22,892,400
	Perf. 11						
2515	25¢ Christmas Tree	.45	.15	2.00	(4)	1.25	599,400,000
	Booklet Stamp, Perf. 11½ x 11 on two or three sides						
2516	Single (2515) from booklet pane	.45	.15			1.25	
a	Booklet pane of 10	4.50	—			6.00	32,030,400
	Issues of 1991, Perf. 13						
2517	29¢ F Stamp, Jan. 22	.50	.15	2.50	(4)	1.25	
	Coil Stamp, Perf. 10 Vertically						
2518	29¢ Tulip (2517), Jan. 22	.50	.15	4.00	(3)	1.25	
	Booklet Stamps, Perf. 11 on two or three sides						
2519	F Stamp, single from booklet	.50	.15			1.25	
a	Booklet pane of 10, Jan. 22	5.00				7.25	
2520	F Stamp, single from booklet	.50	.15			1.25	
a	Booklet pane of 10, Jan. 22	5.50				7.25	
	#2519 has bull's-eye perforations that measure approximately 11.2. #2520 has less-pronounced black lines in the leaf, which is a much brighter green than on #2519.						
	Perf. 11						
2521	4¢ Makeup Rate, Jan. 22	.15	.15	.40	(4)	1.25	
	Self-Adhesive, Die-Cut, Imperf.						
2522	29¢ F Flag, single from pane	.50	.25			1.25	
a	Pane of 12	6.00				8.25	
	Coil Stamps, Perf. 10 Vertically						
2523	29¢ Flag Over Mt. Rushmore, intaglio printing, Mar. 29	.50	.15	4.75	(3)	1.25	
b	Imperf. pair	20.00					
2523A	29¢ Flag Over Mt. Rushmore, gravure printing, July 4	.50	.15	4.50	(3)	1.25	
	Perf. 11						
2524	29¢ Tulip, Apr. 5	.50	.15	2.25	(4)	1.25	
a	Perf. 13	.50	.15				
	Coil Stamps, Roulette 10 Vertically						
2525	29¢ Tulip, Aug. 16	.50	.15	4.50	(3)	1.25	
	Perf. 10 Vertically						
2526	29¢ Tulip, Mar. 3	.50	.15	4.75	(3)		
	Booklet Stamp, Perf. 11 on two or three sides						
2527	29¢ Tulip (2524), single from bklt.	.50	.15			1.25	
a	Booklet pane of 10, Apr. 5	5.00				7.25	
b	As "a," vertically imperf. between —						

2511a

2508   2509

2510   2511

2512

2513

2514   2515

2517   2519   2520   2521

2522

2523   2523A

2524   2525   2526

317

2528

2529

2530

2531

2531A

2532

2533

2534

2535

2537

2538

2539

2540

2542

2543

2545

2546

2547

2548

2549

2541

2549a

	Issues of 1991 (continued), Perf. 10	Un	U	PB	#	FDC	Q
	Flag With Olympic Rings Booklet Issue, Apr. 21						
2528	29¢ U.S. Flag, Olympic Rings, single from booklet	.50	.15			1.25	
a	Booklet pane of 10	5.00				7.25	
	Perf. 10 Vertically						
2529	19¢ Fishing Boat, Aug. 8	.35	.15	3.50	(3)	1.25	
a	New printing	.35	.15	3.75	(3)		
	Ballooning Booklet Issue, May 17, Perf. 10						
2530	19¢ Overhead View of Balloon, single from booklet	.35	.15			1.25	
a	Booklet pane of 10	3.50				4.75	
	#2530 was issued only in booklets. All stamps are imperf. on one side or on one side and bottom.						
	Perf. 11						
2531	29¢ Flags on Parade, May 30	.50	.15	2.25	(4)	1.25	
	Self-Adhesive, Die-Cut, Imperf.						
2531A	29¢ Liberty Torch, single stamp from pane	.58	.25			1.25	
a	Pane of 18, June 25	10.50				12.00	
	Perf. 11						
2532	50¢ Founding of Switzerland, Feb. 22	1.00	.25	5.00	(4)	2.00	100,000,000
2533	29¢ Vermont Statehood, Mar. 1	.50	.15	2.50	(4)	1.25	181,,000
2534	29¢ Savings Bonds, Apr. 30	.50	.15	2.50	(4)	1.25	150,560,000
	Perf. 12¹/₂ x 13						
2535	29¢ Love, May 9	.50	.15	2.50	(4)	1.25	631,330,000
	Booklet Stamp, Perf. 11 on two or three sides						
2536	29¢ (2535), single from booklet	.50	.15			1.25	
a	Booklet pane of 10, May 9	5.00				7.25	
	Perf. 11						
2537	52¢ Love, May 9	.90	.20	4.50	(4)	2.00	200,000,000
	Literary Arts Issue, William Saroyan, May 22						
2538	29¢ Portrait of Saroyan	.50	.15	2.50	(4)	1.25	161,498,000
2539	$1 USPS Logo/Olympic Rings, Sept. 29	1.75	.50	7.75	(4)	1.25	
2540	$2.90 Priority Mail, July 7	5.00	2.50	25.00	(4)	6.00	
2541	$9.95 Domestic Express Mail, June 16	17.50	7.50	85.00	(4)	20.00	
2542	$14 International Express Mail, Aug. 31	22.50	10.00	110.00	(4)	28.00	
2543	$2.90 Space Vehicle, 1993	5.80	—	25.00	(4)		
	Fishing Flies Booklet Issue, May 31, Perf. 11 Horizontally						
2545	29¢ Royal Wulff	.50	.15			1.25	148,983,600
2546	29¢ Jock Scott	.50	.15			1.25	148,983,600
2547	29¢ Apte Tarpon Fly	.50	.15			1.25	148,983,600
2548	29¢ Lefty's Deceiver	.50	.15			1.25	148,983,600
2549	29¢ Muddler Minnow	.50	.15			1.25	148,983,600
a	Booklet pane of 5, #2545-49	2.50	—			4.50	148,983,600
	#2545-49 were issued only in booklets. All stamps are imperf. at sides or imperf. at sides and bottom.						

	Issues of 1991 (continued), Perf. 11	Un	U	PB	#	FDC	Q
	Performing Arts Issue, Cole Porter, June 8, Perf. 11						
2550	29¢ Portrait of Porter at Piano, Sheet Music	.50	.15	2.50	(4)	1.25	149,848,000
a	Vertical pair, imperf. horizontally	650.00					
2551	29¢ Operations Desert Shield/ Desert Storm, July 2	.50	.15	2.50	(4)	1.25	200,003,000
	Booklet Stamp, Perf. 11 on one or two sides						
2552	29¢ Operations Desert Shield/ Desert Storm (2551), July 2, single from booklet	.50	.15			1.25	200,000,000
a	Booklet pane of 5	2.50	—	4.50			40,000,000
	Summer Olympic Games Issue, July 12						
2553	29¢ Pole Vaulter	.50	.15			1.25	34,005,120
2554	29¢ Discus Thrower	.50	.15			1.25	34,005,120
2555	29¢ Women Sprinters	.50	.15			1.25	34,005,120
2556	29¢ Javelin Thrower	.50	.15			1.25	34,005,120
2557	29¢ Women Hurdlers	.50	.15			1.25	34,005,120
a	Strip of 5, #2553-57	2.50		5.50	(10)	3.25	34,005,120
2558	29¢ Numismatics, Aug. 13	.50	.15	2.50	(4)	1.25	150,310,000
	World War II Miniature Sheet, Sept. 3						
2559	Sheet of 10 and central label	5.80	—			6.00	15,218,000
a	29¢ Burma Road	.58	.29			1.25	15,218,000
b	29¢ America's First Peacetime Draft	.58	.29			1.25	15,218,000
c	29¢ Lend-Lease Act	.58	.29			1.25	15,218,000
d	29¢ Atlantic Charter	.58	.29			1.25	15,218,000
e	29¢ Arsenal of Democracy;	.58	.29			1.25	15,218,000
f	29¢ Destroyer *Reuben James*	.58	.29			1.25	15,218,000
g	29¢ Civil Defense	.58	.29			1.25	15,218,000
h	29¢ Liberty Ship	.58	.29			1.25	15,218,000
i	29¢ Pearl Harbor	.58	.29			1.25	15,218,000
j	29¢ U.S. Declaration of War	.58	.29			1.25	15,218,000
2560	29¢ Basketball, Aug. 28	.50	.15	2.50	(4)	1.25	149,810,000
2561	29¢ District of Columbia, Sept. 7	.50	.15	2.50	(4)	1.25	149,260,000
	Comedians Booklet Issue, Aug. 29, Perf. 11 on two or three sides						
2562	29¢ Stan Laurel and Oliver Hardy	.58	.15			1.25	139,995,600
2563	29¢ Edgar Bergen and Dummy Charlie McCarthy	.58	.15			1.25	139,995,600
2564	29¢ Jack Benny	.58	.15			1.25	139,995,600
2565	29¢ Fanny Brice	.58	.15			1.25	139,995,600
2566	29¢ Bud Abbott and Lou Costello	.58	.15			1.25	139,995,600
a	Booklet pane of 10, 2 each of #2562-66	6.00	—			7.25	69,997,800
b	As "a," scarlet and bright violet omitted	650.00					
	#2562-66 issued only in booklets. All stamps are imperf. at top or bottom, or at top or bottom and right side.						
	Black Heritage Issue, Jan Matzeliger, Sept. 15, Perf. 11						
2567	29¢ Portrait of Matzeliger and Shoe-Lasting Machine Diagram	.50	.15	2.50	(4)	1.25	148,973,000

2550

2551

2553

2554

2555

2556

2557   2557a

a   b   c   d   e

1941: A World at War

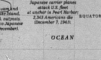

f   g   h   i   j   2559

2562   2563   2564   2565   2566   2566a

2661

2558   2560   2567

2568 **2569** **2570** **2571** **2572**

2573 **2574** **2575** **2576** **2577** **2577a**

2579 **2581**

2578

2582 **2583** **2584** **2585**

2595 **2596** **2597**

2594

2604 **2605** **2606**

2607

	Issues of 1991 (continued), Perf. 11	Un	U	PB	#	FDC	Q
	Space Exploration Booklet Issue, Oct. 1						
2568	29¢ Mercury, Mariner 10	.50	.15			1.25	33,394,800
2569	29¢ Venus, Mariner 2	.50	.15			1.25	33,394,800
2570	29¢ Earth, Landsat	.50	.15			1.25	33,394,800
2571	29¢ Moon, Lunar Orbiter	.50	.15			1.25	33,394,800
2572	29¢ Mars, Viking Orbiter	.50	.15			1.25	33,394,800
2573	29¢ Jupiter, Pioneer 11	.50	.15			1.25	33,394,800
2574	29¢ Saturn, Voyager 2	.50	.15			1.25	33,394,800
2575	29¢ Uranus, Voyager 2	.50	.15			1.25	33,394,800
2576	29¢ Neptune, Voyager 2	.50	.15			1.25	33,394,800
2577	29¢ Pluto	.50	.15			1.25	33,394,800
a	Booklet pane of 10, #2568-77	6.00	—			7.25	33,394,800
	#2568-77 issued only in booklets. All stamps are imperf. at top or bottom, or at top or bottom and right side.						
	Christmas Issue, Oct. 17, Perf. 11						
2578	29¢ Madonna and Child, by Romano	.58	.15	2.50	(4)	1.25	401,000,000
a	Booklet pane of 10	5.80					30,000,000
2579	29¢ Santa Claus Sliding Down Chimney	.58	.15	2.50	(4)	1.25	900,000,000
	Booklet Stamps						
2580	29¢ Santa Claus (2579), Type I, single from booklet	.58	.15			1.25	
2581	29¢ Santa Claus, Type II, single from booklet	.58	.15			1.25	
a	Pair, #2580, 2581	1.16	.25			3.50	28,000,000
	The extreme left brick in top row of chimney is missing from Type II, #2581.						
2582	29¢ Santa Claus Checking List, single from booklet	.58	.15			1.25	
a	Booklet pane of 4	2.40	—			3.50	28,000,000
2583	29¢ Santa Claus Leaving Present Under Tree, single from booklet	.58	.15			1.25	
a	Booklet pane of 4	2.40	—			3.50	28,000,000
2584	29¢ Santa Claus Going Up Chimney, single from booklet	.58	.15			1.25	
a	Booklet pane of 4	2.40	—			3.50	28,000,000
2585	29¢ Santa Claus Flying Away in Sleigh, single from booklet	.58	.15			1.25	
a	Booklet pane of 4	2.40	—			3.50	28,000,000
	#2582-85 issued only in booklets. All stamps are imperf. at top or bottom, or at top or bottom and right side.						
	Issues of 1992						
	Coil Stamps, Perf. 10 Vertically						
2594	29¢ Pledge of Allegiance	.50	.15			1.25	
a	Booklet of 10	5.00	—				
2595	29¢ Eagle and Shield (brown lettering)	.50	.25				
a	Pane of 17 + label	8.50					
2596	29¢ Eagle and Shield (green lettering)	.50	.25				
a	Pane of 17 + label	8.50					
2597	29¢ Eagle and Shield (red lettering)	.50	.25				
a	Pane of 17 + label	8.50					
	Issues of 1991						
2604	10¢ Eagle and Shield, Dec. 13	.20	.20	3.25	(3)		
2605	10¢ Eagle	.20	.20				
2606	10¢ Eagle	.20	.20				
2607	23¢ Flag	.46	.46	4.50	(3)		

	Issues of 1992, Perf. 11	Un	U	PB	#	FDC	Q
2608	23¢ USA, July 21	.40	.15	3.75	(3)		
2608A	23¢ USA (Bureau)	.40	.15	3.75	(3)		
2608B	23¢ USA (violet)	.40	.40	3.75	(3)		
2609	29¢ Flag Over White House, April 23	.50	.15	5.00	(3)	1.25	
	Winter Olympic Games Issue						
2611	29¢ Hockey	.50	.15			1.25	32,000,000
2612	29¢ Figure Skating	.50	.15			1.25	32,000,000
2613	29¢ Speed Skating	.50	.15			1.25	32,000,000
2614	29¢ Skiing	.50	.15			1.25	32,000,000
2615	29¢ Bobsledding	.50	.15			1.25	32,000,000
a	Strip of 5, #2611-15	2.90	—	5.50	(10)		
2616	29¢ World Columbian Stamp Expo, Jan. 24	.50	.15	2.50	(4)	1.25	148,665,000
	Black Heritage Issue						
2617	29¢ W.E.B. DuBois, Jan. 31	.50	.15	2.50	(4)	1.25	149,990,000
2618	29¢ Love, Feb. 6	.50	.15	2.50	(4)	1.25	835,000,000
2619	29¢ Olympic Baseball, April 3	.50	.15	2.50	(4)	1.25	160,000,000
	First Voyage of Christopher Columbus Issue, April 24						
2620	29¢ Seeking Queen Isabella's Support	.50	.15			1.25	40,005,000
2621	29¢ Crossing The Atlantic	.50	.15			1.25	40,005,000
2622	29¢ Approaching Land	.50	.15			1.25	40,005,000
2623	29¢ Coming Ashore	.50	.15			1.25	40,005,000
a	Block of 4, #2620-23	2.00	1.00	2.50	(4)	3.00	

What type of skating uses a "rake"?

Figure skating, an Olympic event since 1908, often involves numerous spins and jumps for the skater. That's why figure skates have jagged teeth, known as "toe rakes" located on the front of the blade, which is only one eighth of an inch thick. Toe rakes help skaters dig into the ice for balanced spins, smooth landings and quick maneuvers. **(#2612)**

2608   **2608A**   **2608B**

2609

2611   **2612**   **2613**   **2614**   **2615**   **2615a**

2619

2616   **2617**   **2618**

2620   **2621**   **2623a**

2622   **2623**

2624

2625

2626

2627

2628

2629

	Issues of 1992 (continued), Perf. 10¹/₂	Un	U		Q
	The Voyages of Columbus Souvenir Sheets, May 22				
2624	First Sighting of Land, sheet of 3	2.10	—		2,000,000
a	1¢ deep blue	.15	.15		
b	4¢ ultramarine	.15	.15		
c	$1 salmon	2.00	1.00		
2625	Claiming a New World, sheet of 3	8.10	—		2,000,000
a	2¢ brown violet	.15	.15		
b	3¢ green	.15	.15		
c	$4 crimson lake	8.00	4.00		
2626	Seeking Royal Support, sheet of 3	1.70	—		2,000,000
a	5¢ chocolate	.15	.15		
b	30¢ orange brown	.60	.30		
c	50¢ slate blue	1.00	.50		
2627	Royal Favor Restored, sheet of 3	6.28	—		2,000,000
a	6¢ purple	.15	.15		
b	8¢ magenta	.16	.15		
c	$3 yellow green	6.00	3.00		
2628	Reporting Discoveries, sheet of 3	4.50	—		2,000,000
a	10¢ black brown	.20	.15		
b	15¢ dark green	.30	.15		
c	$2 brown red	4.00	2.00		
2629	$5 Christopher Columbus, sheet of 1	10.00	—		2,000,000

Who reigned over the Ocean sea?

After returning from his first mission in 1493, Columbus and his officers presented themselves before Queen Isabella and King Ferdinand. He was dubbed "Admiral of the Ocean Sea" and given a grand reception. The title allowed Columbus to judge admiralty cases (including piracy, ship-wreck and wage disputes) anywhere in the Atlantic Ocean. **(#2628)**

	Issues of 1992 (continued), Perf. 11	Un	U	PB	#	FDC	Q
2630	29¢ New York Stock Exchange Bicentennial, May 17	.50	.15	2.50	(4)	1.25	148,000,000
	Space Adventures Issue, May 29						
2631	29¢ Cosmonaut, US Space Shuttle	.50	.15			1.25	37,315,000
2632	29¢ Astronaut, Russian Space Station	.50	.15			1.25	37,315,000
2633	29¢ Sputnik, Vostok, Apollo Command and Lunar Modules	.50	.15			1.25	37,315,000
2634	29¢ Soyuz, Mercury and Gemini Spacecraft	.50	.15			1.25	37,315,000
a	Block of 4, #2631-34	2.00		2.50	(4)	3.00	
2635	29¢ Alaska Highway, 50th Anniversary, May 30	.50	.15	2.50	(4)	1.25	146,610,000
a	Black (engr.) omitted	—					
2636	29¢ Kentucky Statehood Bicentennial, June 11	.50	.15	2.50	(4)	1.25	160,000,000
	Summer Olympic Games Issue, June 1						
2637	29¢ Soccer	.50	.15			1.25	32,000,000
2638	29¢ Gymnastics	.50	.15			1.25	32,000,000
2639	29¢ Volleyball	.50	.15			1.25	32,000,000
2640	29¢ Boxing	.50	.15			1.25	32,000,000
2641	29¢ Swimming	.50	.15			1.25	32,000,000
a	Strip of 5, #2637-41	2.50	—	5.50	(10)	4.00	
	Hummingbirds Issue, June 15						
2642	29¢ Ruby-Throated	.50	.15			1.25	87,728,000
2643	29¢ Broad-Billed	.50	.15			1.25	87,728,000
2644	29¢ Costa's	.50	.15			1.25	87,728,000
2645	29¢ Rufous	.50	.15			1.25	87,728,000
2646	29¢ Calliope	.50	.15			1.25	87,728,000
a	Booklet pane of 5, #2642-46	2.50	—			4.00	

Where does the Alaska Highway run?

The Alaska Highway connects Dawson Creek, British Columbia, Canada, with Delta Junction in central Alaska. The 1,422-mile strip of road was created in 1942 as a military supply route during World War II, and was once known as the Alcan (*A*laska and *Can*ada) Highway. Although the route is the only major road connecting Alaska to the rest of Canada and the U.S., only a fourth of it is actually paved. **(#2635)**

2630

2631   **2632**   **2634a**

2633   **2634**

2636

2635

2637   **2638**   **2639**   **2640**   **2641**   **2641a**

Indian Paintbrush	Fragrant Water Lily	Meadow Beauty	Jack-in-the-Pulpit	California Poppy
2647	2648	2649	2650	2651
Large-flowered Trillium	Tickseed	Shooting Star	Stream Violet	Bluets
2652	2653	2654	2655	2656
Herb Robert	Marsh Marigold	Sweet White Violet	Claret Cup Cactus	White Mountain Avens
2657	2658	2659	2660	2661
Sessile Bellwort	Blue Flag	Harlequin Lupine	Twinflower	Common Sunflower
2662	2663	2664	2665	2666

Sego Lily

Virginia Bluebells

Ohi'a Lehua

Rosebud Orchid

Showy Evening Primrose

Issues of 1992 (continued), Perf. 11	Un	U	FDC	Q
Wildflowers Issue, July 24				
2647 29¢ Indian Paintbrush	.50	.15	1.25	11,000,000
2648 29¢ Fragrant Water Lily	.50	.15	1.25	11,000,000
2649 29¢ Meadow Beauty	.50	.15	1.25	11,000,000
2650 29¢ Jack-in-the-Pulpit	.50	.15	1.25	11,000,000
2651 29¢ California Poppy	.50	.15	1.25	11,000,000
2652 29¢ Large-Flowered Trillium	.50	.15	1.25	11,000,000
2653 29¢ Tickseed	.50	.15	1.25	11,000,000
2654 29¢ Shooting Star	.50	.15	1.25	11,000,000
2655 29¢ Stream Violet	.50	.15	1.25	11,000,000
2656 29¢ Bluets	.50	.15	1.25	11,000,000
2657 29¢ Herb Robert	.50	.15	1.25	11,000,000
2658 29¢ Marsh Marigold	.50	.15	1.25	11,000,000
2659 29¢ Sweet White Violet	.50	.15	1.25	11,000,000
2660 29¢ Claret Cup Cactus	.50	.15	1.25	11,000,000
2661 29¢ White Mountain Avens	.50	.15	1.25	11,000,000
2662 29¢ Sessile Bellwort	.50	.15	1.25	11,000,000
2663 29¢ Blue Flag	.50	.15	1.25	11,000,000
2664 29¢ Harlequin Lupine	.50	.15	1.25	11,000,000
2665 29¢ Twinflower	.50	.15	1.25	11,000,000
2666 29¢ Common Sunflower	.50	.15	1.25	11,000,000
2667 29¢ Sego Lily	.50	.15	1.25	11,000,000
2668 29¢ Virginia Bluebells	.50	.15	1.25	11,000,000
2669 29¢ Ohi'a Lehua	.50	.15	1.25	11,000,000
2670 29¢ Rosebud Orchid	.50	.15	1.25	11,000,000
2671 29¢ Showy Evening Primrose	.50	.15	1.25	11,000,000

How tall can a sunflower grow?

Common sunflowers usually grow from three to 10 feet, and often have more than one flower head. The heads can produce up to 1,000 seeds.

Sunflower oil is ranked as the third most abundantly produced vegetable oil because the seeds are so rich in protein. The larger seeds of these golden beauties can also be salted and sold as a snack.

Sunflowers can be grown almost anywhere. The U.S. states with the greatest sunflower seed production are Minnesota and Texas. **(#2666)**

	Issues of 1992 (continued), Perf. 11	Un	U	PB	#	FDC	Q
	Wildflowers Issue (continued)						
2672	29¢ Fringed Gentian	.50	.15			1.25	11,000,000
2673	29¢ Yellow Lady's Slipper	.50	.15			1.25	11,000,000
2674	29¢ Passionflower	.50	.15			1.25	11,000,000
2675	29¢ Bunchberry	.50	.15			1.25	11,000,000
2676	29¢ Pasqueflower	.50	.15			1.25	11,000,000
2677	29¢ Round-Lobed Hepatica	.50	.15			1.25	11,000,000
2678	29¢ Wild Columbine	.50	.15			1.25	11,000,000
2679	29¢ Fireweed	.50	.15			1.25	11,000,000
2680	29¢ Indian Pond Lily	.50	.15			1.25	11,000,000
2681	29¢ Turk's Cap Lily	.50	.15			1.25	11,000,000
2682	29¢ Dutchman's Breeches	.50	.15			1.25	11,000,000
2683	29¢ Trumpet Honeysuckle	.50	.15			1.25	11,000,000
2684	29¢ Jacob's Ladder	.50	.15			1.25	11,000,000
2685	29¢ Plains Prickly Pear	.50	.15			1.25	11,000,000
2686	29¢ Moss Campion	.50	.15			1.25	11,000,000
2687	29¢ Bearberry	.50	.15			1.25	11,000,000
2688	29¢ Mexican Hat	.50	.15			1.25	11,000,000
2689	29¢ Harebell	.50	.15			1.25	11,000,000
2690	29¢ Desert Five Spot	.50	.15			1.25	11,000,000
2691	29¢ Smooth Solomon's Seal	.50	.15			1.25	11,000,000
2692	29¢ Red Maids	.50	.15			1.25	11,000,000
2693	29¢ Yellow Skunk Cabbage	.50	.15			1.25	11,000,000
2694	29¢ Rue Anemone	.50	.15			1.25	11,000,000
2695	29¢ Standing Cypress	.50	.15			1.25	11,000,000
2696	29¢ Wild Flax	.50	.15			1.25	11,000,000
a	Pane of 50, #2647-96	25.00	—			32.50	11,000,000

How many kinds of wildflowers exist?

More than 250,000 different species of flowering plants bloom in the world — 20,000 that are native to the U.S. and Canada. About half of these flowering plants are classified as "wildflowers."

The Jacob's Ladder is one of 300 phlox wildflowers, which are annuals (they live for only one season) or perennials (they return every year). The Jacob's Ladder and all other phlox flowers have five leafy sepals, five pollen-filled stamens and five petals. (**#2684**)

Fringed Gentian

2672

Yellow Lady's Slipper

2673

Passionflower

2674

Bunchberry

2675

Pasqueflower

2676

Round-lobed Hepatica

2677

Wild Columbine

2678

Fireweed

2679

Indian Pond Lily

2680

Turk's Cap Lily

2681

Dutchman's Breeches

2682

Trumpet Honeysuckle

2683

Jacob's Ladder

2684

Plains Prickly Pear

2685

Moss Campion

2686

Bearberry

2687

Mexican Hat

2688

Harebell

2689

Desert Five Spot

2690

Smooth Solomon's Seal

2691

Red Maids

2692

Yellow Skunk Cabbage

2693

Rue Anemone

2694

Standing Cypress

2695

Wild Flax

2696

a   b   c   d   e

1942: Into the Battle

f   g   h   i   j   2697

2698

Dorothy Parker
American Writer 1893–1967

2699

Theodore von Kármán
Aerospace Scientist

Minerals USA — Azurite
Minerals USA — Copper
Minerals USA — Variscite
Minerals USA — Wulfenite

2700   2701   2703a
2702   2703

Giraffe
Giant Panda
Flamingo
King Penguins
White Bengal Tiger

2705   2709a
2706
2707
2708
2709

Juan Rodríguez CABRILLO
Explorer of California 1542

2704

	Issues of 1992 (continued), Perf. 11	Un	U	PB	#	FDC	Q
	World War II Issue Miniature Sheet, Aug. 17						
2697	Sheet of 10 and central label	5.25	2.90				12,000,000
a	29¢ B-25s Take Off to Raid Tokyo	.52	.29			1.25	12,000,000
b	29¢ Food and Other Commodities Rationed	.52	.29			1.25	12,000,000
c	29¢ U.S. Wins Battle of the Coral Sea	.52	.29			1.25	12,000,000
d	29¢ Corregidor Falls to Japanese	.52	.29			1.25	12,000,000
e	29¢ Japan Invades Aleutian Islands	.52	.29			1.25	12,000,000
f	29¢ Allies Decipher Secret Enemy Codes	.52	.29			1.25	12,000,000
g	29¢ Yorktown Lost	.52	.29			1.25	12,000,000
h	29¢ Millions of Women Join War Effort	.52	.29			1.25	12,000,000
i	29¢ Marines Land on Guadalcanal	.52	.29			1.25	12,000,000
j	29¢ Allies Land in North Africa	.52	.29			1.25	12,000,000
2698	29¢ Dorothy Parker, Aug. 22	.50	.15	2.50	(4)	1.25	105,000,000
2699	29¢ Dr. Theodore von Karman, Aug. 31	.50	.15	2.50	(4)	1.25	142,500,000
	Minerals Issue, Sept. 17						
2700	29¢ Azurite	.50	.15			1.25	36,831,000
2701	29¢ Copper	.50	.15			1.25	36,831,000
2702	29¢ Variscite	.50	.15			1.25	36,831,000
2703	29¢ Wulfenite	.50	.15			1.25	36,831,000
a	Block of 4, #2700-03	2.00	1.10	2.50	(4)	3.00	
2704	29¢ Juan Rodriguez Cabrillo, Sept. 28	.50	.15	2.50	(4)	1.25	85,000,000
	Wild Animals Issue, Oct. 1, Perf. 11 Horizontal						
2705	29¢ Giraffe	.50	.15			1.25	80,000,000
2706	29¢ Giant Panda	.50	.15			1.25	80,000,000
2707	29¢ Flamingo	.50	.15			1.25	80,000,000
2708	29¢ King Penguins	.50	.15			1.25	80,000,000
2709	29¢ White Bengal Tiger	.50	.15			1.25	80,000,000
a	Booklet pane of 5, #2705-09	2.50	—			4.00	

What was the Algonquin Round Table?

Dorothy Parker, the famous writer, would meet regularly with other known writers at the Algonquin Hotel in New York City in the 1920s. The group became known as the Algonquin Round Table. Parker was known for her poetry and short stories, which were widely published. She was also one of *The New Yorker*'s first regular contributors, and later wrote the magazine's book review columns. **(#2698)**

	Issues of 1992 (continued), Perf. 11½ x 11	Un	U	PB	#	FDC	Q
	Christmas Issue, Oct. 22						
2710	29¢ Madonna and Child by Giovanni Bellini	.50	.15	2.50	(4)	1.25	300,000,000
a	Booklet pane of 10	5.00					349,254,000
2711	29¢ Horse and Rider	.50	.15			1.25	125,000,000
2712	29¢ Toy Train	.50	.15			1.25	125,000,000
2713	29¢ Toy Steamer	.50	.15			1.25	125,000,000
2714	29¢ Toy Ship	.50	.15			1.25	125,000,000
a	Block of 4, #2711-14	2.00		2.50	(4)	3.00	
	Perf. 11						
2715	29¢ Horse and Rider	.50	.15			1.25	102,137,500
2716	29¢ Toy Train	.50	.15			1.25	102,137,500
2717	29¢ Toy Steamer	.50	.15			1.25	102,137,500
2718	29¢ Toy Ship	.50	.15			1.25	102,137,500
a	Booklet pane of 4, #2715-18	2.00	—			3.00	
2719	29¢ Toy Train (self-adhesive)	.58	.15			1.25	21,600,000
a	Booklet pane of 18	10.50					
2720	29¢ Happy New Year	.50	.15	2.50	(4)		

Whose New Year celebration lasts four days?

Most people in the U.S. celebrate the new year by going to a party on New Year's Eve, blowing horns and throwing confetti when the clock strikes twelve. But the Chinese New Year is different — it's four days long. And it happens anytime between January 21 and February 19, starting with the first new moon after the sun enters Aquarius. On the last day of the festivities, adults dress up as dragons to entertain the children. **(#2720)**

2710

2711 2712 2714a

2713 2714

2715 2716 2718a

2717 2718

2719   2719a

2720

2721

2722

2723

2724   2725   2726   2727   2728

2729   2730

2735

2732

2736

2733

2737

2734

2731

2737b

2741   2742   2743   2744   2745   2745a

	Issues of 1993	Un	U	PB	#	FDC	Q
	American Music Series						
2721	29¢ Elvis Presley	.50	.15	2.50	(4)		517,000,000
	Perf. 10						
2722	29¢ Oklahoma!	.50	.15	2.50	(4)		150,000,000
2723	29¢ Hank Williams	.50	.15	2.50	(4)		152,000,000
2724	29¢ Elvis Presley	.50	.15				14,285,715
2725	29¢ Bill Haley	.50	.15				14,285,715
2726	29¢ Clyde McPhatter	.50	.15				14,285,715
2727	29¢ Ritchie Valens	.50	.15				14,285,715
2728	29¢ Otis Redding	.50	.15				14,285,715
2729	29¢ Buddy Holly	.50	.15				14,285,715
2730	29¢ Dinah Washington	.50	.15				14,285,715
a	Vertical strip of 7, #2724-30	3.50	—				
	Perf. 11 Horizontal						
2731	29¢ Elvis Presley	.50	.15				98,841,000
2732	29¢ Bill Haley (2725)	.50	.15				32,947,000
2733	29¢ Clyde McPhatter (2726)	.50	.15				32,947,000
2734	29¢ Ritchie Valens (2727)	.50	.15				32,947,000
2735	29¢ Otis Redding	.50	.15				65,894,000
2736	29¢ Buddy Holly	.50	.15				65,894,000
2737	29¢ Dinah Washington	.50	.15				65,894,000
a	Booklet pane, 2 #2731, 1 each #2732-37	4.00	—				
b	Booklet pane of 4, #2731, #2735-37	2.00	—				
2738-40 Not assigned							
	Space Fantasy Issue, Jan. 25						
	Perf. 11 Vertical on 1 or 2 sides						
2741	29¢ multicolored	.50	.15				140,000,000
2742	29¢ multicolored	.50	.15				140,000,000
2743	29¢ multicolored	.50	.15				140,000,000
2744	29¢ multicolored	.50	.15				140,000,000
2745	29¢ multicolored	.50	.15				140,000,000
a	Booklet pane of 5, #2741-45	2.50					

Who's the "Queen of the Blues"?

Dinah Washington, born Ruth Lee Jones in 1924, was crowned "Queen of the Blues" for her nationwide popularity as a singer and piano player.

Washington began singing when she was 11, when her mother taught her religious songs, and Ruth frequently played piano at her church. She toured as a gospel singer, and linked up with boogie-woogie clubs by the time she was 18. She went on to play hundreds of big city clubs, TV specials and international jazz festivals before her death in 1963. **(#2737)**

	Issues of 1993 (continued), Perf. 11	Un	U	PB	#	FDC	Q
2746	29¢ Percy Lavon Julian	.50	.15	2.50	(4)		105,000,000
2747	29¢ Oregon Trail	.50	.15	2.50	(4)		110,000,000
2748	29¢ World University Games	.50	.15	2.50	(4)		110,000,000
2749	29¢ Grace Kelly	.50	.15	2.50	(4)		172,870,000
	Circus Issue, Apr. 6						
2750	29¢ Clown	.50	.15				65,625,000
2751	29¢ Ringmaster	.50	.15				65,625,000
2752	29¢ Trapeze Artist	.50	.15				65,625,000
2753	29¢ Elephant	.50	.15				65,625,000
a	Block of 4 #2750-53	2.00	1.10	3.50	(6)		
2754	29¢ Cherokee Strip	.50	.15	2.50	(4)		110,000,000
2755	29¢ Dean Acheson	.50	.15	2.50	(4)		115,870,000
b	As "a," black omitted	—					
	Sporting Horses Issue, May 1, Perf. 11 x 11½						
2756	29¢ Steeplechase	.50	.15				40,000,000
2757	29¢ Thoroughbred Racing	.50	.15				40,000,000
2758	29¢ Harness Racing	.50	.15				40,000,000
2759	29¢ Polo	.50	.15				40,000,000
a	Block of 4, #2756-59	2.00	1.10	2.50	(4)		

2746

2747

2748

2749

2753a

2752   2753
2750   2751

2754

2759a

2756   2757
2758   2759

2755

341

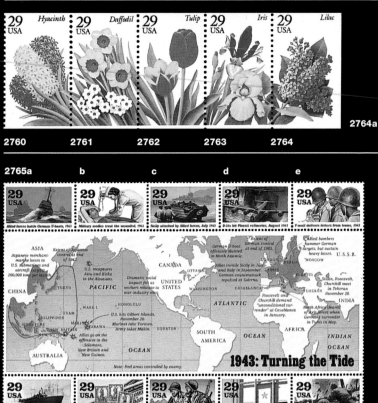

Hyacinth 29 USA · Daffodil 29 USA · Tulip 29 USA · Iris 29 USA · Lilac 29 USA

2764a

2760 2761 2762 2763 2764

2765a   b   c   d   e

1943: Turning the Tide

f   g   h   i   j

2766

2767

2768

2769

2770

2770a

	Issues of 1993 (continued), Perf. 11	Un	U	PB	#	FDC	Q
	Garden Flowers Issue, May 15, Perf. 11 Vertical						
2760	29¢ Hyacinth	.50	.15				199,784,500
2761	29¢ Daffodil	.50	.15				199,784,500
2762	29¢ Tulip	.50	.15				199,784,500
2763	29¢ Iris	.50	.15				199,784,500
2764	29¢ Lilac	.50	.15				199,784,500
a	Booklet pane of 5, #2760-64	2.50	—				
b	As "a," black omitted	—					
c	As "a," imperf.	—					
	World War II Issue Miniature Sheet, May 31, Perf. 11						
2765	Sheet of 10 and central label	5.80	3.00				
a	29¢ Allied Forces Battle German U-boats	.58	.30				12,000,000
b	29¢ Military Medics Treat the Wounded	.58	.30				12,000,000
c	29¢ Sicily Attacked by Allied Forces	.58	.30				12,000,000
d	29¢ B-24s Hit Ploesti Refineries	.58	.30				12,000,000
e	29¢ V-Mail Delivers Letters from Home	.58	.30				12,000,000
f	29¢ Italy Invaded by Allies	.58	.30				12,000,000
g	29¢ Bonds and Stamps Help War Effort	.58	.30				12,000,000
h	29¢ "Willie and Joe" Keep Spirits High	.58	.30				12,000,000
i	29¢ Gold Stars Mark World War II Losses	.58	.30				12,000,000
j	29¢ Marines Assault Tarawa	.58	.30				12,000,000
2766	29¢ Joe Louis	.50	.15	2.50	(4)		160,000,000
	American Music Series, July 14						
2767	29¢ Show Boat	.50	.15				128,735,000
2768	29¢ Porgy & Bess	.50	.15				128,735,000
2769	29¢ Oklahoma!	.50	.15				128,735,000
2770	29¢ My Fair Lady	.50	.15				128,735,000
a	Booklet pane of 4, #2767-70	2.00					

	Issues of 1993 (continued), Perf. 10	Un	U	PB	#	FDC	Q
	Country & Western, American Music Series						
2771	29¢ Hank Williams (2775)	.50	.15				25,000,000
2772	29¢ Patsy Cline (2777)	.50	.15				25,000,000
2773	29¢ The Carter Family (2776)	.50	.15				25,000,000
2774	29¢ Bob Willis (2778)	.50	.15				25,000,000
a	Block or horiz. strip of 4, #2771-74	2.00	1.10				
	Booklet Stamps, Perf. 11 Horizontal						
2775	29¢ Hank Williams	.50	.15				170,000,000
2776	29¢ The Carter Family	.50	.15				170,000,000
2777	29¢ Patsy Cline	.50	.15				170,000,000
2778	29¢ Bob Willis	.50	.15				170,000,000
a	Booklet pane of 4, #2775-78	2.00	—				
	National Postal Museum Issue, July 30, Perf. 11						
2779	Independence Hall, Benjamin Franklin, Printing Press, Colonial Post Rider	.50	.15				37,500,000
2780	Pony Express Rider, Civil War Soldier, Concord Stagecoach	.50	.15				37,500,000
2781	Biplane, Charles Lindbergh, Railway Mail Car, 1931 Model A Ford Mail Truck	.50	.15				37,500,000
2782	California Gold Rush Miner's Letter, Barcode and Circular Date Stamp	.50	.15				37,500,000
a	Block or strip of 4, #2779-82	2.00	1.10	2.50	(4)		
	American Sign Language Issue, Sept. 20, Perf. 11½						
2783	29¢ Recognizing Deafness	.50	.15				41,840,000
2784	29¢ American Sign Language	.50	.15				41,840,000
a	Pair, #2783-84	1.00	.20				
	Classic Books Issues, Oct. 23						
2785	29¢ *Rebecca of Sunnybrook Farm*	.50	.15				37,550,000
2786	29¢ *Little House on the Prairie*	.50	.15				37,550,000
2787	29¢ *The Adventures of Huckleberry Finn*	.50	.15				37,550,000
2788	29¢ *Little Women*	.50	.15				37,550,000
a	Block or horiz. strip of 4, #2785-88	2.00	1.10				

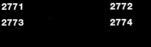

2771

2773

2772

2774

2774a

2775

2776

2777

2778

2778a

2779

2781

2780

2782

2782a

2783

2784

2784a

2787

2785

2788

2786

2788a

2791

2792

2789

2790

2793

2794

2794a

2799　　　　**2800**

2801　　　　**2802**　　　　　　　　　**2802a**

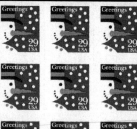

2804

2806

2805

2803a

346　　　　　　　**2803**

2594B

	Issues of 1993 (continued), Perf. 10	Un	U	PB	#	FDC	Q
	Christmas Issue, Oct. 21						
2789	29¢ Madonna and Child	.50	.15				500,000,000
	Booklet Stamps, Perf. 11½ x 11 on 2 or 3 sides						
2790	29¢ Madonna and Child	.50	.15				500,000,000
a	Booklet pane of 4	2.00	—				
	Perf. 11½						
2791	29¢ Jack-in-the-Box	.50	.15				250,000,000
2792	29¢ Red-Nosed Reindeer	.50	.15				250,000,000
2793	29¢ Snowman	.50	.15				250,000,000
2794	29¢ Toy Soldier	.50	.15				250,000,000
a	Block or strip of 4, #2791-94	2.00	1.10				
	Booklet Stamps, Perf 11 x 10 on 2 or 3 sides						
2795	29¢ Toy Soldier (2794)	.50	.15				200,000,000
2796	29¢ Snowman (2793)	.50	.15				200,000,000
2797	29¢ Red-Nosed Reindeer (2792)	.50	.15				200,000,000
2798	29¢ Jack-in-the-Box (2791)	.50	.15				200,000,000
a	Booklet pane, 3 each #2795-96, 2 each #2797-98	5.00	—				
b	Booklet pane, 3 each #2797-98, 2 each #2795-96	5.00	—				
	Self-adhesive						
2799	29¢ Snowman	.50	.15				120,000,000
2800	29¢ Toy Soldier	.50	.15				120,000,000
2801	29¢ Jack-in-the-Box	.50	.15				120,000,000
2802	29¢ Red-Nosed Reindeer	.50	.15				120,000,000
a	Booklet pane, 3 each #2799-802	6.00					
2803	29¢ Snowman	.50	.15				18,000,000
a	Booklet pane of 18	9.00					
	Perf. 11						
2804	29¢ Northern Mariana Islands	.50	.15				88,300,000
2805	29¢ Columbus Landing in Puerto Rico	.50	.15				105,000,000
2806	29¢ AIDS Awareness	.50	.15				100,000,000
2806a	AIDS booklet version (2806)	.50	.15				250,000,000
2806b	AIDS booklet pane of 5	2.50	—				

	Addendum (1993)						
2452B	5¢ Circus Wagon (2452)	.15	.15	1.10	(3)		
2594B	29¢ Pledge of Allegiance	.50	.15				
c	Booklet of 10	5.00	—				
C128b	50¢ Portrait of Quimby (C128)	.90	.24	4.50	(4)		
C132	40¢ Portrait of Piper (C129)	.80	.22	4.00	(4)		

The Thrill of Favorite Topics on Stamps

- Comprehensive stamp collections devoted to special subjects
- Interesting, informative text in colorfully illustrated books
- Includes protective stamp mounts

There's a Topical Collection Just For You

Whether it's the pure visual appeal of some of America's best stamp designs, the psychological appeal of subjects that evoke fond memories or stir emotions, or the educational appeal of interesting background material on intriguing topics, Topical Stamp Collections contain something for everyone.

World War II

Designed for all those whose lives have been affected by the war, these 44-page deluxe, hardbound books are the first four of five annual editions. They focus on the years 1941, 1942, 1943 and 1994, each features two of the striking World War II miniature sheets of 10 stamps—one to grace the front of the book, the other to be broken up and mounted in sections devoted to such subjects as the Battle of Midway or the bombing of Pearl Harbor. ($15.95 each)

Legends of the Silent Screen

Relive the laughter, drama and thrills of the "Golden Age of Cinema" with this handsome 56-page hardbound book. The "Legends of the Silent Screen"—Charlie Chaplin, Buster Keaton, Harold Lloyd, Clara Bow, Rudolph Valentino and others—are featured on a delightful set of 10 different stamps issued in 1994. A complete group of 20 of these stamps (two for each of the 10 performers) is included with each book. ($24.95)

To Obtain Topical Collections

Some Topical Stamp Collections are available at local post offices and Philatelic Centers. You can also fill out the postage-paid request card in this book or write to:

U.S. POSTAL SERVICE GUIDE
TOPICAL STAMP COLLECTIONS
PHILATELIC FULFILLMENT SERVICE CENTER
PROMOTIONS
PO BOX 419219
KANSAS CITY MO 64179-0998

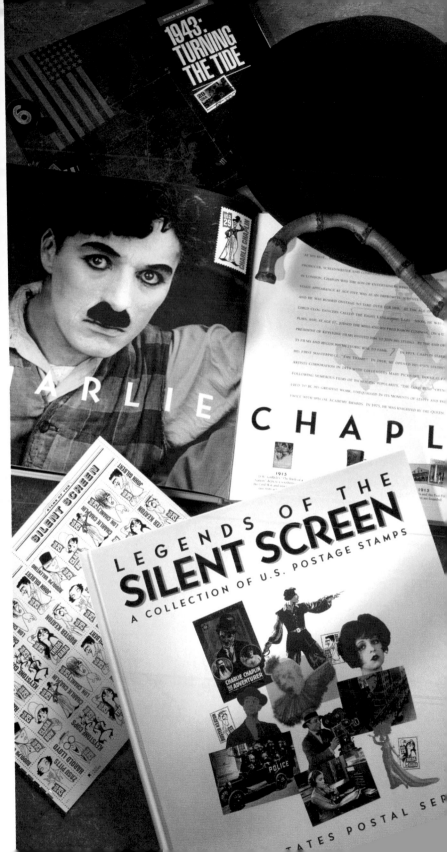

1918-1938

C1   C2   C3   C4

C6   C7   C10

C11   C12

C13   C14

C15   C18

	Issues of 1918, Perf. 11	Un	U	PB	#	FDC	Q
	For prepayment of postage on all mailable matter sent by airmail. All unwatermarked.						
C1	6¢ Curtiss Jenny, Dec. 10	55.00	25.00	650.00	(6)	17,500.00	3,395,900
	Double transfer	80.00	40.00				
C2	16¢ Curtiss Jenny, July 11	80.00	27.50	1,150.00	(6)	22,500.00	3,793,900
C3	24¢ Curtiss Jenny, May 13	75.00	32.50	360.00	(4)	27,500.00	2,134,900
a	Center Inverted	135,000.00		1,100,000.00	(4)		100
	Issues of 1923						
C4	8¢ Airplane Radiator and Wooden Propeller, Aug. 15	20.00	12.00	250.00	(6)	400.00	6,414,600
C5	16¢ Air Service Emblem, Aug. 17	75.00	27.50	1,900.00	(6)	600.00	5,309,300
C6	24¢ De Havilland Biplane, Aug. 21	75.00	22.50	2,250.00	(6)	750.00	5,285,800
	Issues of 1926-27						
C7	10¢ Map of U.S. and Two Mail Planes, Feb. 13, 1926	2.25	.25	40.00	(6)	55.00	42,092,800
	Double transfer	5.00	1.00				
C8	15¢ olive brown (C7), Sept. 18, 1926	2.75	1.90	45.00	(6)	75.00	15,597,300
C9	20¢ yellow green (C7), Jan. 25, 1927	7.00	1.65	95.00	(6)	100.00	17,616,350
	Issue of 1927-28						
C10	10¢ Lindbergh's "Spirit of St. Louis," June 18, 1927	6.00	1.65	140.00	(6)	20.00	20,379,200
a	Booklet pane of 3, May 26, 1928	75.00	50.00			825.00	
	Issue of 1928						
C11	5¢ Beacon on Rocky Mountains, July 25	4.50	.40	175.00	(8)		106,887,700
a	Recut frame line at left	6.00	1.00				
	Issues of 1930						
C12	5¢ Winged Globe, Feb. 10	8.00	.25	160.00	(6)	11.50	97,641,200
a	Horizontal pair, imperf. between	4,500.00					
	Graf Zeppelin Issue, Apr. 19						
C13	65¢ Zeppelin over Atlantic Ocean	250.00	150.00	2,000.00	(6)	1,700.00	93,500
C14	$1.30 Zeppelin Between Continents	500.00	350.00	5,000.00	(6)	1,200.00	72,400
C15	$2.60 Zeppelin Passing Globe	850.00	500.00	7,750.00	(6)	1,450.00	61,300
	Issues of 1931-32, Perf. 10$1/2$ x 11						
C16	5¢ violet (C12), Aug. 19, 1931	4.75	.35	75.00	(4)	175.00	57,340,050
C17	8¢ olive bister (C12), Sept. 26, 1932	1.90	.20	30.00	(4)	15.00	76,648,800
	Issue of 1933, Century of Progress Issue, Oct. 2, Perf. 11						
C18	50¢ Zeppelin, Federal Building at Chicago Exposition and Hangar at Friedrichshafen	75.00	65.00	650.00	(6)	225.00	324,050
	Beginning with #C19, unused values are for never-hinged stamps.						
	Issue of 1934, Perf. 10$1/2$ x 11						
C19	6¢ dull orange (C12), June 30	2.25	.15	25.00	(4)	175.00	302,205,100
	Issues of 1935-37, Trans-Pacific Issue, Perf. 11						
C20	25¢ "China Clipper" over the Pacific, Nov. 22, 1935	1.10	.75	25.00	(6)	20.00	10,205,400
C21	20¢ "China Clipper" over the Pacific, Feb. 15, 1937	8.00	1.25	110.00	(6)	20.00	12,794,600
C22	50¢ carmine (C21), Feb. 15, 1937	7.50	4.00	110.00	(6)	20.00	9,285,300
	Issue of 1938						
C23	6¢ Eagle Holding Shield, Olive Branch and Arrows, May 14	.40	.15	8.00	(4)	15.00	349,946,500
a	Vertical pair, imperf. horizontally	300.00					
b	Horizontal pair, imperf. vertically	10,000.00					
	6¢ ultramarine and carmine	150.00					

	Issue of 1939, Perf. 11	Un	U	PB/LP	#	FDC	Q
	Trans Atlantic Issue, May 16						
C24	30¢ Winged Globe	8.50	1.00	165.00	(6)	45.00	19,768,150
	Issues of 1941-44, Perf. 11 x 10½						
C25	6¢ Twin-Motor Transport, June 25, 1941	.15	.15	.70	(4)	2.25	4,476,527,700
a	Booklet pane of 3, Mar. 18, 1943	3.50	1.00			25.00	
	Singles of #C25a are imperf. at sides or imperf. at sides and bottom.						
b	Horizontal pair, imperf. between	1,500.00					
C26	8¢ olive green (C25), Mar. 21, 1944	.16	.15	1.25	(4)	3.75	1,744,878,650
C27	10¢ violet (C25), Aug. 15, 1941	1.10	.20	8.50	(4)	8.00	67,117,400
C28	15¢ brn. carmine (C25), Aug. 19, 1941	2.25	.35	12.00	(4)	10.00	78,434,800
C29	20¢ bright green (C25), Aug. 27, 1941	1.75	.30	11.00	(4)	12.50	42,359,850
C30	30¢ blue (C25), Sept. 25, 1941	2.00	.30	12.00	(4)	20.00	59,880,850
C31	50¢ orange (C25), Oct. 29, 1941	9.00	3.75	75.00	(4)	40.00	11,160,600
	Issue of 1946						
C32	5¢ DC-4 Skymaster, Sept. 25	.15	.15	.45	(4)	2.00	864,753,100
	Issues of 1947, Perf. 10½ x 11						
C33	5¢ DC-4 Skymaster, Mar. 26	.15	.15	.45	(4)	2.00	971,903,700
	Perf. 11 x 10½						
C34	10¢ Pan American Union Building, Washington, D.C. and Martin 2-0-2, Aug. 30	.25	.15	1.10	(4)	2.00	207,976,550
C35	15¢ Statue of Liberty, N.Y. Skyline and Lockheed Constellation, Aug. 20	.35	.15	1.25	(4)	2.00	756,186,350
a	Horizontal pair, imperf. between	1,750.00					
b	Dry printing	.55	.15	2.50	(4)		
C36	25¢ San Francisco-Oakland Bay Bridge and Boeing Stratocruiser, July 30	.85	.15	3.50	(4)	2.75	132,956,100
	Issues of 1948, Coil Stamp, Perf. 10 Horizontally						
C37	5¢ carmine (C33), Jan. 15	.80	.75	8.50	(2)	2.00	33,244,500
	Perf. 11 x 10½						
C38	5¢ New York City, July 31	.15	.15	3.75	(4)	1.75	38,449,100
	Issues of 1949, Perf. 10½ x 11						
C39	6¢ carmine (C33), Jan. 18	.15	.15	.50	(4)	1.50	5,070,095,200
a	Booklet pane of 6, Nov. 18	9.50	4.00			9.00	
b	Dry printing	.50	.15	2.25	(4)		
c	As "a," dry printing	15.00	—				
	Perf. 11 x 10½						
C40	6¢ Alexandria, Virginia, May 11	.15	.15	.60	(4)	1.25	75,085,000
	Coil Stamp, Perf. 10 Horizontally						
C41	6¢ carmine (C33), Aug. 25	2.75	.15	12.00	(2)	1.25	260,307,500
	Universal Postal Union Issue, Perf. 11 x 10½						
C42	10¢ Post Office Dept. Bldg., Nov. 18	.20	.18	1.40	(4)	1.75	21,061,300
C43	15¢ Globe and Doves Carrying Messages, Oct. 7	.30	.25	1.25	(4)	2.25	36,613,100
C44	25¢ Boeing Stratocruiser and Globe, Nov. 30	.50	.40	5.75	(4)	3.00	16,217,100
C45	6¢ Wright Brothers, Dec. 17	.15	.15	.65	(4)	3.50	80,405,000
	Issue of 1952						
C46	80¢ Diamond Head, Honolulu, Hawaii, Mar. 26	5.50	1.00	27.50	(4)	17.50	18,876,800
	Issue of 1953						
C47	6¢ Powered Flight, May 29	.15	.15	.55	(4)	1.50	78,415,000
	Issue of 1954						
C48	4¢ Eagle in Flight, Sept. 3	.15	.15	1.50	(4)	1.00	50,484,000

C24

C25

C32

C33

C34

C35

C36

C38

C40

C42

C43

C44

C45

C46

C47

C48

353

C49

C51

C53

C54

C55

C56

C57

C58

C59

C62

C63

C64

C66

C67

C68

C69

354

	Issue of 1957, Perf. 11 x 10½	Un	U	PB/LP	#	FDC	Q
C49	6¢ Air Force, Aug. 1	.15	.15	.75	(4)	1.75	63,185,000
	Issues of 1958						
C50	5¢ rose red (C48), July 31	.15	.15	1.50	(4)	1.00	72,480,000
	Perf. 10½ x 11						
C51	7¢ Jet Airliner, July 31	.15	.15	.60	(4)	1.00	1,326,960,000
a	Booklet pane of 6	11.00	*6.00*			9.50	221,190,000
	Coil Stamp, Perf. 10 Horizontally						
C52	7¢ blue (C51), July 31	2.25	.15	14.00	(2)	1.00	157,035,000
	Issues of 1959, Perf. 11 x 10½						
C53	7¢ Alaska Statehood, Jan. 3	.15	.15	.75	(4)	1.00	90,055,200
	Perf. 11						
C54	7¢ Balloon Jupiter, Aug. 17	.15	.15	.75	(4)	1.10	79,290,000
	Perf. 11 x 10½						
C55	7¢ Hawaii Statehood, Aug. 21	.15	.15	.75	(4)	1.00	84,815,000
	Perf. 11						
C56	10¢ Pan American Games, Aug. 27	.24	.24	1.40	(4)	1.00	38,770,000
	Issues of 1959-60						
C57	10¢ Liberty Bell, June 10, 1960	1.25	.70	6.00	(4)	1.25	39,960,000
C58	15¢ Statue of Liberty, Nov. 20, 1959	.35	.15	1.50	(4)	1.25	98,160,000
C59	25¢ Abraham Lincoln, Apr. 22, 1960	.45	.15	1.90	(4)	1.75	
a	Tagged, Dec. 29, 1966	.50	.30			15.00	
	Issues of 1960, Perf. 10½ x 11						
C60	7¢ Jet Airliner, Aug. 12	.15	.15	.60	(4)	1.00	1,289,460,000
	Pair with full horizontal gutter between	—					
a	Booklet pane of 6, Aug. 19	15.00	*7.00*			9.50	
	Coil Stamp, Perf. 10 Horizontally						
C61	7¢ carmine (C60), Oct. 22	4.00	.25	32.50	(2)	1.00	87,140,000
	Issues of 1961-67, Perf. 11						
C62	13¢ Liberty Bell, June 28, 1961	.40	.15	1.65	(4)	1.00	
a	Tagged, Feb. 15, 1967	.75	.50			10.00	
C63	15¢ Statue of Liberty, Jan. 13, 1961	.30	.15	1.25	(4)	1.00	
a	Tagged, Jan. 11, 1967	.32	.20			15.00	
b	As "a," hor. pair, imperf. vertically	15,000.00					
	#C63 has a gutter between the two parts of the design; #C58 does not.						
	Issues of 1962-65, Perf. 10½ x 11						
C64	8¢ Jetliner over Capitol, Dec. 5, 1962	.15	.15	.65	(4)	1.00	
a	Tagged, Aug. 1, 1963	.20	.15			2.00	
b	Bklt. pane of 5 + label, Dec. 5, 1962	6.75	*2.50*			2.00	
c	As "b," tagged, 1964	1.65	*.50*				
	Coil Stamp, Perf. 10 Horizontally						
C65	8¢ carmine (C64), Dec. 5, 1962	.40	.15	3.75	(2)	1.00	
a	Tagged, Jan. 14, 1965	.35	.15			—	
	Issue of 1963, Perf. 11						
C66	15¢ Montgomery Blair, May 3	.60	.55	2.75	(4)	1.10	42,245,000
	Issues of 1963-67, Perf. 11 x 10½						
C67	6¢ Bald Eagle, July 12, 1963	.15	.15	1.80	(4)	1.00	
a	Tagged, Feb. 15, 1967	2.75	1.00			15.00	
	1963 continued, Perf. 11						
C68	8¢ Amelia Earhart, July 24	.20	.15	1.00	(4)	1.75	63,890,000
	Issue of 1964						
C69	8¢ Robert H. Goddard, Oct. 5	.40	.15	1.75	(4)	1.75	62,255,000

	Issues of 1967, Perf. 11	Un	U	PB/LP	#	FDC	Q
C70	8¢ Alaska Purchase, Mar. 30	.24	.15	1.40	(4)	1.00	55,710,000
C71	20¢ "Columbia Jays," by Audubon, Apr. 26 (See also #1241)	.80	.15	3.50	(4)	2.00	165,430,000
	Issues of 1968, Unwmk., Perf. 11 x 10½						
C72	10¢ 50-Star Runway, Jan. 5	.18	.15	.90	(4)	1.00	
b	Booklet pane of 8	2.00	.75			3.50	
c	Booklet pane of 5 + label, Jan. 6	3.75	.75			125.00	
	Coil Stamp, Perf. 10 Vertically						
C73	10¢ carmine (C72), Jan. 5	.30	.15	1.70	(2)	1.00	
a	Imperf. pair	600.00		900.00	(2)		
	Perf. 11						
C74	10¢ U.S. Air Mail Service, May 15	.25	.15	2.00	(4)	1.50	
a	Red (tail stripe) omitted		—				
C75	20¢ USA and Jet, Nov. 22	.35	.15	1.75	(4)	1.10	
	Issue of 1969						
C76	10¢ Moon Landing, Sept. 9	.20	.15	.95	(4)	4.50	152,364,800
a	Rose red omitted	450.00	—				
	Issues of 1971-73, Perf. 10½ x 11						
C77	9¢ Delta Wing Plane, May 15, 1971	.18	.15	.80	(4)	1.00	
	Perf. 11 x 10½						
C78	11¢ Silhouette of Jet, May 7, 1971	.20	.15	.90	(4)	1.00	
a	Booklet pane of 4 + 2 labels	1.10	.75			1.75	
C79	13¢ Winged Airmail Envelope, Nov. 16, 1973	.22	.15	1.05	(4)	1.00	
a	Booklet pane of 5 + label, Dec. 27, 1973	1.25	.75			1.75	
b	Untagged (Bureau precanceled)		.28				
	Perf. 11						
C80	17¢ Statue of Liberty, July 13, 1971	.35	.15	1.50	(4)	1.00	
C81	21¢ USA and Jet, May 21, 1971	.35	.15	1.65	(4)	1.00	
	Coil Stamps, Perf. 10 Vertically						
C82	11¢ carmine (C78), May 7, 1971	.25	.15	.80	(2)	1.00	
a	Imperf. pair	250.00		225.00	(2)		
C83	13¢ carmine (C79), Dec. 27, 1973	.26	.15	1.00	(2)	1.00	
a	Imperf. pair	80.00		110.00	(2)		
	Issues of 1972, National Parks Centennial Issue, City of Refuge, May 3, Perf. 11 (See also #1448-54)						
C84	11¢ Kii Statue and Temple at City of Refuge Historical National Park, Honaunau, Hawaii	.20	.15	.90	(4)	1.00	78,210,000
a	Blue and green omitted	1,250.00					
	Olympic Games Issue, Aug. 17, Perf. 11 x 10½ (See also #1460-62)						
C85	11¢ Skiers and Olympic Rings	.22	.15	2.25	(10)	1.00	96,240,000
	Issues of 1973, Progress in Electronics Issue, July 10, Perf. 11 (See also #1500-02)						
C86	11¢ DeForest Audions	.22	.15	.95	(4)	1.00	58,705,000
a	Vermilion and green omitted	1,500.00					
	Issues of 1974						
C87	18¢ Statue of Liberty, Jan. 11	.38	.25	1.65	(4)	1.00	
C88	26¢ Mount Rushmore National Memorial, Jan. 2	.48	.15	2.00	(4)	1.25	
	Issues of 1976						
C89	25¢ Plane and Globes, Jan. 2	.45	.15	2.10	(4)	1.25	
C90	31¢ Plane, Globes and Flag, Jan. 2	.55	.15	2.30	(4)	1.25	

C70

C71

C72

C74

C75

C76

C77

C78

C79

C80

C81

C84

C85

C86

C87

C88

C89

C90

357

C97

C98

C91　C92a　C93　C94a　C95　C96a
C92　　　　C94　　　　C96

C99　　　　　　　**C100**

C105　　　　　C106　　　　C108a
C107　　　　　C108

C101　　　　C102　　　C104a
C103　　　　C104

C109　　　　　C110　　　　C112a
C111　　　　　C112

	Issues of 1978, Perf. 11	Un	U	PB	#	FDC	Q
	Aviation Pioneers Issue, Wright Brothers, Sept. 23 (See also #C93-96, C99-100, C113-14, C118-19, C128-29)						
C91	31¢ Orville and Wilbur Wright, Flyer A	.60	.30			3.00	157,445,000
C92	31¢ Wright Brothers, Flyer A and Shed	.60	.30			3.00	157,445,000
a	Vert. pair, #C91-92	1.20	.85	2.75	(4)	4.00	
b	As "a," ultramarine and black omitted	900.00					
c	As "a," black omitted	—					
d	As "a," black, yellow, magenta, blue and brown omitted	2,250.00					
	Issues of 1979, Aviation Pioneers Issue, Octave Chanute, Mar. 29						
C93	21¢ Chanute and Biplane Hang-Glider	.70	.32			3.00	29,012,500
C94	21¢ Biplane Hang-Glider and Chanute	.70	.32			3.00	29,012,500
a	Attached pair, #C93-94	1.40	.95	3.50	(4)	4.00	
b	As "a," ultramarine and black omitted	4,000.00					
	Aviation Pioneers Issue, Wiley Post, Nov. 20						
C95	25¢ Wiley Post and "Winnie Mae"	1.10	.35			3.00	32,005,000
C96	25¢ NR-105-W, Post in Pressurized Suit and Portrait	1.10	.35			3.00	32,005,000
a	Attached pair, #C95-96	2.25	.95	9.50	(4)	4.00	
	Olympic Summer Games Issue, Nov. 1 (See also #1790-94)						
C97	31¢ High Jumper	.65	.30	9.50	(12)	1.25	47,200,000
	Issues of 1980-82						
C98	40¢ Philip Mazzei, Oct. 13, 1980	.70	.15	8.75	(12)	1.35	80,935,000
a	Perf. 10½ x 11, 1982	3.00	—				
b	Imperf. pair	3,000.00					
	Issues of 1980, Aviation Pioneers Issues, Blanche Stuart Scott, Dec. 30						
C99	28¢ Portrait of Scott and Biplane	.55	.15	6.75	(12)	1.25	20,190,000
	Glenn Curtiss, Dec. 30						
C100	35¢ Portrait of Curtiss and "Pusher" Biplane	.60	.15	8.00	(12)	1.25	22,945,000
	Issues of 1983, Olympic Summer Games Issue, June 17 (See also #2048-51, 2082-85)						
C101	28¢ Gymnast	.60	.28			1.25	42,893,750
C102	28¢ Hurdler	.60	.28			1.25	42,893,750
C103	28¢ Basketball Player	.60	.28			1.25	42,893,750
C104	28¢ Soccer Player	.60	.28			1.25	42,893,750
a	Block of 4, #C101-04	2.50	1.75	3.50	(4)	3.75	
	Olympic Summer Games Issue, Apr. 8 (See also #2048-51 and 2082-85)						
C105	40¢ Shotputter	.90	.40			1.35	66,573,750
C106	40¢ Gymnast	.90	.40			1.35	66,573,750
C107	40¢ Swimmer	.90	.40			1.35	66,573,750
C108	40¢ Weightlifter	.90	.40			1.35	66,573,750
a	Block of 4, #C105-08	3.60	2.00	4.00	(4)	5.00	
b	As "a," imperf.	1,350.00					
d	As "a," perf. 11 x 10½	4.25	—				
	Olympic Summer Games Issue, Nov. 4 (See also #2048-51 and 2082-85)						
C109	35¢ Fencer	.90	.35			1.25	42,587,500
C110	35¢ Bicyclist	.90	.35			1.25	42,587,500
C111	35¢ Volleyball Players	.90	.35			1.25	42,587,500
C112	35¢ Pole Vaulter	.90	.35			1.25	42,587,500
a	Block of 4, #C109-12	3.60	1.85	6.00	(4)	4.50	

	Issues of 1985, Perf. 11	Un	U	PB	#	FDC	Q
	Aviation Pioneer Issues, Alfred Verville, Feb. 13, Perf. 11						
C113	33¢ Portrait of Verville and Airplane Diagram	.60	.20	3.00	(4)	1.25	168,125,000
a	Imperf. pair	850.00					
	Lawrence and Elmer Sperry, Feb. 13						
C114	39¢ Portrait of Sperrys and Seaplane	.70	.20	3.25	(4)	1.35	167,825,000
a	Imperf, pair	1,250.00					
C115	44¢ Transpacific Airmail, Feb. 15	.80	.20	3.75	(4)	1.35	209,025,000
a	Imperf. pair	800.00					
C116	44¢ Junipero Serra, Aug. 22	.80	.20	6.50	(4)	1.35	164,350,000
a	Imperf. pair	—					
	Issues of 1988						
C117	44¢ New Sweden, Mar. 29	1.00	.20	5.50	(4)	1.35	136,900,000
C118	45¢ Samuel P. Langley, May 14	.80	.20	3.75	(4)	1.40	406,475,000
C119	36¢ Igor Sikorsky, June 23	.65	.20	3.10	(4)	1.25	179,004,000
	Issues of 1989, Perf. 11½ x 11						
C120	45¢ French Revolution, July 14	.80	.22	4.25	(4)	1.40	38,922,000
	America/PUAS Issue, Oct. 12, Perf. 11 (See also #2426)						
C121	45¢ Southeast Carved Wood Figure, Key Marco Cat (A.D. 700-1450), Emblem of the Postal Union of the Americas and Spain	.80	.22	3.75	(4)	1.40	39,325,000
	20th UPU Congress Issue, Future Mail Transportation, Nov. 28 (See also #2434-38)						
C122	45¢ Hypersonic Airliner	.90	.30			1.40	26,590,000
C123	45¢ Air-Cushion Vehicle	.90	.30			1.40	26,590,000
C124	45¢ Surface Rover	.90	.30			1.40	26,590,000
C125	45¢ Shuttle	.90	.30			1.40	26,590,000
a	Block of 4, #C122-25	3.60	2.25	4.50	(4)	5.00	
b	As "a," light blue omitted	1,000.00					

Who pioneered the design of flying boats?

Russian-born Igor Sikorsky was one of the first developers of transoceanic flying boats. He also developed helicopters and airplanes, and built the world's first four-engine airplane in 1913.

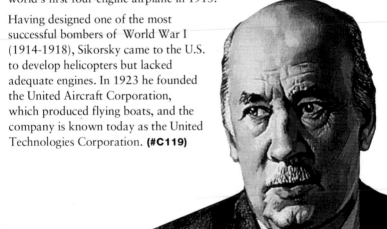

Having designed one of the most successful bombers of World War I (1914-1918), Sikorsky came to the U.S. to develop helicopters but lacked adequate engines. In 1923 he founded the United Aircraft Corporation, which produced flying boats, and the company is known today as the United Technologies Corporation. **(#C119)**

C113

C114

C115

C116

C117

C118

C119

C120

C121

C122   **C123**   **C125a**
C124   **C125**

20ᵗʰ Universal Postal Congress

A glimpse at several potential mail delivery methods of the future is the theme of these four stamps issued by the U.S. in commemoration of the convening of the 20th Universal Postal Congress in Washington, D.C. from November 13 through December 14, 1989. The United States, as host nation to the Congress for the first time in ninety-two years, welcomed more than 1,000 delegates from most of the member nations of the Universal Postal Union to the major international event.

©USPS 1989

C126

C127

C128

C129

C130

C131

CE1

E1

E3

E4

	Issues of 1989 (continued), Imperf.	Un	U	PB	#	FDC	Q
	20th UPU Congress Issue Souvenir Sheet, Nov. 24						
C126	Designs of #C122-25	4.25	3.25			3.00	2,182,400
a-d	Single stamp from sheet	.90	.50				
	Issue of 1990, America/PUAS Issue, Oct. 12, Perf. 11 (See also #2512)						
C127	45¢ Tropical Coast	.80	.20	4.00	(4)	1.40	39,350,000
	Issues of 1991, Aviation Pioneers Issues, Harriet Quimby, Apr. 27						
C128	50¢ Portrait of Quimby and Early Plane	.90	.24	4.50	(4)	2.00	
	William T. Piper, May 17						
C129	40¢ Portrait of Piper and Piper Cub Airplane	.80	.22	4.00	(4)	1.75	
C130	50¢ Antarctic Treaty, June 21	.90	.24	4.50	(4)	2.00	113,000,000
	America/PUAS Issue, Oct. 12						
C131	50¢ Eskimo and Bering Land Bridge	.90	.24	4.75	(4)	2.00	15,260,000
	Airmail Special Delivery Stamps						
	Issues of 1934						
CE1	16¢ Great Seal of the United States, Aug. 30	.55	.65			25.00	
	For imperforate variety see #771.						
	Issue of 1936						
CE2	16¢ red and blue (CE1), Feb. 10	.30	.20	6.50	(4)	17.50	
a	Horizontal pair, imperf. vertically	4,000.00					
	Special Delivery Stamps						
	Issue of 1885, Oct. 1, Perf. 12, Unwmkd.						
E1	10¢ Messenger Running	185.00	29.00	10,000.00	(8)	8,000.00	
	Issue of 1888, Sept. 6						
E2	10¢ blue Messenger Running (E3)	175.00	8.00	10,000.00	(8)		
	Issue of 1893, Jan. 24						
E3	10¢ Messenger Running	110.00	15.00	6,000.00	(8)		
	Issue of 1894, Oct. 10, Line under "Ten Cents"						
E4	10¢ Messenger Running	450.00	14.00	12,000.00	(6)		

Why aren't nuclear weapons allowed on Antarctica?

Twelve countries had research bases on Antarctica by 1959. That same year those countries signed the Antarctic Treaty, an agreement which took effect in 1961. The Treaty allows people to use Antarctica only for peaceful purposes such as expeditions and research. Neither radioactive waste nor nuclear weapons are allowed, and all scientists must be willing to share information with scientists from other countries. Member countries may inspect bases of those suspected of violating the treaty. Antarctic Treaty membership has now grown to 42 countries. **(#C130)**

Issue of 1895, Aug. 16, Perf. 12, Wmkd. (191)					
		Un	U	PB	#	FDC
E5	10¢ blue Messenger Running (E4)	100.00	2.00	*4,000.00*	(6)	
	Double transfer	—	15.00			
	Line of color through "POSTAL DELIVERY"	130.00	9.00			
	Dots in curved frame above messenger	115.00	6.00			
	Issue of 1902, Dec. 9					
E6	10¢ Messenger on Bicycle	55.00	1.90	*2,500.00*	(6)	
	Damaged transfer under "N" of "CENTS"	85.00	3.00			
	Issue of 1908, Dec. 12					
E7	10¢ Mercury Helmet and Olive Branch	40.00	24.00	850.00	(6)	
	Issue of 1911, Jan., Wmkd. (190)					
E8	10¢ ultramarine Messenger on Bicycle (E6)	55.00	2.50	*2,250.00*	(6)	
	Top frame line missing	72.50	3.50			
	Issue of 1914, Sept., Perf. 10					
E9	10¢ ultramarine Messenger on Bicycle (E6)	110.00	3.00	*4,250.00*	(6)	
	Issue of 1916, Oct. 19, Unwmkd.					
E10	10¢ ultramarine Messenger on Bicycle (E6)	200.00	15.00	5,550.00	(6)	
	Issue of 1917, May 2, Perf. 11					
E11	10¢ ultramarine Messenger on Bicycle (E6)	10.00	.25	850.00	(6)	
c	Blue	30.00	.60			
d	Perf. 10 at left	—				
	Issue of 1922, July 12					
E12	10¢ Postman and Motorcycle	18.00	.15	275.00	(6)	400.00
a	10¢ deep ultramarine	25.00	.20			
	Double transfer	35.00	1.00			
	Issues of 1925					
E13	15¢ Postman and Motorcycle, Apr. 11	15.00	.50	150.00	(6)	225.00
E14	20¢ Post Office Truck, Apr. 25	1.65	.85	25.00	(6)	90.00
	Issue of 1927, Nov. 29, Perf. 11 x 10¹/₂					
E15	10¢ gray violet Postman and Motorcycle (E12)	.60	.15	4.00	(4)	90.00
c	Horizontal pair, imperf. between	275.00				
	Cracked plate	35.00				
	Issue of 1931, Aug. 13					
E16	15¢ or. Postman and Motorcycle (E13)	.70	.15	3.75	(4)	125.00
	Beginning with #E17, unused values are for never-hinged stamps.					
	Issues of 1944, Oct. 30					
E17	13¢ Postman and Motorcycle	.60	.15	3.00	(4)	12.00
E18	17¢ Postman and Motorcycle	2.75	1.75	22.50	(4)	12.00
	Issue of 1951, Nov. 30					
E19	20¢ black Post Office Truck (E14)	1.25	.15	5.50	(4)	5.00
	Issues of 1954-57					
E20	20¢ Delivery of Letter, Oct. 13, 1954	.40	.15	2.00	(4)	3.00
E21	30¢ Delivery of Letter, Sept. 3, 1957	.50	.15	2.40	(4)	2.25
	Issues of 1969-71, Perf. 11					
E22	45¢ Arrows, Nov. 21, 1969	1.25	.15	5.50	(4)	3.50
E23	60¢ Arrows, May 10, 1971	1.10	.15	4.75	(4)	3.50

E6   E7

E12   E13

E14   E18

E20   E21

E22   E23

Registration, Certified Mail and Postage Due Stamps

1879-1959

F1

FA1

J2

J19

J25

J33

J69

J78

J88

J98

J101

Issue of 1911, Perf. 12, Wmkd. (190)	Un	U	PB	#	FDC	Q

Registration Stamp
Issued for the prepayment of registry; not usable for postage. Sale discontinued May 28, 1913.

		Un	U	PB	#	FDC	Q
F1	10¢ Bald Eagle, Dec. 11	60.00	3.50	*1,350.00*	(6)	*8,000.00*	

Certified Mail Stamp
For use on First-Class mail for which no indemnity value was claimed, but for which proof of mailing and proof of delivery were available at less cost than registered mail.

Issues of 1955, Perf. 10½ x 11

FA1	15¢ Letter Carrier, June 6	.35	.20	4.00	(4)	3.25	54,460,300

Postage Due Stamps
For affixing by a postal clerk to any mail to denote amount to be collected from addressee because of insufficient prepayment of postage.

Issues of 1879, Printed by American Bank Note Co., Design of J2, Perf. 12, Unwmkd.

J1	1¢ brown	30.00	5.00
J2	2¢ Figure of Value	200.00	4.00
J3	3¢ brown	25.00	2.50
J4	5¢ brown	300.00	30.00
J5	10¢ brown, Sept. 19	350.00	15.00
a	Imperf. pair	*1,600.00*	
J6	30¢ brown, Sept. 19	175.00	35.00
J7	50¢ brown, Sept. 19	225.00	40.00

Special Printing, Soft, Porous Paper

J8	1¢ deep brown	*6,250.00*	
J9	2¢ deep brown	*4,250.00*	
J10	3¢ deep brown	*3,900.00*	
J11	5¢ deep brown	*3,250.00*	
J12	10¢ deep brown	*2,250.00*	
J13	30¢ deep brown	*2,250.00*	
J14	50¢ deep brown	*2,400.00*	
J15	1¢ red brown	30.00	2.50

Issues of 1884, Design of J19

J16	2¢ red brown	40.00	2.50
J17	3¢ red brown	500.00	100.00
J18	5¢ red brown	250.00	15.00
J19	10¢ Figure of Value	225.00	10.00
J20	30¢ red brown	110.00	30.00
J21	50¢ red brown	1,000.00	125.00

Issues of 1891, Design of J25

J22	1¢ bright claret	14.00	.50
J23	2¢ bright claret	15.00	.45
J24	3¢ bright claret	32.50	5.00
J25	5¢ Figure of Value	35.00	5.00
J26	10¢ bright claret	70.00	11.00
J27	30¢ bright claret	250.00	90.00
J28	50¢ bright claret	275.00	90.00

Issues of 1894, Printed by the Bureau of Engraving and Printing, Design of J33, Perf. 12

J29	1¢ vermilion	650.00	200.00	5,250.00	(6)
J30	2¢ vermilion	300.00	60.00	2,400.00	(6)

	Issues of 1894-95, Design of J33, Unwmkd., Perf. 12	Un	U	PB	#
J31	1¢ deep claret, Aug. 14, 1894	22.50	3.00	375.00	(6)
J32	2¢ deep claret, July 20, 1894	17.50	1.75	325.00	(6)
J33	3¢ Figure of Value, Apr. 27, 1895	75.00	20.00	850.00	(6)
J34	5¢ deep claret, Apr. 27, 1895	100.00	22.50	950.00	(6)
J35	10¢ deep claret, Sept. 24, 1894	100.00	17.50	950.00	(6)
J36	30¢ deep claret, Apr. 27, 1895	225.00	60.00		
b	30¢ pale rose	210.00	55.00	2,100.00	(6)
J37	50¢ deep claret, Apr. 27, 1895	500.00	150.00		
a	50¢ pale rose	450.00	135.00	5,000.00	(6)
	Issues of 1895-97, Design of J33, Wmkd. (191)				
J38	1¢ deep claret, Aug. 29, 1895	5.00	.30	190.00	(6)
J39	2¢ deep claret, Sept. 14, 1895	5.00	.20	190.00	(6)
J40	3¢ deep claret, Oct. 30, 1895	35.00	1.00	425.00	(6)
J41	5¢ deep claret, Oct. 15, 1895	37.50	1.00	450.00	(6)
J42	10¢ deep claret, Sept. 14, 1895	40.00	2.00	550.00	(6)
J43	30¢ deep claret, Aug. 21, 1897	300.00	25.00	3,750.00	(6)
J44	50¢ deep claret, Mar. 17, 1896	190.00	20.00	2,250.00	(6)
	Issues of 1910-12, Design of J33, Wmkd. (190)				
J45	1¢ deep claret, Aug. 30, 1910	20.00	2.00		
a	1¢ rose carmine	17.50	1.75	400.00	(6)
J46	2¢ deep claret, Nov. 25, 1910	20.00	.30		
a	2¢ rose carmine	17.50	.30	350.00	(6)
J47	3¢ deep claret, Aug. 31, 1910	350.00	17.50	3,850.00	(6)
J48	5¢ deep claret, Aug. 31, 1910	60.00	3.50		
a	5¢ rose carmine	—	—	600.00	(6)
J49	10¢ deep claret, Aug. 31, 1910	75.00	7.50	1,150.00	(6)
J50	50¢ deep claret, Sept. 23, 1912	600.00	75.00	7,500.00	(6)
	Issues of 1914, Design of J33, Perf. 10				
J52	1¢ carmine lake	40.00	7.50		
J53	2¢ carmine lake	32.50	.20		
J54	3¢ carmine lake	425.00	20.00		
J55	5¢ carmine lake	25.00	1.50		
	5¢ deep claret	—	—		
J56	10¢ carmine lake	40.00	1.00		
J57	30¢ carmine lake	145.00	12.00	2,100.00	(6)
J58	50¢ carmine lake	6,500.00	375.00	50,000.00	(6)
	Issues of 1916, Design of J33, Unwmkd.				
J59	1¢ rose	1,100.00	175.00	8,750.00	(6)
	Experimental Bureau precancel, New Orleans		125.00		
J60	2¢ rose	85.00	10.00	800.00	(6)
	Issues of 1917-25, Design of J33, Perf. 11				
J61	1¢ carmine rose	1.75	.15		
J62	2¢ carmine rose	1.50	.15		
J63	3¢ carmine rose	8.50	.15		
J64	5¢ carmine	8.50	.15		
J65	10¢ carmine rose	12.50	.20		
	Double transfer	—	—		
J66	30¢ carmine rose	60.00	.40		
J67	50¢ carmine rose	75.00	.15		
J68	1/2¢ dull red, Apr. 13, 1925	.70	.15	11.00	(6)

	Issue of 1930-31, Design of J69, Perf. 11				
		Un	U	PB	#
J69	1/2¢ Figure of Value	3.50	1.00	35.00	(6)
J70	1¢ carmine	2.50	.15	27.50	(6)
J71	2¢ carmine	3.00	.15	40.00	(6)
J72	3¢ carmine	15.00	1.00	250.00	(6)
J73	5¢ carmine	14.00	1.50	225.00	(6)
J74	10¢ carmine	30.00	.50	425.00	(6)
J75	30¢ carmine	85.00	1.00	1,000.00	(6)
J76	50¢ carmine	100.00	.30	1,250.00	(6)
	Design of J78				
J77	$1 carmine	25.00	.15		
a	$1 scarlet	20.00	.15	275.00	(6)
J78	$5 "FIVE" on $	30.00	.15		
a	$5 scarlet	25.00	.15		
b	As "a," wet printing	27.50	.15	375.00	(6)
	Issues of 1931-56, Design of J69, Perf. 11 x 101/2				
J79	1/2¢ dull carmine	.75	.15		
J80	1¢ dull carmine	.15	.15		
J81	2¢ dull carmine	.15	.15		
J82	3¢ dull carmine	.25	.15		
b	Scarlet, wet printing	.25	.15		
J83	5¢ dull carmine	.35	.15		
J84	10¢ dull carmine	1.10	.15		
b	Scarlet, wet printing	1.25	.15		
J85	30¢ dull carmine	8.00	.15		
J86	50¢ dull carmine	9.50	.15		
	Design of J78, Perf. 101/2 x 11				
J87	$1 scarlet	35.00	.20	250.00	(4)
	Beginning with #J88, unused values are for never-hinged stamps.				
	Issues of 1959, June 19, Designs of J88, J98 and J101, Perf. 11 x 101/2				
J88	1/2¢ Figure of Value	1.25	.85	165.00	(4)
J89	1¢ carmine rose	.15	.15	.35	(4)
a	"1 CENT" omitted	375.00			
b	Pair, one without "1 CENT"	—			
J90	2¢ carmine rose	.15	.15	.45	(4)
J91	3¢ carmine rose	.15	.15	.50	(4)
J92	4¢ carmine rose	.15	.15	.60	(4)
J93	5¢ carmine rose	.15	.15	.65	(4)
J94	6¢ carmine rose	.15	.15	.70	(4)
a	Pair, one without "6 CENTS"	800.00			
J95	7¢ carmine rose	.15	.15	.80	(4)
J96	8¢ carmine rose	.16	.15	.90	(4)
J97	10¢ carmine rose	.20	.15	1.00	(4)
J98	30¢ Figure of Value	.55	.15	2.75	(4)
J99	50¢ carmine rose	.90	.15	4.50	(4)
	Design of J101				
J100	$1 carmine rose	1.50	.15	7.50	(4)
J101	$5 Outline Figure of Value	8.00	.15	40.00	(4)
	Issues of 1978-85, Designs of J98				
J102	11¢ carmine rose, Jan. 2, 1978	.25	.15	2.00	(4)
J103	13¢ carmine rose, Jan. 2, 1978	.25	.15	2.00	(4)
J104	17¢ carmine rose, June 10, 1985	.40	.15	25.00	(4)

Official and
Penalty Mail Stamps

1873-1991

 O3

 O7

 O11

 O14

 O16

 O18

 O25

 O34

 O37

 O44

 O47

 O52

 O57

 O74

 O76

 O87

 O91

 O121

 O124

 O125

 O126

Official Mail USA
USA 1c
Penalty for private use $300
O127

Official Mail USA
USA 14
Penalty for private use $300
O129A

Official Mail USA
Domestic Letter Rate D
Penalty for private use $300
O139

Official Mail USA
Domestic Mail E
Penalty for private use $300
O140

Official Mail USA
1
Penalty for private use $300
O143

Official Stamps

The franking privilege having been abolished as of July 1, 1873, these stamps were provided for each of the departments of government for the prepayment on official matter. These stamps were supplanted on May 1, 1879 by penalty envelopes and on July 5, 1884 were declared obsolete.

Department of Agriculture: Yellow

		Un	U
O1	1¢ Franklin	90.00	70.00
	Ribbed paper	100.00	65.00
O2	2¢ Jackson	70.00	25.00
O3	3¢ Washington	65.00	3.50
	Double transfer	—	—
O4	6¢ Lincoln	75.00	15.00
O5	10¢ Jefferson	150.00	70.00
	10¢ golden yellow	155.00	72.50
	10¢ olive yellow	165.00	75.00
O6	12¢ Clay	200.00	95.00
	12¢ golden yellow	225.00	100.00
O7	15¢ Webster	150.00	80.00
	15¢ olive yellow	160.00	85.00
O8	24¢ Scott	175.00	80.00
	24¢ golden yellow	190.00	85.00
O9	30¢ Hamilton	225.00	120.00
	30¢ olive yellow	250.00	125.00

Executive Dept. Issue: Carmine

		Un	U
O10	1¢ Franklin	350.00	175.00
O11	2¢ Jackson	225.00	100.00
	Double transfer	—	—
O12	3¢ Washington	275.00	85.00
O13	6¢ Lincoln	400.00	250.00
O14	10¢ Jefferson	375.00	200.00

Dept. of the Interior Issue: Vermilion

		Un	U
O15	1¢ Franklin	20.00	3.50
	Ribbed paper	25.00	4.50
O16	2¢ Jackson	17.50	2.00
O17	3¢ Washington	27.50	2.00
O18	6¢ Lincoln	20.00	2.00
O19	10¢ Jefferson	19.00	4.00
O20	12¢ Clay	30.00	3.00
O21	15¢ Webster	50.00	6.00
	Double transfer of left side	100.00	17.50
O22	24¢ Scott	37.50	5.00
O23	30¢ Hamilton	50.00	6.00
O24	90¢ Perry	110.00	15.00

Dept. of Justice Issue: Purple

		Un	U
O25	1¢ Franklin	60.00	40.00
O26	2¢ Jackson	95.00	40.00
O27	3¢ Washington	95.00	6.00
O28	6¢ Lincoln	90.00	10.00

Dept. of Justice Issue (continued): Purple

		Un	U
O29	10¢ Jefferson	100.00	27.50
	Double transfer	—	—
O30	12¢ Clay	75.00	15.00
O31	15¢ Webster	165.00	50.00
O32	24¢ Scott	450.00	135.00
O33	30¢ Hamilton	400.00	75.00
	Double transfer at top	425.00	85.00
O34	90¢ Perry	600.00	200.00

Navy Dept. Issue: Ultramarine

		Un	U
O35	1¢ Franklin	45.00	10.00
a	1¢ dull blue	52.50	12.50
O36	2¢ Jackson	32.50	9.00
a	2¢ dull blue	42.50	9.00
	2¢ gray blue	35.00	11.00
O37	3¢ Washington	37.50	4.00
a	3¢ dull blue	42.50	5.50
O38	6¢ Lincoln	32.50	5.00
a	6¢ dull blue	42.50	5.00
	Vertical line through "N" of "NAVY"	65.00	10.00
O39	7¢ Stanton	225.00	70.00
a	7¢ dull blue	250.00	70.00
O40	10¢ Jefferson	45.00	15.00
a	10¢ dull blue	50.00	15.00
	Cracked plate	*125.00*	—
O41	12¢ Clay	57.50	10.00
	Double transfer of left side	110.00	30.00
O42	15¢ Webster	95.00	20.00
O43	24¢ Scott	95.00	25.00
a	24¢ dull blue	110.00	—
O44	30¢ Hamilton	85.00	10.00
O45	90¢ Perry	400.00	70.00
a	Double impression		*3,250.00*

Post Office Dept. Issue: Black

		Un	U
O47	1¢ Figure of Value	7.25	3.00
O48	2¢ Figure of Value	7.00	2.50
a	Double impression	300.00	
O49	3¢ Figure of Value	2.50	.55
	Cracked plate	—	—
O50	6¢ Figure of Value	8.00	1.40
	Vertical ribbed paper	—	7.50
O51	10¢ Figure of Value	40.00	15.00
O52	12¢ Figure of Value	22.50	3.50
O53	15¢ Figure of Value	25.00	5.00
a	Imperf. pair	*600.00*	
	Double transfer	—	—
O54	24¢ Figure of Value	32.50	6.00
O55	30¢ Figure of Value	32.50	5.50
O56	90¢ Figure of Value	47.50	7.50

Issues of 1873 (continued), Perf. 12	Un	U
Dept. of State Issue: Green		
O57 1¢ Franklin	60.00	20.00
O58 2¢ Jackson	125.00	25.00
O59 3¢ Washington	50.00	10.00
Double paper	—	—
O60 6¢ Lincoln	47.50	10.00
O61 7¢ Stanton	90.00	20.00
Ribbed paper	110.00	21.00
O62 10¢ Jefferson	75.00	13.50
Short transfer	100.00	27.50
O63 12¢ Clay	110.00	35.00
O64 15¢ Webster	125.00	25.00
O65 24¢ Scott	250.00	75.00
O66 30¢ Hamilton	250.00	45.00
O67 90¢ Perry	500.00	125.00
O68 $2 Seward	550.00	400.00
O69 $5 Seward	4,250.00	2,000.00
O70 $10 Seward	3,000.00	1,500.00
O71 $20 Seward	2,250.00	800.00
Treasury Dept. Issue: Brown		
O72 1¢ Franklin	22.50	1.75
Double transfer	30.00	3.50
O73 2¢ Jackson	25.00	1.75
Double transfer	—	5.00
Cracked plate	40.00	—
O74 3¢ Washington	16.00	.75
Shaded circle outside right frame line	—	—
O75 6¢ Lincoln	22.50	1.50
Worn plate	24.00	2.50
O76 7¢ Stanton	57.50	10.00
O77 10¢ Jefferson	57.50	3.00
O78 12¢ Clay	57.50	1.75
O79 15¢ Webster	50.00	2.50
O80 24¢ Scott	250.00	30.00
O81 30¢ Hamilton	82.50	3.00
Short transfer top right	—	—
O82 90¢ Perry	87.50	3.00
War Dept. Issue: Rose		
O83 1¢ Franklin	82.50	3.25
O84 2¢ Jackson	75.00	4.50
Ribbed paper	67.50	7.50
O85 3¢ Washington	72.50	1.00
O86 6¢ Lincoln	250.00	2.00
O87 7¢ Stanton	75.00	40.00
O88 10¢ Jefferson	22.50	4.00
O89 12¢ Clay	75.00	2.00
Ribbed paper	90.00	3.50
O90 15¢ Webster	20.00	2.50
Ribbed paper	25.00	4.50

Issues of 1873 (continued), Perf. 12	Un	U
War Dept. Issue (continued): Rose		
O91 24¢ Scott	20.00	3.00
O92 30¢ Hamilton	22.50	2.50
O93 90¢ Perry	50.00	10.00
Issues of 1879, Soft, Porous Paper		
Dept. of Agriculture: Yellow		
O94 1¢ Franklin, issued without gum	1,500.00	
O95 3¢ Washington	175.00	35.00
Dept. of the Interior Issue: Vermilion		
O96 1¢ Franklin	110.00	90.00
O97 2¢ Jackson	2.50	1.00
O98 3¢ Washington	2.00	.60
O99 6¢ Lincoln	3.00	2.50
O100 10¢ Jefferson	32.50	27.50
O101 12¢ Clay	65.00	40.00
O102 15¢ Webster	150.00	65.00
Double transfer	200.00	—
O103 24¢ Scott	2,000.00	
O104-05 Not assigned		
Dept. of Justice Issue: Bluish Purple		
O106 3¢ Washington	50.00	25.00
O107 6¢ Lincoln	110.00	90.00
Post Office Dept. Issue: Black		
O108 3¢ Figure of Value	7.50	1.75
Treasury Dept. Issue: Brown		
O109 3¢ Washington	27.50	2.50
O110 6¢ Lincoln	50.00	16.00
O111 10¢ Jefferson	70.00	17.50
O112 30¢ Hamilton	800.00	125.00
O113 90¢ Perry	825.00	125.00
War Dept. Issue: Rose Red		
O114 1¢ Franklin	2.00	1.50
O115 2¢ Jackson	3.00	1.50
O116 3¢ Washington	3.00	.75
a Imperf. pair	*800.00*	
b Double impression	500.00	
Double transfer	6.00	4.00
O117 6¢ Lincoln	2.50	.80
O118 10¢ Jefferson	20.00	17.50
O119 12¢ Clay	15.00	3.00
O120 30¢ Hamilton	47.50	35.00

Issues of 1910-11, Perf. 12	Un	U

Official Postal Savings Mail

These stamps were used to prepay postage on official correspondence of the Postal Savings Division of the Post Office Department. Discontinued Sept. 23, 1914.

		Un	U
O121	2¢ Postal Savings	9.00	1.10
	Double transfer	12.50	2.00
O122	50¢ dark green Postal Savings	110.00	25.00
O123	$1 ultramarine	100.00	7.00
	Wmkd. (190)		
O124	1¢ dark violet Postal Savings	5.50	1.00
O125	2¢ Postal Savings (O121)	30.00	3.50
O126	10¢ carmine Postal Savings	10.00	1.00

Penalty Mail Stamps

Stamps for use by government departments were reinstituted in 1983. Now known as Penalty Mail stamps, they help provide a better accounting of actual mail costs for official departments and agencies, etc.

Beginning with #O127, unused values are for never-hinged stamps.

Issues of 1983-91, Unwmkd., Perf. 11 x 10½		

		Un	U
O127	1¢, Jan. 12, 1983	.15	.15
O128	4¢, Jan. 12, 1983	.15	.25
O129	13¢, Jan. 12, 1983	.26	.75
O129A	14¢, May 15, 1985	.28	.50
O130	17¢, Jan. 12, 1983	.34	.40

Issues of 1983-91 (continued), Perf 11 x 10½	Un	U

		Un	U
O131, O134, O137, O142 Not assigned			
O132	$1, Jan. 12, 1983	1.75	1.00
O133	$5, Jan. 12, 1983	9.00	5.00
Coil Stamps, Perf. 10 Vertically			
O135	20¢, Jan. 12, 1983	2.00	2.00
a	Imperf. pair	2,000.00	
O136	22¢, May 15, 1985	.60	2.00
Perf. 11			
O138	14¢ D Stamp, Feb. 4, 1985	3.50	5.00
Coil Stamps, Perf. 10 Vertically			
O138A	15¢, June 11, 1988	.30	.50
O138B	20¢, May 19, 1988	.40	.30
O139	22¢ D Stamp, Feb. 4, 1985	4.50	3.00
O140	25¢ E Stamp, Mar. 22, 1988	.50	2.00
O141	25¢, June 11, 1988	.50	.50
Perf. 11			
O143	1¢, July 5, 1989	.15	.15
Perf. 10			
O144	29¢ F Stamp, Jan. 22, 1991	.58	.50
O145	29¢, May 24, 1991	.58	.25
Perf. 11			
O146	4¢, Apr. 6, 1991	.15	.15
O147	19¢, May 24, 1991	.38	.50
O148	23¢, May 24, 1991	.46	.25

Parcel Post and
Special Handling Stamps

1912-1955

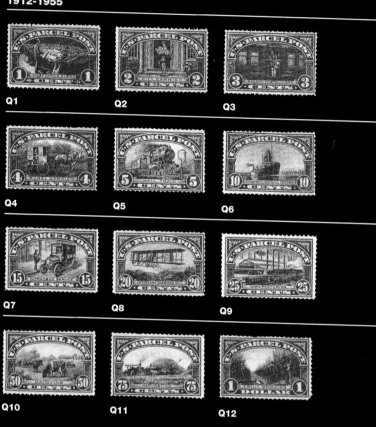

Q1

Q2

Q3

Q4

Q5

Q6

Q7

Q8

Q9

Q10

Q11

Q12

QE1

QE2

QE3

QE4

JQ1

JQ5

Issues of 1913, Wmkd. (190), Perf. 12

		Un	U	PB	#	FDC

Parcel Post Stamps

Issued for the prepayment of postage on parcel post packages only. Beginning July 1, 1913 these stamps were valid for all postal purposes.

		Un	U	PB	#	FDC
Q1	1¢ Post Office Clerk, July 1, 1913	2.50	.85	30.00	(4)	1,500.00
	Double transfer	5.00	3.00			
Q2	2¢ City Carrier, July 1, 1913	3.00	.60	35.00	(4)	1,500.00
	2¢ lake	—				
	Double transfer	—	—			
Q3	3¢ Railway Postal Clerk, Apr. 5, 1913	5.75	4.50	65.00	(4)	3,000.00
	Retouched at lower right corner	15.00	12.50			
	Double transfer	15.00	12.50			
Q4	4¢ Rural Carrier, July 1, 1913	16.00	1.90	250.00	(4)	3,000.00
	Double transfer	—	—			
Q5	5¢ Mail Train, July 1, 1913	15.00	1.25	250.00	(4)	3,000.00
	Double transfer	25.00	5.00			
Q6	10¢ Steamship and Mail Tender	25.00	1.75	300.00	(4)	
	Double transfer	—	—			
Q7	15¢ Automobile Service, July 1, 1913	35.00	7.75	500.00	(4)	
Q8	20¢ Aeroplane Carrying Mail	77.50	15.00	1,050.00	(4)	
Q9	25¢ Manufacturing	35.00	4.00	2,500.00	(6)	
Q10	50¢ Dairying, Mar. 15, 1913	150.00	27.50	1,500.00	(4)	
Q11	75¢ Harvesting	45.00	22.50	3,000.00	(6)	
Q12	$1 Fruit Growing, Jan. 3, 1913	235.00	17.00	20,000.00	(6)	

Special Handling Stamps

Issued for use on parcel post packages to secure the same expeditious handling accorded first class mail matter.

Issues of 1925, 1928-29, 1955, Unwmkd., Perf. 11,

		Un	U	PB	#	FDC
QE1	10¢ Special Handling, 1955	1.00	.80	15.00	(6)	
a	Wet printing, June 25, 1928	2.50	.80			45.00
QE2	15¢ Special Handling, 1955	1.10	.70	27.50	(6)	
a	Wet printing, June 25, 1928	2.50	.70			45.00
QE3	20¢ Special Handling, 1955	1.75	1.00	30.00	(6)	
a	Wet printing, June 25, 1928	3.00	1.00			45.00
QE4	25¢ Special Handling, 1929	14.00	5.50	240.00	(6)	
a	25¢ deep grn., Apr. 11, 1925	22.50	4.50	325.00	(6)	225.00
	"A" and "T" of "STATES" joined at top	37.50	20.00			
	"T" and "A" of "POSTAGE" joined at top	37.50	37.50			

Parcel Post Postage Due Stamps

Issued for affixing by a postal clerk to any parcel post package to denote the amount to be collected from the addressee because of insufficient prepayment of postage. Beginning July 1, 1913 these stamps were valid for use as regular postage due stamps.

Issues of 1912, Wmkd. (190), Perf. 12

		Un	U	PB	#	FDC
JQ1	1¢ Figure of Value, Nov. 27	5.00	2.75	550.00	(6)	
JQ2	2¢ dark green Parcel Post Postage Due, Dec. 9	45.00	13.00	4,000.00	(6)	
JQ3	5¢ dark green Parcel Post Postage Due, Nov. 27	6.50	3.50	675.00	(6)	
JQ4	10¢ dark green Parcel Post Postage Due, Dec. 12	100.00	30.00	10,000.00	(6)	
JQ5	25¢ Figure of Value, Dec. 16	50.00	3.25	4,500.00	(6)	

Migratory Bird Hunting & Conservation Stamps

1934-1959

RW1

RW16

RW26

Migratory Bird Hunting and Conservation Stamps (popularly known as "Duck Stamps"), issued currently by the U.S. Department of the Interior, are sold as hunting permits. While they are sold through many post offices, they are not usable for postage.

Issues of 1934-60	Un	U	PB	#	Q
Department of Agriculture Duck Stamps					
RW1 1934, $1 Mallards Alighting	450.00	85.00	6,000.00	(6)	635,001
a Imperf. pair	—				
b Vert. pair, imperf. horiz.	—				
RW2 1935, $1 Canvasbacks Taking to Flight	400.00	100.00	7,000.00	(6)	448,204
RW3 1936, $1 Canada Geese in Flight	210.00	50.00	2,500.00	(6)	603,623
RW4 1937, $1 Scaup Ducks Taking to Flight	170.00	35.00	1,750.00	(6)	783,039
RW5 1938, $1 Pintail Drake and Hen Alighting	175.00	35.00	1,800.00	(6)	1,002,715
Department of the Interior Duck Stamps					
RW6 1939, $1 Green-winged Teal	125.00	15.00	1,250.00	(6)	1,111,561
RW7 1940, $1 Black Mallards	125.00	15.00	1,250.00	(6)	1,260,810
RW8 1941, $1 Family of Ruddy Ducks	115.00	15.00	1,000.00	(6)	1,439,967
RW9 1942, $1 Baldpates	115.00	15.00	1,050.00	(6)	1,383,629
RW10 1943, $1 Wood Ducks	50.00	15.00	425.00	(6)	1,169,352
RW11 1944, $1 White-fronted Geese	40.00	15.00	400.00	(6)	1,487,029
RW12 1945, $1 Shoveller Ducks in Flight	40.00	10.00	300.00	(6)	1,725,505
RW13 1946, $1 Redhead Ducks	35.00	9.00	260.00	(6)	2,016,841
RW14 1947, $1 Snow Geese	35.00	9.00	260.00	(6)	1,722,677
RW15 1948, $1 Buffleheads in Flight	30.00	9.00	250.00	(6)	2,127,603
RW16 1949, $2 Goldeneye Ducks	40.00	7.00	250.00	(6)	1,954,734
RW17 1950, $2 Trumpeter Swans in Flight	45.00	7.00	325.00	(6)	1,903,644
RW18 1951, $2 Gadwall Ducks	45.00	5.00	325.00	(6)	2,167,767
RW19 1952, $2 Harlequin Ducks	45.00	5.00	325.00	(6)	2,296,628
RW20 1953, $2 Blue-winged Teal	50.00	5.00	350.00	(6)	2,268,446
RW21 1954, $2 Ring-necked Ducks	45.00	5.00	325.00	(6)	2,184,550
RW22 1955, $2 Blue Geese	45.00	5.00	325.00	(6)	2,369,940
RW23 1956, $2 American Merganser	45.00	5.00	325.00	(6)	2,332,014
RW24 1957, $2 American Eider	45.00	5.00	340.00	(6)	2,355,190
RW25 1958, $2 Canada Geese	45.00	5.00	325.00	(6)	2,176,425
RW26 1959, $3 Labrador Retriever Carrying Mallard Drake	60.00	5.00	300.00	(4)	1,626,115
RW27 1960, $3 Redhead Ducks	60.00	5.00	285.00	(4)	1,725,634

	Issues of 1961-93	Un	U	PB	#	Q
	Department of the Interior Duck Stamps (continued)					
RW28	1961, $3 Mallard Hen and Ducklings	65.00	5.00	285.00	(4)	1,344,236
RW29	1962, $3 Pintail Drakes Coming in for Landing	70.00	6.00	350.00	(4)	1,147,212
RW30	1963, $3 Pair of Brant Landing	70.00	6.00	350.00	(4)	1,448,191
RW31	1964, $3 Hawaiian Nene Geese	70.00	6.00	1,750.00	(6)	1,573,155
RW32	1965, $3 Three Canvasback Drakes	65.00	6.00	325.00	(4)	1,558,197
RW33	1966, $3 Whistling Swans	65.00	5.00	300.00	(4)	1,805,341
RW34	1967, $3 Old Squaw Ducks	65.00	5.00	300.00	(4)	1,934,697
RW35	1968, $3 Hooded Mergansers	50.00	5.00	225.00	(4)	1,837,139
RW36	1969, $3 White-winged Scoters	50.00	5.00	225.00	(4)	2,072,108
RW37	1970, $3 Ross's Geese	47.50	5.00	225.00	(4)	2,420,244
RW38	1971, $3 Three Cinnamon Teal	27.50	5.00	125.00	(4)	2,441,664
RW39	1972, $5 Emperor Geese	20.00	5.00	85.00	(4)	2,179,628
RW40	1973, $5 Steller's Eiders	17.00	5.00	85.00	(4)	2,113,594
RW41	1974, $5 Wood Ducks	15.00	5.00	75.00	(4)	2,190,268
RW42	1975, $5 Canvasbacks Decoy, 3 Flying Canvasbacks	10.00	5.00	50.00	(4)	2,218,589
RW43	1976, $5 Family of Canada Geese	10.00	5.00	50.00	(4)	2,248,394
RW44	1977, $5 Pair of Ross's Geese	12.00	5.00	55.00	(4)	2,180,625
RW45	1978, $5 Hooded Merganser Drake	10.00	5.00	52.50	(4)	2,196,758
RW46	1979, $7.50 Green-winged Teal	12.00	5.00	55.00	(4)	2,209,572
RW47	1980, $7.50 Mallards	12.00	5.00	55.00	(4)	2,103,021
RW48	1981, $7.50 Ruddy Ducks	12.00	5.00	55.00	(4)	1,907,114
RW49	1982, $7.50 Canvasbacks	11.00	5.00	55.00	(4)	1,926,253
RW50	1983, $7.50 Pintails	11.00	5.00	55.00	(4)	1,867,998
RW51	1984, $7.50 Widgeons	11.00	5.00	55.00	(4)	1,913,509
RW52	1985, $7.50 Cinnamon Teal	11.00	5.00	55.00	(4)	1,780,760
RW53	1986, $7.50 Fulvous Whistling Duck	11.00	5.00	55.00	(4)	1,794,448
a	Black omitted	3,250.00				
RW54	1987, $10 Redheads	14.00	5.00	60.00	(4)	1,663,112
RW55	1988, $10 Snow Goose	14.00	5.00	65.00	(4)	1,394,923
RW56	1989, $12.50 Lesser Scaup	17.50	5.00	80.00	(4)	
RW57	1990, $12.50 Black Bellied Whistling Duck	17.50	6.00	85.00	(4)	
RW58	1991, $15 King Eiders	20.00	6.00	100.00	(4)	
RW59	1992, $15 Spectacled Eider	20.00	6.00	100.00	(4)	
RW60	1993, $15 Canvasbacks	20.00	6.00	100.00	(4)	

RW39

RW46

RW54

RW57

RW58

RW59

TAKE PRIDE IN AMERICA
BUY DUCK STAMPS
SAVE WETLANDS

SEND IN ALL BIRD BANDS

IT IS UNLAWFUL TO HUNT WATERFOWL OR USE THIS STAMP
AS A NATIONAL WILDLIFE REFUGE ENTRANCE PASS UNLESS
YOU SIGN YOUR NAME IN INK ON THE FACE OF THIS STAMP.

(back)

Stamped Envelopes

1853-1886

U19   **U45**   **U46**

U62   **U69**   **U85**

U97

	Issues of 1853-64	Un	U

Represented below is only a partial listing of stamped envelopes. At least one example is listed for most die types; most die types exist on several colors of envelope paper. Values are for cut squares; prices for entire envelopes are higher. Color in italic is the color of the envelope paper; when no color is specified, envelope paper is white. "W" with catalog number indicates wrapper instead of envelope.

		Un	U
U1	3¢ red Washington (top label 13mm wide), *buff*	185.00	17.50
U4	3¢ red Washington (top label 15mm wide)	200.00	17.50
U5	3¢ red (label has octagonal ends)	3,500.00	350.00
U7	3¢ red (label 20mm wide)	500.00	77.50
U9	3¢ red (label 14½mm)	17.50	2.00
U12	6¢ red Washington, *buff*	85.00	55.00
U14	6¢ green Washington, *buff*	170.00	80.00
U15	10¢ green Washington (label 15½mm wide)	130.00	60.00
U17	10¢ green (label 20mm)	195.00	95.00
a	10¢ pale green	170.00	95.00
U19	1¢ blue Franklin (period after "POSTAGE"), *buff*	27.50	12.50
U23	1¢ blue (bust touches inner frame line), *orange*	400.00	350.00
U24	1¢ blue (no period after "POSTAGE"), *buff*	185.00	90.00
U27	3¢ red, no label, *buff*	17.50	12.50
U28	3¢ + 1¢ (U12 and U9)	325.00	225.00
U30	6¢ red Wash., no label	2,000.00	1,250.00
U33	10¢ green, no label, *buff*	1,000.00	250.00
U34	3¢ pink Washington (outline lettering)	17.50	5.00
U36	3¢ pink, *blue* (letter sheet)	70.00	50.00
U39	6¢ pink Washington, *buff*	60.00	55.00
U40	10¢ yellow green Wash.	27.50	27.50
U42	12¢ red, brn. Wash., *buff*	170.00	150.00
U44	24¢ Washington, *buff*	180.00	140.00
U45	40¢ blk., red Wash., *buff*	275.00	275.00
U46	2¢ black Jackson ("U.S. POSTAGE." downstroke, tail of "2" unite near point)	30.00	15.00
U49	2¢ black ("POSTAGE." downstroke and tail of "2" touch but do not merge), *orange*	975.00	
U50	2¢ blk. Jack. ("U.S. POST." stamp 24-25mm wide), *buff*	9.00	8.50

	Issues of 1863-86	Un	U
W51	2¢ blk. Jack. ("U.S. POST." stamp 24-25mm wide), *buff*	150.00	150.00
U54	2¢ blk. Jack. ("U.S. POST." stp. 25½-26½mm), *buff*	11.00	9.00
W55	2¢ blk. Jack. ("U.S. POST." stp. 25½-26½mm), *buff*	75.00	50.00
U58	3¢ pink Washington (solid lettering)	6.00	1.50
U60	3¢ brown Washington	37.50	20.00
U62	6¢ pink Washington	45.00	25.00
U64	6¢ purple Washington	40.00	20.00
U66	9¢ lemon Washington, *buff*	350.00	200.00
U67	9¢ orange Washington, *buff*	90.00	72.50
U68	12¢ brn. Wash., *buff*	350.00	195.00
U69	12¢ red brown Wash., *buff*	85.00	50.00
U70	18¢ red Washington, *buff*	85.00	80.00
U71	24¢ bl. Washington, *buff*	90.00	72.50
U72	30¢ green Washington, *buff*	60.00	50.00
U73	40¢ rose Washington, *buff*	75.00	*200.00*
U75	1¢ blue Franklin (bust points to end of "N" of "ONE"), *amber*	27.50	22.50
U78	2¢ brown Jackson (bust narrow at back; small, thick numerals)	35.00	12.50
U84	3¢ grn. Washington ("ponytail" projects below bust), *cream*	7.50	3.00
U85	6¢ dark red Lincoln (neck very long at back)	16.00	12.50
a	6¢ vermilion	12.50	12.50
U88	7¢ verm. Stanton (figures 7 normal), *amber*	42.50	*165.00*
U89	10¢ olive blk. Jefferson	375.00	375.00
U92	10¢ brown Jefferson, *amber*	65.00	45.00
U93	12¢ plum Clay (chin prominent)	105.00	60.00
U97	15¢ red orange Webster (has side whiskers), *amber*	135.00	165.00
U99	24¢ purple Scott (locks of hair project, top of head)	110.00	90.00
U103	30¢ black Hamilton (back of bust very narrow), *amber*	175.00	200.00
U105	90¢ carmine Perry (front of bust very narrow, pointed)	130.00	185.00
U113	1¢ lt. blue Frank. (lower part of bust points to end of "E" in "ONE")	1.25	.75
a	1¢ dark blue	7.00	5.00

	Issues of 1874-86	Un	U
U114	1¢ lt. blue (lower part of bust points to end of "E" in "Postage"), amber	3.75	3.00
U122	2¢ brown Jackson (bust narrow at back; numerals thin)	85.00	35.00
U128	2¢ brown Jackson (numerals in long ovals)	37.50	27.50
U132	2¢ brown, die 3 (left numeral touches oval)	50.00	20.00
U134	2¢ brown Jackson (similar to U128-31 but "O" of "TWO" has center netted instead of plain)	500.00	110.00
U139	2¢ brown (bust broad; numerals short, thick)	37.50	30.00
U142	2¢ verm. Jackson (U139)	5.00	2.25
U149	2¢ verm. Jackson (similar to U139-48 but circles around ovals much heavier)	45.00	25.00
W155	2¢ verm. Jackson (like U149 but middle stroke of "N" as thin as verticals), manila	15.00	8.00
U156	2¢ verm. Jackson (bottom of bust cut almost semi-circularly)	525.00	100.00
U159	3¢ grn. Wash. (thin letters, long numerals)	17.50	5.00
U163	3¢ grn. Wash. (thick letters, "ponytail" does not project below bust)	1.00	.25
U169	3¢ grn. (top of head egg-shaped; "ponytail" knot projects as point), amber	180.00	90.00
U172	5¢ Taylor, die 1 (numerals have thick, curved tops)	9.00	7.00
U177	5¢ blue, die 2 (numerals have long, thin tops)	6.50	5.25
U183	6¢ red Lincoln (neck short at back), cream	15.00	9.00
U186	7¢ verm. Stanton (figures turned up at ends), amber	85.00	52.50
U187	10¢ brown Jefferson (very large head)	27.50	15.00
U190	10¢ choc. Jeff. (knot of "ponytail" stands out) amb.	6.50	5.50
U195	12¢ plum Clay (chin receding)	160.00	72.50
U198	15¢ orange Webster (no side whiskers)	37.50	27.50
U201	24¢ purple Scott (hair does not project)	140.00	100.00
U204	30¢ blk. Hamilton (back of bust rather broad)	60.00	25.00
U212	90¢ carm. Perry (front of bust broad, sloping), amber	140.00	185.00
U218	3¢ red Post Rider, Train (1 line under "POSTAGE")	50.00	22.50
U225	5¢ brown Garfield, blue	45.00	32.50

	Issues of 1883-93	Un	U
U228	2¢ red Washington, amber	4.25	1.75
U234	2¢ red, four wavy lines in oval (wavy lines fine, clear), fawn	4.00	2.50
U236	2¢ red (wavy lines thick, blurred)	5.00	3.00
U240	2¢ red Washington (3½ links over left "2")	45.00	30.00
U244	2¢ red Wash. (2 links below right "2"), amber	110.00	60.00
U249	2¢ red Washington (round "O" in "TWO"), fawn	550.00	325.00
U250	4¢ green Jackson, die 1 (left numeral 2¾mm wide)	3.00	2.50
U256	4¢ green, die 2 (left numeral 3¼mm wide)	4.00	4.00
U259	4¢, die 2, amber manila	7.75	5.00
U262	2¢ brn. Wash. (U234), blue	11.50	8.00
U267	2¢ brn. Wash. (U236)	10.00	5.00
U270	2¢ brown Washington (2 links below right "2")	75.00	32.50
U274	2¢ brown Wash. (round "O" in "TWO"), amber	150.00	65.00
U277	2¢ brn. Washington (extremity of bust below "ponytail" forms point)	.35	.15
U288	2¢ brn. Wash. (extremity of bust is rounded)	140.00	30.00
U294	1¢ blue Franklin, no wavy lines	.50	.20
U302	1¢ dark blue, manila	19.00	8.00
U307	2¢ grn. Washington ("G" of "POSTAGE" has no bar), oriental buff	60.00	25.00
U314	2¢ green ("G" has bar, ear indicated by 1 heavy line), blue	.50	.20
U320	2¢ green (like U314 but ear indicated by 2 curved lines), oriental buff	145.00	37.50
U327	4¢ carmine Jackson, blue	4.00	3.50
U331	5¢ blue Grant (space between beard and collar), amber	3.75	1.75
U335	5¢ blue (collar touches beard), amber	9.00	5.00
U340	30¢ red brown Hamilton (U204), manila	40.00	40.00
U344	90¢ pur. Perry (U212), oriental buff	70.00	75.00
U348	1¢ Columbus and Liberty	2.00	1.00
U351	10¢ slate brown	30.00	25.00

U142

W155

U159

U172

U190

U204

U218

U250

U314

U348

U351

U358

U368

U374

U390

U393

U398

U400

U406

U416

Issues of 1899-16		Un	U
U355	1¢ grn. Frank. (U294), *bl.*	9.00	6.00
U358	2¢ carm. Washington (bust points to first notch of inner oval)	2.50	1.50
U362	2¢ carmine (bust points to middle of second notch of inner oval, "ponytail")	.25	.20
U368	2¢ carm. (same as U362 but hair flowing; no ribbon "ponytail"), *amber*	7.50	6.25
U371	4¢ brown Lincoln (bust pointed, undraped)	15.00	10.00
U374	4¢ brown (head larger; inner oval has no notches)	9.00	7.00
U377	5¢ blue Grant (like U331, U335 but smaller)	8.75	8.50
U379	1¢ green Franklin, horizontal oval	.45	.15
U386	2¢ carm. Wash. (1 short, 2 long vertical lines at right of "CENTS"), *amber*	1.50	.20
U390	4¢ chocolate Grant	18.00	11.00
U393	5¢ blue Lincoln	16.00	9.50
U398	2¢ carm. Washington, recut die (lines at end of "TWO CENTS" all short), *blue*	3.00	.90
U400	1¢ grn. Frank., oval, die 1 (wide "D" in "UNITED")	.25	.15
U401a	1¢ grn. Frank., die 2 (narrow "D"), *amber*	.85	.70
U402b	1¢, grn. die 3 (wide "S" in "STATES"), *oriental buff*	6.00	1.50
U403c	1¢, die 4 (sharp angle at back of bust, "N," "E" of "ONE" are parallel), *blue*	3.50	1.25
U406	2¢ brn. red Wash., die 1 (oval "O" in "TWO" and "C" in "CENTS")	.70	.15
U407a	2¢, die 2 (like die 1, but hair recut in 2 distinct locks, top of head), *amb.*	100.00	45.00
U408b	2¢, die 3 (round "O" in "TWO" and "C" in "CENTS," coarse letters), *or. buff*	6.00	2.50
U411c	2¢ carmine, die 4 (like die 3 but lettering, hair lines fine, clear)	.35	.16
U412d	2¢ carmine Wash., die 5 (all S's wide), *amber*	.55	.35
U413e	2¢ carm., die 6 (like die 1 but front of bust narrow), *oriental buff*	.50	.35
U414f	2¢ carm., die 7 (like die 6 but upper corner of front of bust cut away), *blue*	12.50	7.50
U414g	2¢ carm., die 8 (like die 7 but lower stroke of "S" in "CENTS" straight line; hair as in die 2), *blue*	12.50	7.50

Issues of 1907-32		Un	U
U416	4¢ blk. Wash., die 2 ("F" is 1³/₄mm from left "4")	3.50	2.25
a	4¢, die 1 ("F" is 1mm from left "4")	4.25	3.00
U420	1¢ grn. Frank., round, die 1 ("UNITED" nearer inner circle than outer circle)	.15	.15
U421a	1¢, die 2 (large "U"; "NT" closely spaced), *amber*	300.00	175.00
U423a	1¢ grn. die 3 (knob of hair at back of neck; large "NT" widely spaced), *blue*	.75	.45
b	1¢, die 4 ("UNITED" nearer outer circle than inner)	1.25	.65
c	1¢, die 5 (narrow, oval "C")	.65	.35
U429	2¢ carmine Washington, die 1 (letters broad, numerals vertical, "E" closer than "N" to inner circle)	.15	.15
a	2¢, die 2 (like die 1 but "U" far from left circle), *amber*	9.00	6.00
b	2¢, die 3 (like die 2 but inner circles very thin)	30.00	25.00
U430b	2¢, die 4 (like die 1 but "C" very close to left circle), *amber*	20.00	10.00
c	2¢, die 5 (small head, 8³/₄mm from tip of nose to back of neck; "TS" of "CENTS" close at bottom)	1.10	.35
U431d	2¢, die 6 (like die 6 but "TS" of "CENTS" far apart at bottom; left numeral slopes right), *oriental buff*	3.00	2.00
e	2¢, die 7 (large head, both numerals slope right, T's have short top strokes)	2.75	1.75
U432h	2¢, die 8 (like die 7 but all T's have long top strokes), *blue*	.60	.25
i	2¢, die 9 (narrow, oval "C")	.90	.30

Issues of 1916-62		Un	U
U436	3¢ dk. violet Washington, die 1 (as 2¢)	.50	.16
U440	4¢ black Washington	1.00	.60
U447	2¢ on 3¢ dark violet, rose surcharge	6.00	5.50
U458	Same as U447, black surcharge, bars 2mm apart	.45	.35
U468	Same as U458, bars 1½mm apart	.60	.45
U481	1½¢ brown Washington, die 1 (as U429)	.15	.15
W485	1½¢ brown, *manila*	.75	.15
U490	1½¢ on 1¢ grn. Franklin, black surcharge	3.75	3.50
U499	1½¢ on 1¢, *manila*	10.00	6.00
U510	1½¢ on 1¢ grn., outline numeral in surcharge	1.75	1.25
U522	2¢ carmine Liberty Bell	1.00	.50
a	2¢, center bar of "E" of "Postage" same length as top bar	6.00	4.00
U523	1¢ ol. grn. Mount Vernon	1.10	1.00
U524	1½¢ choc. Mount Vernon	2.00	1.50
U525	2¢ carmine Mount Vernon	.40	.16
a	2¢, die 2 "S" of "POSTAGE" raised	70.00	16.00
U526	3¢ violet Mount Vernon	2.00	.35
U527	4¢ black Mount Vernon	18.00	15.00
U528	5¢ dark blue Mount Vernon	4.00	3.25
U529	6¢ orange Washington	5.00	2.75
U530	6¢ orange Wash., *amber*	10.00	7.50
U531	6¢ or. Washington, *blue*	10.00	8.50
U532	1¢ green Franklin	5.00	1.75
U533	2¢ carmine Wash. (oval)	.70	.25
U534	3¢ dk. violet Washington, die 4 (short N in UNITED, thin crossbar in A of STATES)	.40	.16
U535	1½¢ brown Washington	4.50	3.50
U536	4¢ red violet Franklin	.75	.16
U537	2¢ + 2¢ Wash. (U429)	3.00	1.50
U538	2¢ + 2¢ Washington (U533)	.75	.20
U539	3¢ + 1¢ purple, die 1 (4½mm tall, thick "3")	14.00	10.00
U540	3¢ + 1¢ purple, die 3 (4mm tall, thin "3")	.50	.15
a	Die 2 (4½mm tall, thin "3" in medium circle), entire	1,000.00	—
U541	1¼¢ turquoise Franklin	.70	.50
a	Die 2 ("4" 3½mm high), precanceled		2.00
U542	2½¢ dull blue Washington	.80	.50
U543	4¢ brn. Pony Express Rider	.60	.30
U544	5¢ dark blue Lincoln	.80	.20
c	With albino impression of 4¢ (U536)	50.00	—

Issues of 1962-78		Un	U
U545	4¢ + 1¢, type 1 (U536)	1.30	.50
U546	5¢ New York World's Fair	.60	.40
U547	1¼¢ brown Liberty Bell		.15
U548	1⁴⁄₁₀¢ brown Liberty Bell		.15
U548a	1⁶⁄₁₀¢ orange Liberty Bell		.15
U549	4¢ blue Old Ironsides	.75	.15
U550	5¢ purple Eagle	.75	.15
a	Tagged	1.00	.15
U551	6¢ green Statue of Liberty	.70	.15
U552	4¢ + 2¢ brt. bl. (U549)	3.75	2.00
U553	5¢ + 1¢ brt. pur. (U550)	3.50	2.25
U554	6¢ lt. blue Herman Melville	.50	.15
U555	6¢ Youth Conference	.75	.15
U556	1⁷⁄₁₀¢ lilac Liberty Bell		.15
U557	8¢ ultramarine Eagle	.40	.15
U561	6¢ + (2¢) lt. grn.	1.00	.30
U562	6¢ + (2¢) lt. blue	2.00	1.50
U563	8¢ rose red Bowling	.50	.15
U564	8¢ Aging Conference	.50	.15
U565	8¢ Transpo '72	.50	.15
U566	8¢ + 2¢ brt. ultra.	.40	.15
U567	10¢ emerald Liberty Bell	.40	.15
U568	1⁸⁄₁₀¢ Volunteer Yourself		.15
U569	10¢ Tennis Centenary	.30	.16
U571	10¢ Compass Rose	.30	.15
a	Brown "10¢/USA" omitted, entire	110.00	
U572	13¢ Quilt Pattern	.35	.15
U573	13¢ Sheaf of Wheat	.35	.15
U574	13¢ Mortar and Pestle	.35	.15
U575	13¢ Tools	.35	.15
U576	13¢ Liberty Tree	.30	.15
U577	2¢ red Nonprofit		.15
U578	2.1¢ yel. green Nonprofit		.15
U579	2.7¢ green Nonprofit		.15
U580	15¢ orange Eagle, A	.35	.15
U581	15¢ red Uncle Sam	.35	.15
U582	13¢ emerald Centennial	.35	.15
U583	13¢ Golf	.45	.20
U584	13¢ Energy Conservation	.40	.15
d	Blk, red omitted, ent.	200.00	
U585	13¢ Energy Development	.40	.15
U586	15¢ on 16¢ blue USA	.35	.15
U587	15¢ Auto Racing	.35	.15
a	Black omitted, entire	125.00	

U447

U468

W485

U522

U523

U524

U530

U531

U541

U542

U543

U569

U576

U581

Auto Racing

U601   U609   U610

U611   U614

U616   U617

UC1   UC3   UC7

UC14

Issues of 1978-92		Un	U
U588	15¢ on 13¢ (U576)	.35	.15
U590	3.5¢ purple Violins		.15
U591	5.9¢ Auth Nonprofit Org		.15
U592	18¢ violet Eagle, B	.45	.18
U593	18¢ dark blue Star	.45	.18
U594	20¢ brown Eagle, C	.45	.15
U595	15¢ Veterinary Medicine	.35	.15
U596	15¢ Summer Oly. Games	.60	.15
a	Red, grn. omitted, ent.	150.00	
U597	15¢ Highwheeler Bicycle	.40	.15
a	Blue "15¢ USA" omitted, entire	100.00	
U598	15¢ America's Cup	.40	.15
U599	Brown 15¢ Honeybee	.35	.15
a	Brown "15¢ USA" omitted, entire	125.00	
U600	18¢ Blind Veterans	.45	.18
U601	20¢ Capitol Dome	.45	.15
U602	20¢ Great Seal of U.S.	.45	.15
U603	20¢ Purple Heart	.45	.15
U604	5.2¢ Auth Nonprofit Org		.15
U605	20¢ Paralyzed Veterans	.45	.15
U606	20¢ Small Business	.50	.15
U607	22¢ Eagle, D	.55	.15
U608	22¢ Bison	.55	.15
U609	6¢ USS Constitution		.15
U610	8.5¢ Mayflower		.15
U611	25¢ Stars	.60	.15
U612	8.4¢ USF Constellation		.15
U613	25¢ Snowflake	.50	.25
U614	25¢ USA, Stars (Philatelic Mail)	.50	.25
U615	25¢ Stars (lined paper)	.50	.25
U616	25¢ Love	.50	.25
U617	25¢ Space hologram	.60	.28
U618	25¢ Football hologram	.50	.25
U619	29¢ Star	.58	.29
U620	11.1¢ Birds		.20
U621	29¢ Love	.58	.29
U622	29¢ Magazine Industry	.58	.29
U623	29¢ Star and Bars	.58	.29
U624	29¢ Country Geese	.58	.58
U625	29¢ Space Shuttle	.58	.29
U626	29¢ Western Americana	.58	.29
U627	29¢ Protect the Environment	.58	.29
U628	19.8¢ Bulk Rate precanceled		.38
U629	29¢ Disabled Americans	.58	.29
U630	29¢ Kitten	.60	.30

Issues of 1929-46, Airmail Envelopes and Aerogrammes		Un	U
UC1	5¢ blue Airplane, die 1 (vertical rudder is not semicircular)	3.50	2.00
	1933 wmk., entire	700.00	700.00
	1937 wmk., entire	—	2000.00
	Bicolored border omitted, entire	600.00	
UC2	5¢ blue, die 2 (vertical rudder is semicircular)	11.00	5.00
	1929 wmk., entire	—	1,500.00
	1933 wmk., entire	600.00	
UC3	6¢ orange Airplane, die 2a ("6" is 6½mm wide)	1.45	.40
a	With #U436a added impression	3,000.00	
UC4	6¢ orange, die 2b ("6" is 6mm wide)	2.75	2.00
UC5	6¢ orange, die 2c ("6" is 5½mm wide)	.75	.30
UC6	6¢ orange, die 3 (vertical rudder leans forward)	1.00	.35
a	6¢ orange, *blue*, entire	3,500.00	2,400.00
UC7	8¢ olive green Airplane	13.00	3.50
UC8	6¢ on 2¢ carm. Washington (U429)	1.25	.65
a	6¢ on 1¢ green (U420)	1,750.00	
c	6¢ on 3¢ purple (U437a)	3,000.00	
UC9	6¢ on 2¢ Wash. (U525)	75.00	40.00
UC10	5¢ on 6¢ orange (UC3)	2.75	1.50
a	Double surcharge	60.00	
	Issues of 1946-58		
UC11	5¢ on 6¢ orange (UC4)	9.00	5.50
UC13	5¢ on 6¢ orange (UC6)	.80	.60
a	Double surcharge	60.00	
UC14	5¢ carm. DC-4, die 1 (end of wing on right is smooth curve)	.75	.20
UC16	10¢ red, DC-4 2-line back inscription, entire, *pale blue*	7.50	6.00
a	"Air Letter" on face, 4-line back inscription	16.00	14.00
	Die-cutting reversed	275.00	
b	10¢ chocolate	400.00	
c	"Air Letter" and "Aerogramme" on face	45.00	12.50
d	3-line back inscription	8.00	8.00
UC17	5¢ Postage Centenary	.40	.25
UC18	6¢ carm. Airplane (UC14), type I (6's lean right)	.35	.15
a	Type II (6's upright)	.75	.25
UC20	6¢ on 5¢ (UC15)	.80	.50
a	6¢ on 6¢ carmine, entire	1,500.00	
b	Double surcharge	250.00	

	Issues of 1929-46	Un	U
UC21	6¢ on 5¢ (UC14)	26.00	17.50
UC22	6¢ on 5¢ (UC14)	3.50	2.50
a	Double surcharge	75.00	
UC23	6¢ on 5¢ (UC17)	1,400.00	
UC25	6¢ red Eagle	.75	.50
UC26	7¢ blue (UC14)	.65	.50
	Issues of 1958-73		
UC27	6¢ + 1¢ orange (UC3)	225.00	225.00
UC28	6¢ + 1¢ orange (UC4)	65.00	75.00
UC29	6¢ + 1¢ (UC5)	37.50	50.00
UC30	6¢ + 1¢ orange (UC5)	1.00	.50
UC32	10¢ Jet Airliner, back inscription in 2 lines	6.00	5.00
a	Type 1, entire	10.00	5.00
UC33	7¢ blue Jet Silhouette	.60	.25
UC34	7¢ carmine (UC33)	.60	.25
UC35	11¢ Jet, Globe, entire	3.00	1.50
a	Red omitted	875.00	
a	Die-cutting reversed	35.00	
UC36	8¢ red Jet Airliner	.50	.15
UC37	8¢ red Jet in Triangle	.35	.15
a	Tagged	1.25	.30
UC39	13¢ John Kennedy, entire	3.00	1.50
a	Red omitted	500.00	
UC40	10¢ Jet in Triangle	.50	.15
UC41	8¢ + 2¢ (UC37)	.65	.15
UC42	13¢ Human Rights, entire	7.50	4.00
	Die-cutting reversed	75.00	
UC43	11¢ Jet in Circle	.50	.15
UC44	15¢ gray, red, white and blue Birds in Flight	1.50	1.10
UC45	10¢ + (1¢) (UC40)	1.50	.20
UC46	15¢ (UC44) red, white, bl.	.75	.40
	Issues of 1973-91		
UC47	13¢ red Bird in Flight	.30	.15
UC48	18¢ USA, entire	.90	.30
UC50	22¢ red and bl. USA, entire	.90	.40
UC51	22¢ blue USA, entire	.70	.25
	Die-cutting reversed	25.00	
UC52	22¢ Summer Olympic Games	1.50	.22
UC53	30¢ blue, red, brn. Tour the United States, entire	.65	.30
a	Red "30" omitted	75.00	
UC54	30¢ yellow, magenta, blue and black (UC53), entire	.65	.30
	Die-cutting reversed	20.00	
UC55	30¢ Made in USA, entire	.65	.30
UC56	30¢ World Communications Year, entire	.65	.30
	Die-cutting reversed	27.50	
UC57	30¢ Olympic Games, entire	.65	.30
UC58	36¢ Landsat, entire	.72	.36
UC59	36¢ Tourism Week, entire	.72	.36

	Issues of 1973-91	Un	U
UC60	36¢ Mark Twain/ Halley's Comet, entire	.72	.36
UC61	39¢ Envelope	.78	.40
UC62	39¢ Montgomery Blair	.78	.40
UC63	45¢ Eagle, entire, blue	.90	.45
a	White paper	.90	.45
	Issues of 1873-75 Official Envelopes		
	Post Office Department Numeral 9 1/2mm high		
UO1	2¢ black, lemon	11.00	6.00
	Numeral 10 1/2mm high		
UO5	2¢ black, lemon	5.00	3.00
UO9	3¢ black, amber	35.00	24.00
	Postal Service		
UO16	blue, amber	32.50	22.50
	War Department		
UO20	3¢ dk. red Washington	45.00	35.00
UO26	12¢ dark red Clay	95.00	35.00
UO39	10¢ vermilion Jefferson	180.00	
UO48	2¢ red Jackson, amber	22.50	12.50
UO55	3¢ red Washington, fawn	4.00	1.50
	Issues of 1983-91 (Entires), Penalty Mail Envelopes		
UO73	20¢ blue Great Seal	1.00	30.00
UO74	22¢ (seal embossed)	.65	5.00
UO75	22¢ (seal typographed)	.60	20.00
UO76	25¢ Great Seal, E	.65	20.00
UO77	25¢ black, blue Great Seal (seal embossed)	.65	5.00
UO78	25¢ (seal typographed)	.65	25.00
UO79	45¢ (stars illegible)	1.25	40.00
UO80	65¢ (stars illegible)	1.50	50.00
UO81	45¢ (stars clear)	1.25	40.00
UO82	65¢ (stars clear)	1.50	50.00
UO83	29¢ Great Seal, F	1.00	10.00

UC21

UC25

UC26

UC30

UO1

UO16

UO20

Postal Cards

1873-1968

UX14

UX27

UX56

Issues of 1873-1918	Un	U

Represented below is only a partial listing of postal cards. Values are for entire cards. Color in italic is color of card. Cards preprinted with written address or message usually sell for much less.

		Un	U
UX1	1¢ brown Liberty, wmkd. (90 x 60mm)	300.00	15.00
UX3	1¢ brown Liberty, wmkd. (53 x 36mm)	60.00	2.25
UX4	1¢ blk. Liberty, wmkd USPOD in monogram	1,750.00	300.00
UX5	1¢ blk. Liberty, unwmkd.	50.00	.40
UX6	2¢ blue Liberty, *buff*	20.00	17.50
a	2¢ dark blue, *buff*	25.00	19.00
UX7	1¢ (UX5), inscribed "Nothing But The Address"	50.00	.35
a	23 teeth below "One Cent"	500.00	30.00
b	Printed on both sides	575.00	400.00
UX8	1¢ brown Jefferson, large "one-cent" wreath	35.00	1.25
c	1¢ chocolate	60.00	6.00
UX9	1¢ blk. Jefferson, *buff*	10.00	.55
a	1¢ blk., *dark buff*	16.50	1.25
UX10	1¢ black Grant	25.00	1.40
UX11	1¢ blue Grant	10.00	2.50
UX12	1¢ black Jefferson, wreath smaller than UX14	27.50	.40
UX13	2¢ blue Liberty, *cream*	125.00	75.00
UX14	1¢ Jefferson	22.50	.40
UX15	1¢ black John Adams	30.00	15.00
UX16	2¢ black Liberty	9.00	9.00
UX17	1¢ black McKinley	4,000.00	2,250.00
UX18	1¢ black McKinley, facing left	9.00	.30
UX19	1¢ black McKinley, triangles in top corners	27.50	.50
UX20	1¢ (UX19), correspondence space at left	40.00	5.00
UX21	1¢ blue McKinley, shaded background	90.00	6.50
a	1¢ bronze blue, *bluish*	165.00	12.50
UX22	1¢ blue McKinley, white background	12.50	.25
UX23	1¢ red Lincoln, solid background	6.00	5.50
UX24	1¢ red McKinley	8.00	.25
UX25	2¢ red Grant	1.25	8.50
UX26	1¢ green Lincoln, solid background	7.00	6.00
UX27	1¢ Jefferson, *buff*	.25	.25
a	1¢ green, *cream*	3.50	.60
UX27C	1¢ green Jefferson, *gray*, die I	2,000.00	150.00
UX28	1¢ green Lincoln, *cream*	.60	.30
a	1¢ green, *buff*	1.50	.60
UX29	2¢ red Jefferson, *buff*	35.00	2.00
a	2¢ lake, *cream*	45.00	2.50

Issues of 1917-68	Un	U

		Un	U
c	2¢ vermilion, *buff*	275.00	60.00
UX30	2¢ red Jefferson, *cream*	19.00	1.50
	Surcharged in one line by canceling machine.		
UX31	1¢ on 2¢ red Jefferson	3,500.00	3,500.00
	Surcharged in two lines by canceling machine.		
UX32	1¢ on 2¢ red Jeff., *buff*	40.00	12.50
a	1¢ on 2¢ vermilion	95.00	60.00
b	Double surcharge	—	82.50
UX33	1¢ on 2¢ red Jefferson, *cream*	7.50	1.75
a	Inverted surcharge	55.00	
b	Double surcharge	55.00	35.00
d	Triple surcharge	350.00	
	Surcharged in two lines by press printing.		
UX34	1¢ on 2¢ red (UX29)	500.00	45.00
UX35	1¢ on 2¢ red Jefferson, *cream*	200.00	30.00
UX36	1¢ on 2¢ red (UX25)		28,500.00
UX37	3¢ red McKinley, *buff*	3.75	9.00
UX38	2¢ carmine rose Franklin	.35	.25
a	Double impression	200.00	
	Surcharged by canceling machine in light green.		
UX39	2¢ on 1¢ grn. Jefferson, *buff*	.50	.35
b	Double surcharge	17.50	20.00
UX40	2¢ on 1¢ green (UX28)	.65	.45
	Surcharged typographically in dark green.		
UX41	2¢ on 1¢ green Jefferson, *buff*	3.50	1.50
a	Invrtd surchge lower left	75.00	125.00
UX42	2¢ on 1¢ green (UX29)	5.00	2.00
a	Surcharged on back	80.00	
UX43	2¢ carmine Lincoln	.25	1.00
UX44	2¢ FIPEX	.25	1.00
b	Dk. vio. blue omitted	450.00	225.00
UX45	4¢ Statue of Liberty	1.50	40.00
UX46	3¢ purple Statue of Liberty	.40	.20
a	"N GOD WE TRUST"	12.00	25.00
UX47	2¢ + 1¢ carmine rose Franklin	160.00	250.00
UX48	4¢ red violet Lincoln	.25	.20
UX49	7¢ World Vacationland	3.00	35.00
UX50	4¢ U.S. Customs	.40	1.00
a	Blue omitted	450.00	
UX51	4¢ Social Security	.40	1.00
b	Blue omitted	700.00	
UX52	4¢ blue & red Coast Guard	.30	1.00
UX53	4¢ Bureau of the Census	.30	1.00
UX54	8¢ blue & red (UX49)	3.00	35.00
UX55	5¢ emerald Lincoln	.30	.50
UX56	5¢ Women Marines	.35	1.00

Issues of 1970-83		Un	U
UX57	5¢ Weather Services	.30	1.00
a	Yellow, black omitted	700.00	
b	Blue omitted	650.00	
c	Black omitted	600.00	
UX58	6¢ brown Paul Revere	.30	1.00
a	Double impression	300.00	
UX59	10¢ blue & red (UX49)	3.00	35.00
UX60	6¢ America's Hospitals	.30	1.00
a	Blue, yellow omitted	700.00	
UX61	6¢ USF Constellation	.60	3.00
a	Address side blank	300.00	
UX62	6¢ black Monument Valley	.35	3.00
UX63	6¢ Gloucester, MA	.35	3.00
UX64	6¢ blue John Hanson	.25	1.00
UX65	6¢ magenta Liberty	.25	1.00
UX66	8¢ orange Samuel Adams	.25	1.00
UX67	12¢ Visit USA/ Ship's Figurehead	.35	30.00
UX68	7¢ Charles Thomson	.30	5.00
UX69	9¢ John Witherspoon	.25	1.00
UX70	9¢ blue Caesar Rodney	.25	1.00
UX71	9¢ Federal Court House	.25	1.00
UX72	9¢ green Nathan Hale	.25	1.00
UX73	10¢ Cincinnati Music Hall	.30	1.00
UX74	10¢ John Hancock	.30	1.00
UX75	10¢ John Hancock	.30	.15
UX76	14¢ Coast Guard Eagle	.40	15.00
UX77	10¢ Molly Pitcher	.30	1.00
UX78	10¢ George Rogers Clark	.30	1.00
UX79	10¢ Casimir Pulaski	.30	1.00
UX80	10¢ Olympic Sprinter	.50	1.00
UX81	10¢ Iolani Palace	.30	1.00
UX82	14¢ Olympic Games	.50	10.00
UX83	10¢ Salt Lake Temple	.25	1.00
UX84	10¢ Landing of Rochambeau	.25	1.00
UX85	10¢ Battle of Kings Mtn.	.25	1.00
UX86	19¢ Drake's Golden Hinde	.55	10.00
UX87	10¢ Battle of Cowpens	.25	2.50
UX88	12¢ violet Eagle, nondenominated	.30	.50
UX89	12¢ lt. bl. Isaiah Thomas	.30	.50
UX90	12¢ Nathanael Greene	.30	1.00
UX91	12¢ Lewis and Clark	.30	3.00
UX92	13¢ buff Robert Morris	.30	.50
UX93	13¢ buff Robert Morris	.30	.50
UX94	13¢ "Swamp Fox" Francis Marion	.30	.75
UX95	13¢ LaSalle Claims Louisiana	.30	.75
UX96	13¢ Academy of Music	.30	.75
UX97	13¢ Old Post Office, St. Louis, Missouri	.30	.75
UX100	13¢ Olympic Yachting	.30	.75

Issues of 1984-90		Un	U
UX101	13¢ Ark and Dove, Maryland	.30	.75
UX102	13¢ Olympic Torch	.30	.75
UX103	13¢ Frederic Baraga	.30	.75
UX104	13¢ Dominguez Adobe	.30	.75
UX105	14¢ Charles Carroll	.30	.50
UX106	14¢ green Charles Carroll	.30	.15
UX107	25¢ Clipper Flying Cloud	.70	5.00
UX108	14¢ brt. grn. George Wythe	.30	.50
UX109	14¢ Settlement of Connecticut	.30	.75
UX110	14¢ Stamp Collecting	.30	.75
UX111	14¢ Francis Vigo	.30	.75
UX112	14¢ Settling of Rhode Island	.30	.75
UX113	14¢ Wisconsin Territory	.30	.75
UX114	14¢ National Guard	.30	.75
UX115	14¢ Self-Scouring Plow	.30	.50
UX116	14¢ Constitutional Convention	.30	.50
UX117	14¢ Stars and Stripes	.30	.50
UX118	14¢ Take Pride in America	.30	.50
UX119	14¢ Timberline Lodge	.30	.50
UX120	15¢ Bison and Prairie	.30	.25
UX121	15¢ Blair House	.30	.30
UX122	28¢ Yorkshire	.60	3.00
UX123	15¢ Iowa Territory	.30	.30
UX124	15¢ Ohio, Northwest Terr.	.30	.30
UX125	15¢ Hearst Castle	.30	.30
UX126	15¢ The Federalist Papers	.30	.30
UX127	15¢ Hawk and Desert	.30	.30
UX128	15¢ Healy Hall	.30	.30
UX129	15¢ Blue Heron and Marsh	.30	.30
UX130	15¢ Settling of Oklahoma	.30	.30
UX131	21¢ Geese and Mountains	.42	3.00
UX132	15¢ Seagull and Seashore	.30	.30
UX133	15¢ Deer and Waterfall	.30	.30
UX134	15¢ Hull House, Chicago	.30	.30
UX135	15¢ Ind. Hall, Philadelphia	.30	.30
UX136	15¢ Inner Harbor, Baltimore	.30	.30
UX137	15¢ Bridge, New York	.30	.30
UX138	15¢ Capitol, Washington	.30	.30
	#UX139-42 issued in sheets of 4 plus 2 inscribed labels, rouletted 9½ on 2 or 3 sides.		
UX139	15¢ (UX135)	.30	.90
UX140	15¢ The White House	.30	.90
UX141	15¢ (UX137)	.30	.90
UX142	15¢ (UX138)	.30	.90
a	Sheet of 4, #UX139-42	1.20	
UX143	15¢ The White House	1.00	1.00
UX144	15¢ Jefferson Memorial	1.00	1.00
UX145	15¢ Papermaking	.30	.30
UX146	15¢ World Literacy Year	.30	.30

UX70

Casimir Pulaski, Savannah, 1779

UX79

Historic Preservation

UX81

HISTORIC PRESERVATION

UX83

"Swamp Fox" Francis Marion, 1782

UX94

Settling of Connecticut, 1636

UX109

Settling of Rhode Island, 1636

UX112

Wisconsin Territory, 1836

UX113

Self scouring steel plow, 1837

UX115

Constitutional Convention, 1787

UX116

Take Pride in America 14 USA

UX118

Historic Preservation USA 14

UX119

America the Beautiful USA 21

UX131

UX143

UX144

395

UXC19

UXC20

UXC23

Issues of 1990-93	Un	U
UX147 15¢ George Caleb Bingham	1.00	1.00
UX148 15¢ Isaac Royall House	.30	.30
UX150 15¢ Stanford University	.30	.30
UX151 15¢ Constitution Hall	1.00	1.00
UX152 15¢ Chgo. Orchestra Hall	.30	.30
UX153 19¢ Flag	.38	.19
UX154 19¢ Carnegie Hall	.38	.38
UX155 19¢ Old Red, UT-Galveston	.38	.38
UX156 19¢ Bill of Rights	.38	.38
UX157 19¢ Notre Dame	.38	.38
UX158 30¢ Niagara Falls	.60	.60
UX159 19¢ The Old Mill	.38	.38
UX160 19¢ Wadsworth Atheneum, Hartford, CT	.38	.38
UX161 19¢ Cobb Hall, University of Chicago	.38	.38
UX162 19¢ Waller Hall, Willamette University	.38	.38
UX163 19¢ America's Cup	1.00	1.00
UX164 19¢ Columbia River Gorge	.38	.38
UX165 19¢ Ellis Island Immigration Museum	.38	.38
UX166 19¢ National Cathedral	.38	.38
UX167 19¢ Wren Building	.38	.38
UX168 19¢ Holocaust Memorial	1.00	1.00
UX169 19¢ Fort Recovery	.38	.38
UX170 19¢ Playmakers Theatre	.38	.38
UX171 19¢ O'Kane Hall	.38	.38
UX172 19¢ Beecher Hall	.38	.38
UX173 19¢ Massachusetts Hall	.38	.38

Issues of 1892-1988, Paid Reply Postal Cards
Prices are: Un=unsevered, U=severed card.

		Un	U
UY1	1¢ + 1¢ black Grant	35.00	7.50
UY6	1¢ + 1¢ green G. and M. Washington, double frame line around instructions	140.00	22.50
UY7	1¢ + 1¢ green G. and M. Washington, single frame line	1.00	.50
UY12	3¢ + 3¢ red McKinley	9.00	25.00
UY18	4¢ + 4¢ Lincoln	2.50	2.50
UY23	6¢ + 6¢ John Adams	.75	2.00
UY31	12¢ + 12¢ Eagle, nondenominated	.75	2.00
UY39	15¢ + 15¢ Bison and Prairie	.75	1.00

Issues of 1949-88	Un	U
Airmail Postal Cards		
UXC1 4¢ orange Eagle	.45	.75
UXC2 5¢ red Eagle (C48)	1.50	.75
UXC3 5¢ UXC2 redrawn—"Air Mail-Postal Card" omitted	6.00	2.00
UXC4 6¢ red Eagle	.45	.75
UXC5 11¢ Visit The USA	.50	12.50
UXC6 6¢ Virgin Islands	.40	6.00
a Red, yellow omitted	1,700.00	
UXC7 6¢ Boy Scout World Jamboree	.40	6.00
UXC8 13¢ blue & red (UXC5)	1.25	8.00
UXC9 8¢ Stylized Eagle	.60	2.00
UXC10 9¢ red & blue (UXC5)	.50	1.00
UXC11 15¢ Commerce Department Travel Service	1.50	12.50
UXC12 9¢ black Grand Canyon	.50	8.00
UXC13 15¢ black Niagara Falls	.65	15.00
UXC14 11¢ Stylized Eagle	.70	2.00
UXC15 18¢ Eagle Weather Vane	.85	7.00
UXC16 21¢ Angel Weather Vane	.80	7.50
UXC17 21¢ Curtiss Jenny	.75	6.00
UXC18 21¢ Olympic Gymnast	.95	10.00
UXC19 28¢ First Transpacific Flight	.90	4.00
UXC20 28¢ Gliders	.90	3.00
UXC21 28¢ Olympic Speed Skater	.90	2.00
UXC22 33¢ China Clipper	.90	2.00
UXC23 33¢ AMERIPEX '86	.65	2.00
UXC24 36¢ DC-3	.70	1.00
UXC25 40¢ Yankee Clipper	.80	1.00
Issues of 1913-91, Official Mail Postal Cards		
UZ1 1¢ black Numeral	325.00	150.00
UZ2 13¢ blue Great Seal	.50	35.00
UZ3 14¢ blue Great Seal	.50	35.00
UZ4 15¢ blue Great Seal	.50	30.00
UZ5 19¢ blue Great Seal	.38	5.00

Collect Every First Day Issue

- Features every stamp issued each year
- Complete with First Day cancellation and informative text
- A convenient, affordable way to collect

The U.S. Postal Service's Souvenir Pages Subscription Program is your ticket to all the year's stamp issues. It's a great way to collect and learn about the stamps and stamp subjects honored during the year.

Fun and Attractive

A Souvenir Page is issued for every stamp—all definitives and commemoratives, as well as airmails, coil stamps and booklet panes. Each Souvenir Page includes the featured stamp(s), postmarked with a First Day of Issue cancellation, mounted on an 8" x 10½" page. Information on relevant philatelic specifications and a lively narrative about the history of the stamp's subject are included.

Affordable Collectibles

Souvenir Pages are printed in a limited quantity each year.

The cost of a Souvenir Page currently is approximately $1.25 per page. (In the rare event that the face value of the stamp[s] affixed exceeds $1.25, the price will be the face value.)

Money-back Guarantee

If you are ever dissatisfied, return your Souvenir Pages within 30 days for a full refund. For more information and an order form, fill out request card in this book or write to:

**U.S. POSTAL SERVICE GUIDE
SOUVENIR PAGES PROGRAM
PHILATELIC FULFILLMENT SERVICE CENTER
PO BOX 449980
KANSAS CITY MO 64144-9980**

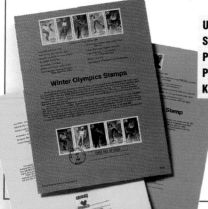

Winter Olympics Stamps

Souvenir Pages

With First Day Cancellations

The Postal Service offers Souvenir Pages for new stamps. The series began with a page for the Yellowstone Park Centennial stamp issued March 1, 1972. The Pages feature one or more stamps tied by the first day cancel, along with technical data and information on the subject of the issue. More than just collectors' items, Souvenir Pages make wonderful show and conversation pieces. Souvenir Pages are issued in limited editions. Number in parentheses ( ) indicates number of stamps on page if there are more than one.

1972

72-0	Family Planning	450.00
72-1	Yellowstone Park	100.00
72-1c	Yellowstone Park with DC cancel	—
72-2	2¢ Cape Hatteras	100.00
72-3	14¢ Fiorello LaGuardia	110.00
72-4	11¢ City of Refuge Park	110.00
72-5	6¢ Wolf Trap Farm Park	37.50
72-6	Colonial Craftsmen (4)	20.00
72-7	15¢ Mount McKinley	30.00
72-8	6¢-11¢ Olympic Games (4)	20.00
72-8e	Olympic Games with broken red circle on 6¢ stamp	—
72-9	PTA	9.50
72-10	Wildlife Conservation (4)	10.00
72-11	Mail Order	7.75
72-12	Osteopathic Medicine	7.50
72-13	Tom Sawyer	7.50
72-14	7¢ Benjamin Franklin	9.25
72-15	Christmas (2)	10.00
72-16	Pharmacy	7.50
72-17	Stamp Collecting	7.50

1973

73-1	$1 Eugene O'Neill	17.50
73-1e	$1 Eugene O'Neill picture perf. error	—
73-2	Love	10.00
73-3	Pamphleteer	6.75
73-4	George Gershwin	7.75
73-5	Broadside	8.00
73-6	Copernicus	6.50
73-7	Postal Employees	8.75
73-8	Harry S. Truman	6.25
73-9	Post Rider	8.00
73-10	21¢ Amadeo Gianninni	6.25
73-11	Boston Tea Party (4)	8.25

73-12	6¢-15¢ Electronics (4)	7.25
73-13	Robinson Jeffers	4.75
73-14	Lyndon B. Johnson	5.25
73-15	Henry O. Tanner	5.25
73-16	Willa Cather	4.25
73-17	Colonial Drummer	5.75
73-18	Angus Cattle	4.25
73-19	Christmas (2)	7.00
73-20	13¢ Winged Envelope airmail	3.50
73-21	10¢ Crossed Flags	3.50
73-22	10¢ Jefferson Memorial	3.50
73-23	13¢ Winged Envelope airmail coil (2)	3.50

1974

74-1	26¢ Mount Rushmore airmail	5.75
74-2	ZIP Code	4.75
74-2e	ZIP Code with date error 4/4/74	—
74-3	18¢ Statue of Liberty airmail	7.50
74-4	18¢ Elizabeth Blackwell	3.25
74-5	VFW	3.25
74-6	Robert Frost	3.50
74-7	Expo '74	3.25
74-8	Horse Racing	3.50
74-9	Skylab	6.75
74-10	UPU (8)	6.50
74-11	Mineral Heritage (4)	6.75
74-12	Fort Harrod	3.25
74-13	Continental Congress (4)	5.00
74-14	Chautauqua	2.75
74-15	Kansas Wheat	2.75
74-16	Energy Conservation	2.75
74-17	6.3¢ Liberty Bell coil (2)	4.00
74-18	Sleepy Hollow	3.50
74-19	Retarded Children	3.25
74-20	Christmas (3)	6.25

1975

75-1	Benjamin West	3.25
75-2	Pioneer/Jupiter	6.25
75-3	Collective Bargaining	3.50
75-4	8¢ Sybil Ludington	3.25

75-5	Salem Poor	3.25
75-6	Haym Salomon	3.25
75-7	18¢ Peter Francisco	3.25
75-8	Mariner 10	6.00
75-9	Lexington & Concord	3.50
75-10	Paul Dunbar	4.25
75-11	D.W. Griffith	3.50
75-12	Bunker Hill	3.50
75-13	Military Uniforms (4)	6.50
75-14	Apollo Soyuz (2)	6.50
75-15	International Women's Year	3.25
75-16	Postal Service Bicentennial (4)	5.25
75-17	World Peace Through Law	3.25
75-18	Banking & Commerce (2)	3.25
75-19	Christmas (2)	4.25
75-20	3¢ Francis Parkman	4.00
75-21	11¢ Freedom of the Press	2.50
75-22	24¢ Old North Church	2.75
75-23	Flag over Independence Hall (2)	2.75
75-24	9¢ Freedom to Assemble (2)	2.50
75-25	Liberty Bell coil (2)	4.00
75-26	Eagle & Shield	2.50

1976

76-1	Spirit of '76 (3)	4.25
76-1e	Spirit of '76 with cancellation error Jan. 2, 1976 (3)	—
76-2	25¢ and 31¢ Plane and Globes airmails (2)	4.00
76-3	Interphil '76	2.75
76-4	State Flags, DE to VA (10)	8.75
76-5	State Flags, NY to MS (10)	8.75
76-6	State Flags, IL to WI (10)	8.75
76-7	State Flags, CA to SD (10)	8.75

76-8	State Flags, MT to HI (10)	8.75
76-9	9¢ Freedom to Assemble coil (2)	2.50
76-10	Telephone Centennial	2.75
76-11	Commercial Aviation	2.50
76-12	Chemistry	2.75
76-13	7.9¢ Drum coil (2)	2.75
76-14	Benjamin Franklin	2.75
76-15	Bicentennial souvenir sheet	9.00
76-15E	Bicentennial souvenir sheet with perforation and numerical errors	1,000.00
76-16	18¢ Bicentennial souvenir sheet	9.00
76-17	24¢ Bicentennial souvenir sheet	9.00
76-18	31¢ Bicentennial souvenir sheet	9.00
76-19	Declaration of Independence (4)	5.25
76-20	Olympics (4)	6.25
76-21	Clara Maass	2.50
76-22	Adolph S. Ochs	2.50
76-23	Christmas (3)	4.25
76-24	7.7¢ Saxhorns coil (2)	2.50

1977

77-1	Washington at Princeton	2.75
77-2	Flag over Capitol booklet pane (9¢ and 13¢) Perf. 10 (8)	20.00
77-3	Sound Recording	2.50
77-4	Pueblo Pottery (4)	3.50
77-5	Lindbergh Flight	3.50
77-6	Colorado Centennial	2.25
77-7	Butterflies (4)	3.25
77-8	Lafayette	2.50
77-9	Skilled Hands (4)	3.25
77-10	Peace Bridge	2.50
77-11	Battle of Oriskany	2.50
77-12	Alta, CA, First Civil Settlement	2.50
77-13	Articles of Confederation	2.50
77-14	Talking Pictures	2.75
77-15	Surrender at Saratoga	3.75
77-16	Energy (2)	2.50
77-17	Christmas, Mailbox and Christmas, Valley Forge, Omaha cancel (2)	2.50
77-18	Same, Valley Forge cancel	2.50
77-19	10¢ Petition for Redress coil (2)	4.50
77-20	10¢ Petition for Redress sheet (2)	3.25
77-21	1¢-4¢ Americana (5)	3.25

1978

78-1	Carl Sandburg	2.50
78-2	Indian Head Penny	2.50
78-3	Captain Cook, Anchorage cancel (2)	3.25
78-4	Captain Cook, Honolulu cancel (2)	3.25
78-5	Harriet Tubman	3.25
78-6	American Quilts (4)	2.75
78-7	16¢ Statue of Liberty sheet and coil (2)	2.75
78-8	29¢ Sandy Hook Lighthouse	2.75
78-9	American Dance (4)	3.25
78-10	French Alliance	2.50

78-11	Early Cancer Detection	2.50
78-12	"A" (15¢) sheet and coil (2)	4.50
78-13	Jimmie Rodgers	4.75
78-14	CAPEX '78 (8)	7.50
78-15	Oliver Wendell Holmes coil	2.75
78-16	Photography	2.50
78-17	Fort McHenry Flag sheet and coil (2)	2.75
78-18	George M. Cohan	2.50
78-19	Rose booklet single	2.75
78-20	8.4¢ Piano coil (2)	3.25
78-21	Viking Missions	4.25
78-22	28¢ Remote Outpost	3.25
78-23	American Owls (4)	3.50
78-24	31¢ Wright Brothers airmails (2)	3.50
78-25	American Trees (4)	3.50
78-26	Christmas, Madonna	2.50
78-27	Christmas, Hobby Horse	2.50
78-28	$2 Kerosene Lamp	7.50

1979

79-1	Robert F. Kennedy	2.50
79-2	Martin Luther King, Jr.	5.00
79-3	International Year of the Child	2.50
79-4	John Steinbeck	2.50
79-5	Albert Einstein	2.75
79-6	21¢ Octave Chanute airmails (2)	3.50
79-7	Pennsylvania Toleware (4)	2.75
79-8	American Architecture (4)	3.25
79-9	Endangered Flora (4)	3.50
79-10	Seeing Eye Dogs	2.50
79-11	$1 Lamp & Candle	7.25
79-12	Special Olympics	2.75
79-13	$5 Lantern	20.00
79-14	30¢ Schoolhouse	4.75
79-15	10¢ Summer Olympics (2)	4.25
79-16	50¢ Whale Oil Lamp	5.00
79-17	John Paul Jones	3.25
79-18	Summer Olympics (4)	5.50
79-19	Christmas, Madonna	3.25
79-20	Christmas, Santa Claus	3.25
79-21	3.1¢ Guitar coil (2)	5.75
79-22	31¢ Summer Olympics airmail	6.25
79-23	Will Rogers	2.75
79-24	Vietnam Veterans	2.75
79-25	25¢ Wiley Post airmails (2)	4.25

1980

80-1	W.C. Fields	3.00
80-2	Winter Olympics (4)	6.50
80-3	Windmills booklet pane (10)	5.00
80-4	Benjamin Banneker	5.00
80-5	Letter Writing (6)	3.50
80-6	1¢ Ability to Write (2)	3.25
80-7	Frances Perkins	2.25
80-8	Dolley Madison	4.00
80-9	Emily Bissell	2.25
80-10	3.5¢ Violins coil (2)	4.00
80-11	Helen Keller/ Anne Sullivan	3.00
80-12	Veterans Administration	2.25

80-13	General Bernardo de Galvez	2.25
80-14	Coral Reefs (4)	2.75
80-15	Organized Labor	4.00
80-16	Edith Wharton	3.75
80-17	Education	2.75
80-18	Indian Masks (4)	3.00
80-19	American Architecture (4)	3.00
80-20	40¢ Philip Mazzei airmail	3.25
80-21	Christmas, Madonna	3.25
80-22	Christmas, Antique Toys	4.00
80-23	Sequoyah	2.25
80-24	28¢ Blanche Scott airmail	2.25
80-25	35¢ Glenn Curtiss airmail	2.25

1981

81-1	Everett Dirksen	2.25
81-2	Whitney M. Young	4.00
81-3	"B" (18¢) sheet and coil (3)	3.00
81-4	"B" (18¢) booklet pane (8)	3.00
81-5	12¢ Freedom of Conscience sheet and coil (3)	2.75
81-6	Flowers block (4)	2.50
81-7	Flag and Anthem sheet and coil (3)	2.75
81-8	Flag and Anthem booklet pane (8 - 6¢ and 18¢)	3.00
81-9	American Red Cross	2.25
81-10	George Mason	2.25
81-11	Savings & Loans	2.25
81-12	Wildlife booklet pane (10)	2.75
81-13	Surrey coil (2)	4.00
81-14	Space Achievement (8)	7.50
81-15	17¢ Rachel Carson (2)	2.25
81-16	35¢ Charles Drew, MD	3.25
81-17	Professional Management	2.25
81-18	17¢ Electric Auto coil (2)	4.50
81-19	Wildlife Habitat (4)	2.75
81-20	International Year of the Disabled	2.25
81-21	Edna St. Vincent Millay	2.25
81-22	Alcoholism	3.00
81-23	American Architecture (4)	3.25
81-24	Babe Zaharias	3.00
81-25	Bobby Jones	3.00
81-26	Frederic Remington	2.50
81-27	"C" (20¢) sheet and coil (3)	4.25
81-28	"C" (18¢) booklet pane (10)	4.25
81-29	18¢ and 20¢ Hoban (2)	2.50
81-30	Yorktown/ Virginia Capes (2)	3.00
81-31	Christmas, Madonna	3.00
81-32	Christmas, Bear on Sleigh	3.00
81-33	John Hanson	2.25
81-34	Fire Pumper coil (2)	7.00
81-35	Desert Plants (4)	2.75
81-36	9.3¢ Mail Wagon coil (3)	6.00

81-37	Flag over Supreme Court sheet and coil (3)	4.25
81-38	Flag over Supreme Court booklet pane (6)	4.00

1982

82-1	Sheep booklet pane (10)	3.50
82-2	Ralph Bunche	4.25
82-3	13¢ Crazy Horse (2)	2.25
82-4	37¢ Robert Millikan	2.00
82-5	Franklin D. Roosevelt	2.25
82-6	Love	2.25
82-7	5.9¢ Bicycle coil (4)	7.50
82-8	George Washington	3.50
82-9	10.9¢ Hansom Cab coil (2)	6.00
82-10	Birds & Flowers, AL-GE (10)	12.00
82-11	Birds & Flowers, HI-MD (10)	12.00
82-12	Birds & Flowers, MA-NJ (10)	12.00
82-13	Birds & Flowers, NM-SC (10)	12.00
82-14	Birds & Flowers, SD-WY (10)	12.00
82-15	USA/Netherlands	2.25
82-16	Library of Congress	2.25
82-17	Consumer Education coil (2)	3.75
82-18	Knoxville World's Fair (4)	2.50
82-19	Horatio Alger	2.25
82-20	2¢ Locomotive coil (2)	5.25
82-21	Aging Together	2.25
82-22	The Barrymores	3.75
82-23	Mary Walker	2.25
82-24	Peace Garden	2.25
82-25	America's Libraries	2.25
82-26	Jackie Robinson	15.00
82-27	4¢ Stagecoach coil (3)	4.25
82-28	Touro Synagogue	2.25
82-29	Wolf Trap Farm Park	2.25
82-30	American Architecture (4)	2.50
82-31	Francis of Assisi	2.25
82-32	Ponce de Leon	2.25
82-33	13¢ Kitten & Puppy (2)	3.25
82-34	Christmas, Madonna	3.25
82-35	Christmas, Seasons Greetings (4)	4.00
82-36	2¢ Igor Stravinsky (2)	3.25

1983

83-1	1¢, 4¢, 13¢ Penalty Mail (5)	3.25
83-2	1¢ and 17¢ Penalty Mail (4)	3.25
83-3	Penalty Mail coil (2)	3.25
83-4	$1 Penalty Mail	5.00
83-5	$5 Penalty Mail	10.00
83-6	Science & Industry	2.00
83-7	5.2¢ Antique Sleigh coil (4)	5.25
83-8	Sweden/USA Treaty	2.50
83-9	3¢ Handcar coil (3)	4.00
83-10	Balloons (4)	2.75
83-11	Civilian Conservation Corps	2.00
83-12	40¢ Olympics airmails (4)	3.50
83-13	Joseph Priestley	2.00
83-14	Volunteerism	2.00
83-15	Concord/German Immigration	2.00
83-16	Physical Fitness	2.00

83-17	Brooklyn Bridge	2.50
83-18	TVA	2.00
83-19	4¢ Carl Schurz (5)	2.00
83-20	Medal of Honor	3.00
83-21	Scott Joplin	4.00
83-22	Thomas H. Gallaudet	2.00
83-23	28¢ Olympics (4)	4.75
83-24	5¢ Pearl S. Buck (4)	2.00
83-25	Babe Ruth	10.00
83-26	Nathaniel Hawthorne	2.00
83-27	3¢ Henry Clay (7)	2.00
83-28	13¢ Olympics (4)	4.00
83-29	$9.35 Eagle booklet single	140.00
83-30	$9.35 Eagle booklet pane (3)	190.00
83-31	1¢ Omnibus coil (3)	4.00
83-32	Treaty of Paris	2.50
83-33	Civil Service	2.00
83-34	Metropolitan Opera	2.50
83-35	Inventors (4)	3.00
83-36	1¢ Dorothea Dix (3)	2.00
83-37	Streetcars (4)	2.50
83-38	5¢ Motorcycle coil (4)	5.25
83-39	Christmas, Madonna	2.50
83-40	Christmas, Santa Claus	2.50
83-41	35¢ Olympics airmails (4)	3.50
83-42	Martin Luther	2.50
83-43	Flag over Supreme Court booklet pane (10)	3.50

1984

84-1	Alaska Statehood	2.00
84-2	Winter Olympics (4)	3.25
84-3	FDIC	2.00
84-4	Harry S. Truman	2.00
84-5	Love	2.00
84-6	Carter G. Woodson	3.00
84-7	11¢ RR Caboose coil (2)	4.00
84-8	Soil & Water Conservation	2.00
84-9	Credit Union Act	2.00
84-10	40¢ Lillian M. Gilbreth	2.00
84-11	Orchids (4)	3.00
84-12	Hawaii Statehood	2.00
84-13	7.4¢ Baby Buggy coil (3)	4.00
84-14	National Archives	2.00
84-15	20¢ Summer Olympics (4)	4.50
84-16	New Orleans World's Fair	2.00
84-17	Health Research	2.00
84-18	Douglas Fairbanks	2.50
84-19	Jim Thorpe	6.00
84-20	10¢ Richard Russell (2)	2.00
84-21	John McCormack	2.50
84-22	St. Lawrence Seaway	2.00
84-23	Migratory Bird Hunting and Conservation Stamp Act	4.50
84-24	Roanoke Voyages	2.00
84-25	Herman Melville	2.00
84-26	Horace Moses	2.00
84-27	Smokey Bear	5.00
84-28	Roberto Clemente	8.00
84-29	30¢ Frank C. Laubach	2.00
84-30	Dogs (4)	4.00
84-31	Crime Prevention	2.00
84-32	Family Unity	3.75
84-33	Eleanor Roosevelt	3.00
84-34	Nation of Readers	3.00

84-35	Christmas, Madonna	3.00
84-36	Christmas, Santa Claus	3.00
84-37	Hispanic Americans	2.00
84-38	Vietnam Veterans Memorial	3.75

1985

85-1	Jerome Kern	3.25
85-2	7¢ Abraham Baldwin (3)	3.25
85-3	"D" (22¢) sheet and coil (3)	2.50
85-4	"D" (22¢) booklet pane (10)	4.00
85-5	"D" (22¢) Penalty Mail sheet and coil (3)	2.50
85-6	11¢ Alden Partridge (2)	2.00
85-7	33¢ Alfred Verville airmail	2.25
85-8	39¢ Lawrence & Elmer Sperry airmail	2.25
85-9	44¢ Transpacific airmail	2.25
85-10	50¢ Chester Nimitz	2.75
85-11	Mary McLeod Bethune	3.50
85-12	39¢ Grenville Clark	2.00
85-13	14¢ Sinclair Lewis (2)	2.00
85-14	Duck Decoys (4)	3.00
85-15	14¢ Iceboat coil (2)	5.00
85-16	Winter Special Olympics	2.00
85-17	Flag over Capitol sheet and coil (3)	2.75
85-18	Flag over Capitol booklet pane (5)	3.50
85-19	12¢ Stanley Steamer coil (2)	5.00
85-20	Seashells booklet pane (10)	5.00
85-21	Love	3.75
85-22	10.1¢ Oil Wagon coil (3)	4.00
85-23	12.5¢ Pushcart coil (2)	4.00
85-24	John J. Audubon	2.50
85-25	$10.75 Eagle booklet single	42.50
85-26	$10.75 Eagle booklet pane (3)	100.00
85-27	6¢ Tricycle coil (4)	4.00
85-28	Rural Electrification Administration	2.00
85-29	14¢ and 22¢ Penalty Mail sheet and coil (4)	3.75
85-30	AMERIPEX '86	2.00
85-31	9¢ Sylvanus Thayer (3)	3.00
85-32	3.4¢ School Bus coil (7)	5.00
85-33	11¢ Stutz Bearcat coil (2)	4.00
85-34	Abigail Adams	2.00
85-35	4.9¢ Buckboard coil (5)	5.00
85-36	8.3¢ Ambulance coil (3)	4.00
85-37	Frederic Bartholdi	3.75
85-38	8¢ Henry Knox (3)	2.00
85-39	Korean War Veterans	2.75
85-40	Social Security Act	3.00
85-41	44¢ Father Junipero Serra airmail	2.50
85-42	World War I Veterans	2.50
85-43	6¢ Walter Lippman (4)	2.50
85-44	Horses (4)	4.00

85-45	Public Education	2.50
85-46	International Youth Year (4)	3.25
85-47	Help End Hunger	2.50
85-48	21.1¢ Letters coil (2)	3.00
85-49	Christmas, Madonna	2.50
85-50	Christmas, Poinsettias	2.50
85-51	18¢ Washington/ Washington Monument coil (2)	3.50

1986

86-1	Arkansas Statehood	2.25
86-2	25¢ Jack London	2.00
86-3	Stamp Collecting booklet pane (4)	4.75
86-4	Love	2.50
86-5	Sojourner Truth	2.50
86-6	5¢ Hugo L. Black (5)	3.25
86-7	Republic of Texas (2)	2.25
86-8	$2 William Jennings Bryan	4.25
86-9	Fish booklet pane (5)	4.25
86-10	Public Hospitals	1.75
86-11	Duke Ellington	3.00
86-12	Presidents, Washington-Harrison (9)	5.00
86-13	Presidents, Tyler-Grant (9)	5.00
86-14	Presidents, Hayes-Wilson (9)	5.00
86-15	Presidents, Harding-Johnson (9)	5.00
86-16	Polar Explorers (4)	3.50
86-17	17¢ Belva Ann Lockwood (2)	3.00
86-18	1¢ Margaret Mitchell (3)	1.75
86-19	Statue of Liberty	5.00
86-20	4¢ Father Flanagan (3)	1.75
86-21	17¢ Dog Sled coil (2)	3.50
86-22	56¢ John Harvard	2.75
86-23	Navajo Blankets (4)	3.25
86-24	3¢ Paul Dudley White, MD (8)	2.00
86-25	$1 Bernard Revel	2.75
86-26	T.S. Eliot	1.75
86-27	Wood-Carved Figurines (4)	2.75
86-28	Christmas, Madonna	2.00
86-29	Christmas, Village Scene	2.00
86-30	5.5¢ Star Route Truck coil (4)	5.00
86-31	25¢ Bread Wagon coil	5.00

1987

87-1	8.5¢ Tow Truck coil (5)	2.75
87-2	Michigan Statehood	2.50
87-3	Pan American Games	2.00
87-4	Love	2.00
87-5	7.1¢ Tractor coil (5)	2.75
87-6	14¢ Julia Ward Howe (2)	2.00
87-7	Jean Baptiste Pointe Du Sable	3.00
87-8	Enrico Caruso	3.00
87-9	2¢ Mary Lyon (3)	2.00
87-10	Reengraved 2¢ Locomotive coil (6)	3.00
87-11	Girl Scouts	4.00
87-12	10¢ Canal Boat coil (5)	3.00
87-13	Special Occasions booklet pane (10)	6.00
87-14	United Way	2.50
87-15	Flag with Fireworks	2.50
87-16	Flag over Capitol coil, prephosphored paper (2)	4.00
87-17	Wildlife, Swallow-Squirrel (10)	5.50
87-18	Wildlife, Armadillo-Rabbit (10)	5.50
87-19	Wildlife, Tanager-Ladybug (10)	5.50
87-20	Wildlife, Beaver-Prairie Dog (10)	5.50
87-21	Wildlife, Turtle-Fox (10)	5.50
87-22	Delaware Statehood	2.75
87-23	U.S./Morocco Friendship	2.50
87-24	William Faulkner	2.50
87-25	Lacemaking (4)	4.00
87-26	10¢ Red Cloud (3)	2.00
87-27	$5 Bret Harte	11.00
87-28	Pennsylvania Statehood	3.00
87-29	Drafting of the Constitution booklet pane (5)	4.50
87-30	New Jersey Statehood	3.00
87-31	Signing of Constitution	2.50
87-32	Certified Public Accountants	4.00
87-33	5¢ Milk Wagon and 17.5¢ Racing Car coils (4)	4.50
87-34	Locomotives booklet pane (5)	10.00
87-35	Christmas, Madonna	2.50
87-36	Christmas, Ornaments	2.50
87-37	Flag with Fireworks booklet-pair	4.00

1988

88-1	Georgia Statehood	3.00
88-2	Connecticut Statehood	3.00
88-3	Winter Olympics	2.50
88-4	Australia Bicentennial	2.75
88-5	James Weldon Johnson	3.00
88-6	Cats (4)	5.00
88-7	Massachusetts Statehood	3.00
88-8	Maryland Statehood	3.00
88-9	3¢ Conestoga Wagon coil (8)	3.50
88-10	Knute Rockne	3.50
88-11	"E" (25¢) Earth sheet and coil (3)	3.00
88-12	"E" (25¢) Earth booklet pane (10)	6.00
88-13	"E" (25¢) Penalty Mail coil (2)	3.00
88-14	44¢ New Sweden airmail	3.00
88-15	Pheasant booklet pane (10)	6.00
88-16	Jack London booklet pane (6)	4.00
88-17	Jack London booklet pane (10)	5.75
88-18	Flag with Clouds	2.50
88-19	45¢ Samuel Langley airmail	3.00
88-19A	20¢ Penalty Mail coil (2)	3.00
88-20	Flag over Yosemite coil (2)	3.00
88-21	South Carolina Statehood	3.00
88-22	Owl & Grosbeak booklet pane (10)	5.00
88-23	15¢ Buffalo Bill Cody (2)	3.00
88-24	15¢ and 25¢ Penalty Mail coils (4)	4.00
88-25	Francis Ouimet	3.00
88-26	45¢ Harvey Cushing, MD	2.50
88-27	New Hampshire Statehood	3.00
88-28	36¢ Igor Sikorsky airmail	3.00
88-29	Virginia Statehood	3.00
88-30	10.1¢ Oil Wagon coil, precancel (3)	4.00
88-31	Love	3.00
88-32	Flag with Clouds booklet pane (6)	6.00
88-33	16.7¢ Popcorn Wagon coil (2)	3.00
88-34	15¢ Tugboat coil (2)	3.00
88-35	13.2¢ Coal Car coil (2)	3.00
88-36	New York Statehood	3.00
88-37	45¢ Love	3.00
88-38	8.4¢ Wheel Chair coil (3)	3.00
88-39	21¢ Railroad Mail Car coil (2)	3.00
88-40	Summer Olympics	3.00
88-41	Classic Cars booklet pane (5)	6.00
88-42	7.6¢ Carreta coil (4)	3.00
88-43	Honeybee coil (2)	3.00
88-44	Antarctic Explorers (4)	3.00
88-45	5.3¢ Elevator coil (5)	3.00
88-46	20.5¢ Fire Engine coil (2)	4.00
88-47	Carousel Animals (4)	3.00
88-48	$8.75 Eagle	22.50
88-49	Christmas, Madonna	3.00
88-50	Christmas, Snow Scene	3.00
88-51	21¢ Chester Carlson	2.50
88-52	Special Occasions booklet pane (6), Love You	5.00
88-53	Special Occasions booklet pane (6), Thinking of You	5.00
88-54	24.1¢ Tandem Bicycle coil (2)	3.00
88-55	20¢ Cable Car coil (2)	3.00
88-56	13¢ Patrol Wagon coil (2)	3.00
88-57	23¢ Mary Cassatt	2.50
88-58	65¢ H.H. "Hap" Arnold	2.50

1989

89-1	Montana Statehood	3.00
89-2	A. Philip Randolph	3.50
89-3	Flag over Yosemite coil, prephosphored paper (2)	3.50
89-4	North Dakota Statehood	3.00
89-5	Washington Statehood	3.00
89-6	Steamboats booklet pane (5)	5.00
89-7	World Stamp Expo '89	3.00
89-8	Arturo Toscanini	3.00
89-9	U.S. House of Representatives	3.00
89-10	U.S. Senate	3.00
89-11	Executive Branch	3.00
89-12	South Dakota Statehood	3.00
89-13	7.1¢ Tractor coil, precancel (4)	2.75
89-14	$1 Johns Hopkins	3.50
89-15	Lou Gehrig	7.50
89-16	1¢ Penalty Mail	3.50
89-17	45¢ French Revolution airmail	3.00
89-18	Ernest Hemingway	3.00
89-19	$2.40 Moon Landing	12.50
89-20	North Carolina Statehood	3.00
89-21	Letter Carriers	2.50
89-22	28¢ Sitting Bull	2.50
89-23	Drafting of the Bill of Rights	2.50
89-24	Prehistoric Animals (4)	7.50
89-25	25¢ and 45¢ PUAS-America (2)	3.50
89-26	Christmas, Madonna	7.50
89-27	Christmas, Antique Sleigh	6.50
89-28	Eagle and Shield, self-adhesive	3.50
89-29	$3.60 World Stamp Expo '89 souvenir sheet	9.00

89-30	Classic Mail Transportation (4)	3.50
89-31	$1.80 Future Mail Transportation souvenir sheet	6.00
89-32	45¢ Future Mail Transportation airmails (4)	5.50
89-33	$1 Classic Mail Transportation souvenir sheet	5.00

1990

90-1	Idaho Statehood	3.00
90-2	Love sheet and booklet pane (11)	7.50
90-3	Ida B. Wells	3.00
90-4	U.S. Supreme Court	3.00
90-5	15¢ Beach Umbrella booklet pane (10)	5.00
90-6	5¢ Luis Munoz Marin (5)	3.00
90-7	Wyoming Statehood	3.00
90-8	Classic Films (4)	6.00
90-9	Marianne Moore	3.00
90-10	$1 Seaplane coil (2)	5.00
90-11	Lighthouses booklet pane (5)	6.00
90-12	Plastic Flag stamp	5.00
90-13	Rhode Island Statehood	4.00
90-14	$2 Bobcat	7.50
90-15	Olympians (5)	8.00
90-16	Indian Headdresses booklet pane (10)	9.00
90-17	5¢ Circus Wagon coil (5)	4.00
90-18	40¢ Claire Lee Chennault	4.50
90-19	Federated States of Micronesia/ Marshall Islands (2)	4.00
90-20	Creatures of the Sea (4)	5.00
90-21	25¢ and 45¢ PUAS/America (2)	4.00
90-22	Dwight D. Eisenhower	3.00
90-23	Christmas, Madonna, sheet and booklet pane (11)	7.50
90-24	Christmas,Yule Tree, sheet and booklet pane (11)	7.50

1991

91-1	"F" (29¢) Flower sheet and coil (3)	4.00
91-2	"F" (29¢) Flower booklet panes (20)	12.50
91-3	4¢ Makeup	3.50
91-4	"F" (29¢) ATM booklet single	4.00
91-5	"F" (29¢) Penalty Mail coil (2)	4.00
91-6	4¢ Steam Carriage coil (7)	4.00
91-7	50¢ Switzerland	4.00
91-8	Vermont Statehood	4.00
91-9	19¢ Fawn (2)	4.00
91-10	Flag over Mount Rushmore coil (2)	4.00
91-11	35¢ Dennis Chavez	4.00
91-12	Flower sheet and booklet pane (11)	7.50
91-13	4¢ Penalty Mail (8)	4.00
91-14	Wood Duck booklet panes (20)	12.50
91-15	23¢ Lunch Wagon coil (2)	4.00
91-16	Flag with Olympic Rings (10)	7.50
91-17	50¢ Harriet Quimby	4.00
91-18	Savings Bond	4.00
91-19	Love sheet and booklet pane, 52¢ Love (12)	12.50
91-20	19¢ Balloon booklet pane (10)	7.50
91-21	40¢ William Piper airmail	4.00

91-22	William Saroyan	4.00
91-23	Penalty Mail coil and 19¢ and 23¢ sheet (4)	5.00
91-24	5¢ Canoe and 10¢ Tractor-Trailer coils (4)	4.00
91-25	Flags on Parade	4.00
91-26	Fishing Flies booklet pane (5)	7.50
91-27	52¢ Hubert H. Humphrey	4.00
91-28	Cole Porter	4.00
91-29	50¢ Antarctic Treaty airmail	4.00
91-30	1¢ Kestrel, 3¢ Bluebird and 30¢ Cardinal (3)	4.00
91-31	Torch ATM booklet single	4.00
91-32	Desert Shield/ Desert Storm sheet and booklet pane (11)	4.00
91-33	Flag over Mount Rushmore coil, gravure printing (darker, 3)	4.00
91-34	Summer Olympics (5)	8.00
91-35	Flower coil, slit perforations (3)	4.00
91-36	Numismatics	4.00
91-37	Basketball	8.00
91-48	19¢ Fishing Boat coil (3)	4.00
91-49	Comedians booklet pane (10)	8.00
91-50	World War II miniature sheet (10)	8.00
91-51	District of Columbia	4.00
91-52	Jan Matzeliger	4.00
91-53	$1 USPS/ Olympic Logo	7.50
91-54	Space Exploration booklet pane (10)	8.00
91-55	50¢ PUASP/America airmail	4.00
91-56	Christmas, Madonna sheet and booklet pane (11)	8.00
91-57	Christmas, Santa Claus sheet and booklet pane (11)	8.00
91-58	5¢ Canoe coil, gravure printing (red, 6)	4.00
91-59	(10¢) Eagle and Shield, self-adhesive (3)	4.00
91-60	23¢ Flag presort	4.00
91-61	$9.95 Express Mail	25.00
91-62	$2.90 Priority Mail	9.00
91-63	$14.00 Express Mail International	35.00

1992

92-01	Winter Olympic Games (5)	8.00
92-02	World Columbian Stamp Expo '92	4.00
92-03	W.E.B. Du Bois	4.00
92-04	Love	4.00
92-05	75¢ Wendell Willkie	4.00
92-06	29¢ Flower coil, round perforations (2)	4.00
92-07	Earl Warren	4.00
92-08	Olympic Baseball	8.00
92-09	Flag over White House, coil (2)	4.00
92-10	First Voyage of Columbus (4)	8.00
92-11	N.Y. Stock Exchange	4.00
92-18	Space Adventures (4)	8.00
92-19	Alaska Highway	4.00
92-20	Kentucky Statehood	4.00
92-21	Summer Olympic Games (5)	8.00
92-22	Hummingbirds (5)	8.00
92-23	Wildflowers (10)	6.00
92-24	Wildflowers (10)	6.00
92-25	Wildflowers (10)	6.00
92-26	Wildflowers (10)	6.00
92-27	Wildflowers (10)	6.00
92-28	World War II (10)	8.00
92-30	Dorothy Parker	4.00
92-31	Theodore von Karman	4.00

92-33	Minerals (4)	8.00
92-35	Juan Rodriguez Cabrillo	4.00
92-36	Wild Animals (5)	8.00
92-38	Christmas Contemporary, sheet and booklet pane (8)	10.00
92-39	Christmas Traditional, sheet and booklet pane (11)	12.00
92-40	Pumpkinseed Sunfish	4.00
92-41	Circus Wagon	5.00
92-42	Happy New Year	6.00

1993

93-01	Elvis	15.00
93-02	Space Fantasy (5)	10.00
93-03	Percy Lavon Julian	5.00
93-04	Oregon Trail	5.00
93-05	World University Games	5.00
93-06	Grace Kelly	5.00
93-07	Oklahoma!	5.00
93-08	Circus	7.50
93-09	Thomas Jefferson	5.00
93-10	Cherokee Strip	5.00
93-11	Dean Acheson	5.00
93-12	Sporting Horses	7.50
93-13	USA coil	5.00
93-14	Garden Flowers (5)	7.50
93-15	Eagle and Shield, coil	5.00
93-16	World War II (10)	7.50
93-17	Futuristic Space Shuttle	12.50
93-18	Hank Williams, sheet	7.50
93-19	Rock & Roll/Rhythm & Blues, sheet single, booklet pane (8)	12.50
93-20	Joe Louis	5.00
93-21	Red Squirrel	5.00
93-22	Broadway Musicals, booklet pane (4)	7.50
93-23	National Postal Museum, strip (4)	7.50
93-24	Rose	5.00
93-25	American Sign Language, pair	5.00
93-26	Country & Western Music, sheet and booklet pane (4)	7.50
93-27	African Violets, booklet pane (10)	7.50
93-28	Official Mail	5.00
93-29	Contemporary Christmas, booklet pane (10), sheet and self-adhesive stamps	12.00
93-30	Traditional Christmas, sheet, booklet pane (4)	12.00
93-31	Classic Books (4)	7.50
93-32	Mariana Islands	7.50
93-33	Pine Cone	5.00
93-34	Columbus' Landing in Puerto Rico	7.50
93-35	AIDS Awareness	10.00

1994

94-01	Winter Olympics (5)	—
94-02	Edward R. Murrow	—
94-03	Love (sunrise)	—
94-04	Dr. Allison Davis	—
94-05	Eagle	—
94-06	Happy New Year	—
94-07	Love (birds)	—
94-08	Postage & Mailing Ctr.	—
94-09	Buffalo Soldiers	—
94-10	Silent Screen Stars (10)	—
94-11	Garden Flowers (5)	—
94-12	Victory at Saratoga	—
94-13	Tractor Trailer	—
94-14	World Cup Soccer (3)	—
94-15	World Cup Soccer S/S	—
94-16	World War II (10)	—
94-17	Love (bird)	—
94-18	Statue of Liberty	—

NOTE: Numbers and prices may be changed without notice, due to additional USPS stamp issues and/or different information that may become available on older issues.

403

History on Panels

- Includes block of four or more mint-condition commemorative stamps mounted on 8½" x 11¼" high-quality paper

Valuable, Elegant Keepsakes

Since the American Commemorative Panel series began in 1972, collectors have recognized these keepsakes as significant milestones in philatelic history. These limited-edition panels are available individually and on an advance subscription basis.

Accompanying the acetate-mounted block of four or more mint stamps are intaglio-printed reproductions of historical steel line engravings and informative articles on the stamp subject.

For Subscription Information

For more information, use the postage-paid request card in this book or write to:

**U.S. POSTAL SERVICE GUIDE
COMMEMORATIVE PANEL PROGRAM
PHILATELIC FULFILLMENT SERVICE CENTER
PO BOX 449980
KANSAS CITY MO 64144-9980**

American Commemorative Panels

The Postal Service offers American Commemorative Panels for each new commemorative stamp and special Christmas and Love stamp issued. The series began in 1972 with the Wildlife Commemorative Panel. The panels feature mint stamps complemented by fine reproductions of steel line engravings and the stories behind the commemorated subjects.

1972

1	Wildlife	7.00
2	Mail Order	6.75
3	Osteopathic Medicine	7.00
4	Tom Sawyer	6.75
5	Pharmacy	7.00
6	Christmas, Angels	11.00
7	Christmas, Santa Claus	11.00
7e	Same with error date (1882)	—
8	Stamp Collecting	6.75

1973

9	Love	9.50
10	Pamphleteers	7.75
11	George Gershwin	8.25
12	Posting a Broadside	7.75
13	Copernicus	7.75
14	Postal People	7.75
15	Harry S. Truman	9.00
16	Post Rider	9.00
17	Boston Tea Party	27.50
18	Electronics	7.50
19	Robinson Jeffers	7.50
20	Lyndon B. Johnson	9.50
21	Henry O. Tanner	7.50
22	Willa Cather	7.50
23	Drummer	11.00
24	Angus Cattle	7.50
25	Christmas, Madonna	11.00
26	Christmas Tree, Needlepoint	11.00

1974

27	VFW	7.50
28	Robert Frost	7.50
29	Expo '74	9.00
30	Horse Racing	9.00
31	Skylab	10.00
32	Universal Postal Union	9.00
33	Mineral Heritage	9.00
34	First Kentucky Settlement	7.50
35	Continental Congress	9.00
35c	Same with corrected logo	—

36	Chautauqua	7.50
37	Kansas Wheat	7.50
38	Energy Conservation	7.50
39	Sleepy Hollow	7.50
40	Retarded Children	7.50
41	Christmas, Currier & Ives	11.00
42	Christmas, Angel Altarpiece	10.50

1975

43	Benjamin West	7.00
44	Pioneer	11.50
45	Collective Bargaining	7.50
46	Contributors to the Cause	7.50
47	Mariner 10	11.50
48	Lexington & Concord	7.75
49	Paul Laurence Dunbar	7.50
50	D.W. Griffith	7.50
51	Bunker Hill	7.75
52	Military Uniforms	8.50
53	Apollo Soyuz	11.50
54	World Peace Through Law	7.50
54c	Same with August 15, 1975 date	—
55	Women's Year	7.50
56	Postal Service Bicentennial	9.00
57	Banking and Commerce	8.50
58	Early Christmas, Card	10.50
59	Christmas, Madonna	10.50

1976

60	Spirit of '76	12.50
61	Interphil 76	12.00
62	State Flags	22.50
63	Telephone	9.00
64	Commercial Aviation	13.00
65	Chemistry	10.00
66	Benjamin Franklin	10.50
67	Declaration of Independence	10.50

68	12th Winter Olympics	12.50
69	Clara Maass	10.00
70	Adolph S. Ochs	10.00
70c	Same with charter logo	—
71	Christmas, Winter Pastime	13.50
71c	Same with charter logo	—
72	Christmas, Nativity	13.50
72c	Same with charter logo	—

1977

73	Washington at Princeton	20.00
73c	Same with charter logo	—
74	Sound Recording	25.00
74c	Same with charter logo	—
75	Pueblo Art	90.00
75c	Same with charter logo	—
76	Solo Transatlantic Lindbergh Flight	100.00
77	Colorado Statehood	17.50
78	Butterflies	19.00
79	Lafayette	17.50
80	Skilled Hands	17.50
81	Peace Bridge	17.50
82	Battle of Oriskany	17.50
83	Alta, CA, Civil Settlement	17.50
84	Articles of Confederation	25.00
85	Talking Pictures	17.50
86	Surrender at Saratoga	24.00
87	Energy	17.50
88	Christmas, Valley Forge	20.00
89	Christmas, Mailbox	35.00

1978

90	Carl Sandburg	11.00
91	Captain Cook	17.50
92	Harriet Tubman	11.00
93	Quilts	19.00
94	Dance	14.00
95	French Alliance	14.00
96	Early Cancer Detection	12.00
97	Jimmie Rodgers	15.00
98	Photography	11.00
99	George M. Cohan	19.00
100	Viking Missions	35.00
101	Owls	35.00
102	Trees	32.50
103	Christmas, Madonna	15.00
104	Christmas, Hobby Horse	17.50

1979

105	Robert F. Kennedy	10.50
106	Martin Luther King, Jr.	10.00
107	International Year of the Child	10.00
108	John Steinbeck	10.00
109	Albert Einstein	10.50
110	Pennsylvania Toleware	10.00
111	Architecture	9.50
112	Endangered Flora	10.00
113	Seeing Eye Dogs	10.50
114	Special Olympics	13.00
115	John Paul Jones	12.50
116	15¢ Olympics	15.00
117	Christmas, Madonna	14.00
118	Christmas, Santa Claus	14.00
119	Will Rogers	13.00
120	Vietnam Veterans	12.50
121	10¢, 31¢ Olympics	14.00

1980

122	W.C. Fields	14.00
123	Winter Olympics	9.50
124	Benjamin Banneker	9.50
125	Frances Perkins	9.50
126	Emily Bissell	9.50
127	Helen Keller/ Anne Sullivan	9.50
128	Veterans Administration	9.50
129	General Bernardo de Galvez	9.50
130	Coral Reefs	11.00
131	Organized Labor	9.00
132	Edith Wharton	8.25
133	Education	9.00
134	Indian Masks	12.00
135	Architecture	9.50
136	Christmas, Epiphany Window	13.00
137	Christmas, Toys	13.00

1981

138	Everett Dirksen	9.50
139	Whitney Moore Young	9.50
140	Flowers	11.00
141	Red Cross	10.00
142	Savings & Loans	9.50
143	Space Achievement	13.75
144	Professional Management	9.00
145	Wildlife Habitats	14.00
146	Int'l. Year of Disabled Persons	9.00
147	Edna St. Vincent Millay	8.50
148	Architecture	9.50
149	Babe Zaharias/ Bobby Jones	11.00
150	James Hoban	9.00
151	Frederic Remington	9.50
152	Battle of Yorktown/ Virginia Capes	9.00
153	Christmas, Bear and Sleigh	12.00
154	Christmas, Madonna	12.50
155	John Hanson	8.50
156	U.S. Desert Plants	11.00

1982

157	Roosevelt	13.50
158	Love	14.75
159	George Washington	20.00
160	State Birds & Flowers	27.50
161	U.S./ Netherlands	20.00
162	Library of Congress	22.50
163	Knoxville World's Fair	14.75
164	Horatio Alger	13.00
165	Aging Together	15.50
166	The Barrymores	16.50
167	Dr. Mary Walker	14.00
168	Peace Garden	15.50
169	America's Libraries	16.00
170	Jackie Robinson	25.00
171	Touro Synagogue	14.50
172	Architecture	16.00
173	Wolf Trap Farm Park	14.50
174	Francis of Assisi	16.00
175	Ponce de Leon	16.00
176	Christmas, Madonna	20.00
177	Christmas, Season's Greetings	20.00
178	Kitten & Puppy	22.50

1983

179	Science and Industry	7.00
180	Sweden/ USA Treaty	7.00
181	Balloons	9.50
182	Civilian Conservation Corps	7.00
183	40¢ Olympics	9.00
184	Joseph Priestley	7.50
185	Voluntarism	6.50
186	Concord/German Immigration	6.50
187	Physical Fitness	6.75
188	Brooklyn Bridge	7.50
189	TVA	6.50
190	Medal of Honor	9.00
191	Scott Joplin	10.00
192	28¢ Olympics	9.00
193	Babe Ruth	12.50
194	Nathaniel Hawthorne	7.50
195	13¢ Olympics	10.50
196	Treaty of Paris	8.00
197	Civil Service	8.00
198	Metropolitan Opera	8.00
199	Inventors	8.50
200	Streetcars	10.00
201	Christmas, Madonna	12.00
202	Christmas, Santa Claus	12.00
203	35¢ Olympics	10.50
204	Martin Luther	10.00

1984

205	Alaska Statehood	6.50
206	Winter Olympics	8.00
207	FDIC	6.00
208	Love	6.50
209	Carter G. Woodson	8.00
210	Soil and Water Conservation	6.00
211	Credit Union Act	6.00
212	Orchids	8.00
213	Hawaii Statehood	8.00
214	National Archives	6.50
215	20¢ Olympics	8.00
216	Louisiana World Exposition	7.50
217	Health Research	6.00
218	Douglas Fairbanks	6.00
219	Jim Thorpe	10.00
220	John McCormack	6.00
221	St. Lawrence Seaway	8.00
222	Preserving Wetlands	10.00
223	Roanoke Voyages	6.00
224	Herman Melville	6.00
225	Horace Moses	6.00
226	Smokey Bear	10.00
227	Roberto Clemente	12.00
228	Dogs	8.00
229	Crime Prevention	7.50
230	Family Unity	6.00
231	Christmas, Madonna	8.00
232	Christmas, Santa Claus	8.00

233	Eleanor Roosevelt	7.00
234	Nation of Readers	7.00
235	Hispanic Americans	6.00
236	Vietnam Veterans Memorial	10.50

1985

237	Jerome Kern	8.00
238	Mary McLeod Bethune	8.00
239	Duck Decoys	11.00
240	Winter Special Olympics	8.50
241	Love	7.50
242	Rural Electrification Administration	7.00
243	AMERIPEX '86	9.50
244	Abigail Adams	6.50
245	Frederic Auguste Bartholdi	11.00
246	Korean War Veterans	8.00
247	Social Security Act	7.00
248	World War I Veterans	7.00
249	Horses	10.00
250	Public Education	6.50
251	Youth	8.00
252	Help End Hunger	7.00
253	Christmas, Poinsettias	9.00
254	Christmas, Madonna	11.50

1986

255	Arkansas Statehood	7.50
256	Stamp Collecting Booklet	9.50
257	Love	12.00
258	Sojourner Truth	9.50
259	Republic of Texas	10.00
260	Fish Booklet	9.50
261	Public Hospitals	9.00
262	Duke Ellington	9.50
263	U.S. Presidents' Sheet #1	9.00
264	U.S. Presidents' Sheet #2	9.00
265	U.S. Presidents' Sheet #3	9.00
266	U.S. Presidents' Sheet #4	9.00
267	Polar Explorers	9.50
268	Statue of Liberty	9.50
269	Navajo Blankets	9.50
270	T.S. Eliot	9.00
271	Wood-Carved Figurines	7.50

| 272 | Christmas, Madonna | 7.00 |
| 273 | Christmas, Village Scene | 7.00 |

1987

274	Michigan Statehood	7.00
275	Pan American Games	7.00
276	Love	12.00
277	Jean Baptiste Pointe Du Sable	7.50
278	Enrico Caruso	7.50
279	Girl Scouts	7.50
280	Special Occasions Booklet	7.00
281	United Way	7.00
282	#1 American Wildlife	9.00
283	#2 American Wildlife	9.00
284	#3 American Wildlife	9.00
285	#4 American Wildlife	9.00
286	#5 American Wildlife	9.00
287	Delaware Statehood	7.00
288	Morocco/U.S. Diplomatic Relations	7.00
289	William Faulkner	7.00
290	Lacemaking	7.00
291	Pennsylvania Statehood	7.00
292	Constitution Booklet	7.00
293	New Jersey Statehood	7.00
294	Signing of the Constitution	7.00
295	Certified Public Accountants	8.00
296	Locomotives Booklet	8.00
297	Christmas, Madonna	9.00
298	Christmas, Ornaments	8.00

1988

299	Georgia Statehood	9.00
300	Connecticut Statehood	9.00
301	Winter Olympics	9.00
302	Australia	9.00
303	James Weldon Johnson	9.00
304	Cats	10.00

305	Massachusetts Statehood	9.00
306	Maryland Statehood	9.00
307	Knute Rockne	15.00
308	New Sweden	9.00
309	South Carolina Statehood	9.00
310	Francis Ouimet	9.00
311	New Hampshire Statehood	9.00
312	Virginia Statehood	9.00
313	Love	10.00
314	New York Statehood	9.00
315	Classic Cars Booklet	9.00
316	Summer Olympics	11.00
317	Antarctic Explorers	9.00
318	Carousel Animals	9.00
319	Christmas, Madonna	11.00
320	Christmas, Village Scene	11.00

1989

321	Montana Statehood	10.00
322	A. Philip Randolph	12.50
323	North Dakota Statehood	10.00
324	Washington Statehood	10.00
325	Steamboats Booklet	10.00
326	World Stamp Expo '89	10.00
327	Arturo Toscanini	10.00
328	U.S. House of Representatives	10.00
329	U.S. Senate	10.00
330	Executive Branch	10.00
331	South Dakota Statehood	10.00
332	Lou Gehrig	12.50
333	French Revolution	10.00
334	Ernest Hemingway	9.00
335	North Carolina Statehood	9.00
336	Letter Carriers	9.00
337	Drafting of the Bill of Rights	9.00
338	Prehistoric Animals	10.00

339	25¢ and 45¢ America/PUAS	10.00
340	Christmas, Traditional and Contemporary	12.50
341	Classic Mail Transportation	10.00
342	Future Mail Transportation	10.00

1990

343	Idaho Statehood	10.00
344	Love	10.00
345	Ida B. Wells	11.00
346	U.S. Supreme Court	10.00
347	Wyoming Statehood	10.00
348	Classic Films	10.00
349	Marianne Moore	10.00
350	Lighthouses Booklet	12.50
351	Rhode Island Statehood	10.00
352	Olympians	12.50
353	Indian Headdresses Booklet	12.50
354	Micronesia/Marshall Islands	12.50
355	Creatures of the Sea	15.00
356	25c and 45c America/PUAS	12.50
357	Dwight D. Eisenhower	10.00
358	Christmas, Traditional and Contemporary	12.50

1991

359	Switzerland	12.50
360	Vermont Statehood	12.50
361	Savings Bonds	10.00
362	29¢ and 52¢ Love	12.50
363	Saroyan	12.50
364	Fishing Flies Booklet	15.00
365	Cole Porter	12.50
366	Antartic Treaty	12.50
367	Desert Shield/Desert Storm	20.00
368	Summer Olympics	12.50
369	Numismatics	12.50
370	Basketball	12.50
371	World War II Miniature Sheet	12.50

372	Comedians Booklet	10.00
373	District of Columbia	12.50
374	Jan Matzeliger	10.00
375	Space Exploration Booklet	15.00
376	America/PUASP	12.50
377	Christmas, Traditional and Contemporary	12.50

1992

378	Winter Olympics	12.50
379	World Columbian Stamp Expo '92	12.50
380	W.E.B. Du Bois	12.50
381	Love	12.50
382	Olympic Baseball	15.00
383	First Voyage of Christopher Columbus	20.00
384	Space Adventures	15.00
385	New York Stock Exchange	12.50
386	Alaska Highway	12.50
387	Kentucky Statehood	12.50
388	Summer Olympics	12.50
389	Hummingbirds Booklet	15.00
390	World War II Miniature Sheet	12.50
391	Dorothy Parker	12.50
392	Theodore von Karman	12.50
393	Minerals	12.50
394	Juan Rodriguez Cabrillo	12.50
395	Wild Animals Booklet	15.00
396	Christmas, Traditional and Contemporary	12.50
397	Columbian Souvenir Sheets	25.00
398	Columbian Souvenir Sheets	25.00
399	Columbian Souvenir Sheets	25.00
400	Wildflowers # 1	15.00
401	Wildflowers # 2	15.00
402	Wildflowers # 3	15.00
403	Wildflowers # 4	15.00
404	Wildflowers # 5	15.00
405	Happy New Year	12.50

1993

406	Elvis	30.00
407	Space Fantasy	17.50
408	Percy Julian	15.00
409	Oregon Trail	15.00
410	World Univ. Games	15.00
411	Grace Kelly	15.00
412	Oklahoma	15.00
413	Circus	15.00
414	Cherokee Strip	15.00
415	Dean Acheson	15.00
416	Sport Horses	15.00
417	Garden Flowers	15.00
418	World War II	15.00
419	Hank Williams	15.00
420	Rock/Roll/R&B	17.50
421	Joe Louis	15.00
422	Broadway Musicals	15.00
423	National Postal Museum	15.00
424	Deaf Communication	15.00
425	Country Western	17.50
426	Youth Classics	15.00
427	Christmas	17.50
428	Mariana Islands	15.00
429	Landing of Columbus	15.00
430	AIDS Awareness	15.00

1994

431	Winter Sports	—
432	Edward R. Murrow	—
433	Allison Davis	—
434	Happy New Year	—
435	Love	—
436	Buffalo Soldiers	—
437	Silent Screen	—
438	Garden Flowers	—
439	World Cup Soccer	—
440	World War II	—
441	Norman Rockwell	—
442	Moon Landing	—
443	Locomotives	—
444	George Meany	—
445	Popular Singers	—
446	James Thurber	—
447	Jazz/Blues	—
448	Wonders of the Sea	—
449	Endangered Birds	—
450	Christmas	—

*1994 issues subject to change.

Subject Index

The numbers listed next to the stamp description are the Scott numbers, and the numbers in parentheses are the numbers of the pages on which the stamps are listed.

410

411

413

416

417

419

421

425

U

Postmasters General of the United States

Appointed by the Continental Congress

1775 Benjamin Franklin, PA
1776 Richard Bache, PA
1782 Ebenezer Hazard, NY

Appointed by the President with the advice and consent of the Senate

1789 Samuel Osgood, MA
1791 Timothy Pickering, PA
1795 Joseph Habersham, GA
1801 Gideon Granger, CT
1814 Return J. Meigs, Jr., OH
1823 John McLean, OH
1829 William T. Barry, KY
1835 Amos Kendall, KY
1840 John M. Niles, CT
1841 Francis Granger, NY
1841 Charles A. Wickliffe, KY
1845 Cave Johnson, TN
1849 Jacob Collamer, VT
1850 Nathan K. Hall, NY
1852 Samuel D. Hubbard, CT
1853 James Campbell, PA
1857 Aaron V. Brown, TN
1859 Joseph Holt, KY
1861 Horatio King, ME
1861 Montgomery Blair, DC
1864 William Dennison, OH
1866 Alexander W. Randall, WI
1869 John A.J. Creswell, MD
1874 James W. Marshall, NJ
1874 Marshall Jewell, CT
1876 James N. Tyner, IN
1877 David McK. Key, TN
1880 Horace Maynard, TN
1881 Thomas L. James, NY
1882 Timothy O. Howe, WI
1883 Walter Q. Gresham, IN
1884 Frank Hatton, IA

1885 William F. Vilas, WI
1888 Don M. Dickinson, MI
1889 John Wanamaker, PA
1893 Wilson S. Bissell, NY
1895 William L. Wilson, WV
1897 James A. Gary, MD
1898 Charles Emory Smith, PA
1902 Henry C. Payne, WI
1904 Robert J. Wynne, PA
1905 George B. Cortelyou, NY
1907 George von L. Meyer, MA
1909 Frank H. Hitchcock, MA
1913 Albert S. Burleson, TX
1921 Will H. Hays, IN
1922 Hubert Work, CO
1923 Harry S. New, IN
1929 Walter F. Brown, OH
1933 James A. Farley, NY
1940 Frank C. Walker, PA
1945 Robert E. Hannegan, MO
1947 Jesse M. Donaldson, IL
1953 Arthur E. Summerfield, MI
1961 J. Edward Day, CA
1963 John A. Gronouski, WI
1965 Lawrence F. O'Brien, MA
1968 W. Marvin Watson, TX
1969 Winton M. Blount, AL

Selected by the Presidentially appointed U.S. Postal Service Board of Governors

1971 Elmer T. Klassen, MA
1975 Benjamin Franklin Bailar, MD
1978 William F. Bolger, CT
1985 Paul N. Carlin, WY
1986 Albert V. Casey, MA
1986 Preston R. Tisch, NY
1988 Anthony M. Frank, CA
1992 Marvin Runyon, TN

...owledgments:

...vice Guide to U.S. Stamps is produced for the United States Postal Service ...nnelley & Sons Co.

...i and Design:

...um, Chicago, IL

...inting:

R.R. Donnelley Book Publishing Services, Crawfordsville, IN

Binding:

R.R. Donnelley Global Software Services, Crawfordsville, IN

U.S. Postal Service:

Editor-in-Chief Joe Brockert, Stamp Services
Print Specialist W. Lee Roberts, Printing Procurement
Contract Administration Peggy Tartal, Stamp Services

Selected stamps for illustrations and advice on content were provided courtesy of:

Richard E. Drews
Stamp King
7139 W. Higgins Rd.
Chicago, IL 60656
(312) 775-2100

Cover Photography:

Jules Frazier

Inside Photography:

Howard Ash Photography
Morrison Photography